The Gift Outright

The land was ours before we were the land's.
She was our land more than a hundred years
Before we were her people. She was ours
In Massachusetts, in Virginia,
But we were England's, still colonials,
Possessing what we still were unpossessed by,
Possessed by what we now no more possessed.
Something we were withholding made us weak
Until we found out that it was ourselves
We were withholding from our land of living,
And forthwith found salvation in surrender.
Such as we were we gave ourselves outright
(The deed of gift was many deeds of war)
To the land vaguely realizing westward,
But still unstoried, artless, unenhanced,
Such as she was, such as she would become.

Robert Frost

The
Adventure
of America

THE
ADVENTURE
OF AMERICA

★　　★　　★　　★　　★

EDITED BY JOHN TOBIAS AND SAVIN HOFFECKER

Conception and Commentary by John Tobias

Introduction by ELEANOR ROOSEVELT

ILLUSTRATED BY STEELE SAVAGE

Published by Bernard Geis Associates

Distributed by Random House

To Poppy,
Rare New England Blossom
and Beloved Wife

Acknowledgments

Thanks are due to the following authors, their representatives and publishers for permission to include certain selections in this anthology.

BRANDT & BRANDT: "Southern Ships and Settlers," "French Pioneers," "Thomas Jefferson," "Nightmare at Noon," and selections from "John Brown's Body," all from *Selected Works of Stephen Vincent Benét*, Holt, Rinehart and Winston, Inc. Copyright 1927, 1928, 1940 by Stephen Vincent Benét. Copyright 1933 by Rosemary and Stephen Vincent Benét. Copyright renewed 1955, 1956, 1961 by Rosemary Carr Benét.

FRANCES VAN SWEARINGEN DIMITY: "The Flag Goes By" by Henry Holcomb Bennett.

DODD, MEAD & COMPANY: "Jesse James" from *Golden Fleece* by William Rose Benét. Copyright 1933, 1935 by Dodd, Mead & Company, Inc. "The Spell of the Yukon" from *The Complete Poems of Robert Service*.

DOUBLEDAY & COMPANY, INC.: "W. C. Fields Makes a Grand Re-entry into Hollywood" as quoted in *W. C. Fields, His Follies and His Fortunes* by Robert Lewis Taylor. Doubleday & Company, Inc., 1949.

DUELL, SLOAN & PEARCE, an affiliate of Meredith Press: "The Little Old Sod Shanty on the Plains" and "The Abolitionist Hymn" from *Song in America* by Burl Ives. Copyright 1962 by Wayfarer Music Co., Inc.

NORMA MILLAY ELLIS: "Travel" by Edna St. Vincent Millay, from *Collected Poems*, Harper & Brothers. Copyright 1921, 1948 by Edna St. Vincent Millay.

BERNARD GEIS ASSOCIATES: "On the Passing of Knickers" by John Tobias and "Lips That Touch Liquor" by J. Gillespie. Copyright 1962 by John Tobias.

HARCOURT, BRACE & WORLD, INC.: "In Just-spring" from *Poems 1923–1954* by E. E. Cummings. Copyright 1923, 1951 by E. E. Cummings.

HOLT, RINEHART AND WINSTON, INC.: "The Ballad of William Sycamore" from *Ballads and Poems* by Stephen Vincent Benét. Copyright 1931 by Stephen Vincent Benét. Copyright renewed © 1959 by Rosemary Carr Benét. "The Blue and the Gray" from *The Blue and the Gray and Other Verses* by Francis Miles Finch, 1909. "Mending Wall" and "The Gift Outright" from *Complete Poems of Robert Frost*. Copyright 1930, 1939 by Holt, Rinehart and Winston, Inc. Copyright 1942 by Robert Frost.

Introduction

This book is history but at the same time it is a new kind of history, and I think for many Americans it will make the past seem closer than ever before. As nations go, our nation is a young nation but much history has already gone into the building of it. There was such a vast area to develop, there were such great resources and the people coming here came with so many dreams, misconceptions sometimes, but dreams have a way of accomplishing miracles. As one reads the pages of this book in which prose and poetry and even mere rhymes call to one's memory, much which may have been read and forgotten is brought back in the words of people themselves who took part in the development of the United States of America.

Knowledge of the past has great value as it illuminates the present, and many of our present problems (the overriding racial difficulties, for instance) will be better understood as one reads this book. It is fascinating history told by someone who has enjoyed delving into every kind of resource material. It will mean much, I think, to young and old and will, I hope, be a book that will find its way into libraries in schools and communities everywhere in this great country. What a saga it is—the first landings, the small population on the Eastern seaboard, and then the surge of adventurers, always adventurers, farther and farther West until they came to the shores of the Pacific.

This book gives us a feel of the people who accomplished this tremendous task, and I think we will be better citizens for having read and understood our history.

ELEANOR ROOSEVELT

Contents

Part Five : Let My People Go!

Part Six : The Blue and the Gray

Part Seven : Growing Pains

Part Eight : Century of New Frontiers

YOU are about to take part in a remarkable adventure—complete with startling discoveries, amazing feats of courage and endurance, the smell of battlesmoke, the gleam of treasure . . .

In fact, it has everything a truly first-class adventure *should* have. Plus one thing more: *it really happened*.

And you have a real stake in it—for it is the adventure of your country.

Where did it begin? In Europe, actually, a long, long time ago; centuries, even, before the birth of Columbus.

How did it begin?

Like most adventures: with ships and with dreams . . .

PART ONE

Of Ships
and Dreams

First — the dream

A sturdy young man stands high on a towering cliff, looking outward, toward the setting sun. The time is a thousand years ago; the place: a rocky point of English coastline called Land's End.

A restless yearning has driven the young man to this desolate spot. He is descended from Saxon and Norse sea rovers, and he longs to follow in their wake, pushing out, conquering, discovering . . .

This is the end of his known world. Ahead of him roll the surging billows of the Atlantic Ocean, stretching westward as far as the eye can see. What lies over the horizon? Nobody knows. The old bards, strumming their harps, sing of raids across the little European seas, of ships hugging the coastlines; but of the mighty ocean— nothing except rumors of sea serpents, darkness and death.

Yet, as his lungs fill with the fresh sea air, his imagination begins to race, and the outgoing tide seems to pull his spirit along with it . . . *Follow me,* it whispers. *Wonders may be waiting for the man who dares my uncharted waters—great treasure, vast new lands where a man can walk like a king. Westward! Sail westward!*

Many restless spirits shared this dream of new horizons a thousand years ago. One of them made up a poem called "The Sea Farer." Read it, and you will smell salt spray and feel the tug of high adventure —that irresistible urge to challenge the unknown which was soon to drive little wooden ships across open water . . . to the vast American wilderness.

THE SEA FARER
(The Youth)

Unknown Saxon Author, Tenth Century
Translated by J. Duncan Spaeth

Oh, wildly my heart
Beats in my bosom and bids me to try
The tumble and surge of seas tumultuous,
Breeze and brine and the breakers' roar.
Daily, hourly, drives me my spirit
Outward to sail, far countries to see.
Liveth no man so large in his soul,
So gracious in giving, so gay in his youth,
In deeds so daring, so dear to his lord,
But frets his soul for his sea adventure,
Fain to try what fortune shall send.
Harping he needs not, nor hoarding of
    treasure;
Nor woman can win him nor joys of the
    world.
Nothing does please but the plunging bil-
    lows;
Ever he longs who is lured by the sea.
Woods are abloom, the wide world awak-
    ens,
Gay are the mansions, the meadows most
    fair;
These are but warnings, that haste on his
    journey
Him whose heart is hungry to taste
The perils and pleasures of the pathless
    deep . . .

Most eager to sample those "perils and pleasures" were the hardy Norsemen. They pushed out from their overpopulated homeland of Scandinavia, raiding the coast of Europe, settling in such far-flung spots as France, Russia, Iceland, Greenland . . . In A.D. 1000, not long after "The Sea Farer" was written, Leif Ericson, a Norse sea captain from Greenland, was driven by a storm into unfamiliar waters, far from home. He and his men spotted a strange coastline, anchored their ship, and went exploring ashore. They found a wealth of timber, streams filled with salmon, clusters of grapevines. Leif named his discovery Wineland.

There's a good chance that those wild grapes were growing on the coast of New England. If so, Leif the Lucky was the first known European to set foot on American soil . . .

However, the wilderness swallowed up primitive Norse attempts to plant a colony, and Wineland the Good faded to a dim, romantic legend in the chronicles of the Norsemen's descendants. The time was not yet ripe for the conquest of a New World.

Four and a half centuries rolled by, while Europe slowly stirred, stretched, and shook itself awake from the long half-sleep of the Middle Ages. In the Italian seaport town of Genoa, the young son of a weaver grew up dreaming of ships and salt-flavored adventure. His name: Christopher Columbus (c. 1446–1506). Columbus got his sea legs in a far different age than that of Leif Ericson. The invention of printing had made communication easier between all parts of the known world, and that world

4

was constantly expanding, as the use of the compass and other instruments took much of the guesswork out of navigation. Countries along the Atlantic coast of Europe— Portugal, Spain, England, France — sent their ships roaming farther and farther from home ports, competing for new lands, treasure, control of trade routes. Above all, sea captains, merchants and kings dreamed of finding a direct water route to the fabulous riches of the Indies.

Columbus was sure he had the answer: sail west to go east! Educated people knew by now that the world was round, but nobody was certain just how *large* a globe it was. Columbus argued that it was smaller than believed, that the fringes of Asia lay not too far out in the Atlantic, beyond the Azores. There had been many rumors of land out there somewhere. Sailing westward, he grew convinced, would prove the shortest route of all to the Indies. (His calculations were actually far off—for which we will be eternally grateful.)

He tried to peddle his scheme to the crowned heads of Europe for several years before Ferdinand and Isabella of Spain, who had finally defeated the Moors in 1492, decided to take a chance on it. The Moorish wars had emptied their treasury. If Columbus had a good sense of direction, the fabulous wealth of Asia would soon refill their coffers (plus giving them the chance to save some heathen souls). If he were wrong, well, after all, they were only gambling a few ships . . .

And so, in the fall of 1492, three small caravels commanded by Columbus left the Canary Islands behind them and headed for the open sea. Many of the men aboard the *Niña,* the *Pinta* and the *Santa Maria* had been forced into service and were terrified and uncertain about where they were going. Columbus, as usual, didn't have a doubt in the world. Here are some early entries from the journal he kept of the trip.

THE ADMIRAL OF THE OCEAN SEA SETS FORTH

Quoted by Washington Irving
in "Life and Voyages of Columbus"

Therefore, your Highnesses . . . determined to send me, Christopher Columbus, to the said parts of India, to see the said princes, and the people and lands, and discover . . . the means to be taken for the conversion of them to our holy faith; and ordered that I should not go by land to the east (by which it is the custom to go) but by a voyage to the west; by which course, unto the present time, we do not know for certain that anyone hath passed . . . and for this purpose bestowed great favors upon me, appointing me high admiral of the Ocean Sea, and perpetual viceroy and governor of all the islands and continents I should discover and gain . . .

But before the admiral of the Ocean Sea could discover or gain anything, he had to deal with the fears of his crew. As land faded from sight, their terror mounted, reinforced by ancient superstitions about sea monsters and other horrors of the deep. They begged him to turn back. In the following poem, you read his answer.

COLUMBUS

by Joaquin Miller

Behind him lay the gray Azores,
Behind the Gates of Hercules;
Before him not the ghost of shores
Before him only shoreless seas.
The good mate said: "Now we must pray,
For lo! the very stars are gone.
Brave Admiral, speak, what shall I say?"
"Why, say, 'Sail on! sail on! and on!' "

"My men grow mutinous day by day;
My men grow ghastly wan and weak."
The stout mate thought of home; a spray
Of salt wave washed his swarthy cheek.
"What shall I say, brave Admiral, say,
If we sight naught but seas at dawn?"
"Why, you shall say at break of day,
'Sail on! sail on! sail on! and on!' "

They sailed and sailed, as winds might blow,
Until at last the blanched mate said:
"Why, now not even God would know
Should I and all my men fall dead.
These very winds forget their way,
For God from these dread seas is gone.
Now speak, brave Admiral, speak
          and say—"
He said, "Sail on! sail on! and on!"

They sailed. They sailed. Then
          spake the mate:
"This mad sea shows his teeth tonight.
He curls his lip, he lies in wait,
With lifted teeth, as if to bite!
Brave Admiral, say but one good word:
What shall we do when hope is gone?"
The words leapt like a leaping sword:
"Sail on! sail on! sail on! and on!"

Then pale and worn, he kept his deck,
And peered through darkness. Ah,
          that night
Of all dark nights! And then a speck—
A light! a light! at last a light!
It grew, a starlit flag unfurled!
It grew to be Time's burst of dawn.
He gained a world; he gave that world
Its grandest lesson: "On! sail on!"

It was on the 12th of October that Columbus' stubbornness paid off with the sight of land—an island of the Bahamas, which he named San Salvador. He landed, bearing the royal standard. Then, with great emotion, he took possession for the King and Queen of Spain.

Just a small, sandy island, but it was to prove the key to the unlocking of a whole New World . . .

Waiting to greet the Admiral was a group of strange, naked people. He named them Indians, in the mistaken belief that these were, indeed, the islands of the Indies. Here is his own colorful account of them.

COLUMBUS DESCRIBES THE INDIANS

from "The Journal of Christopher Columbus"

I, that we might form great friendship, for I knew that they were a people who could be more easily freed and converted to our holy faith by love than by force, gave to some of them red caps, and glass beads to put round their necks, and many other things of little value, which gave them great pleasure, and made them so much our friends that it was a marvel to see. They afterwards came to the ship's boats where we were, swimming and bringing us parrots, cotton threads in skeins, darts, and many other things; and we exchanged them for other things that we gave them, such as glass beads and small bells. In fine, they took all, and gave what they had with good will. It appeared to me to be a race of people very poor in everything. They go as naked as when their mothers bore them, and so do the women, although I did not see more than one young girl. All I saw were youths, none more than thirty years of age. They are very well made, with very handsome bodies, and very good countenances. Their hair is short and coarse, almost like the hairs of a horse's tail. They wear the hairs brought down to the eyebrows, except a few locks behind, which they wear long and never cut. They paint themselves black, and they are the color of the Canarians, neither black nor white. Some paint themselves white, others red, and others of what color they find. Some paint their faces, others the whole body, some only round the eyes, others only on the nose. They neither carry nor know anything of arms, for I showed them swords, and they took them by the blade and cut themselves through ignorance. They have no iron, their darts being wands without iron, some of them having a fish's tooth at the end, and others being pointed in various ways. They are all of fair stature and size, with good faces, and well made. I saw some with marks of wounds on their bodies, and I made signs to ask what it was, and they gave me to understand that people from other adjacent islands came with the intention of seizing them, and that they defended themselves. I believed, and still believe, that they come here from the mainland to take them prisoners. They should be good servants and intelligent, for I observed that they quickly took in what was said to them, and I believe that they would easily be made Christians, as it appeared to me that they had no religion. I, our Lord being pleased, will take hence, at the time of my departure, six natives for your Highnesses, that they may learn to speak.

These misnamed "Indians"—in fact, all American Indians—were actually descended from Mongolian nomads living in what is now the Gobi desert. Thousands of years ago, their homeland started to dry up and they began a series of migrations across Siberia and the Bering Straits, finally reaching the Americas. They gradually separated into different tribes and levels of culture—from highly civilized Incas, Mayas and Aztecs to the primitive savages of San Salvador. When the bearded Columbus and a naked Indian stared for the first time with equal wonder at each other, it meant that man had come full circle in his wanderings about the globe: westward from Europe, eastward from Asia. The world would never be the same for this meeting.

Within a few years after Columbus' first voyage, other explorers had ventured here and there into portions of North and South America. It soon became apparent that these regions were not the fringes of Asia—but a rich new world.

Now came the great age of conquest, as fleets of galleons began to arrive in Spanish harbors, holds packed with Aztec and Inca bullion, jewels, jade . . . Conquistadors and missionaries swarmed over the Americas, exploring most of the southern portion of the United States, from Carolina to California. "Grab the Gold and Convert the Heathen" became the first American dream . . .

Spain was top dog in the New World during most of the sixteenth century. Then, in 1588, Philip II of Spain decided to add England to his personal collection of countries. He sent an Invincible Armada to do the job, but the plucky little British ships proved to be the invincible ones. Helped by a storm, they destroyed the Armada and, with it, Spain's control of the seas and monopoly in the New World.

Now swashbuckling Englishmen take center stage in our drama. Who could blame them for strutting a bit? If they could tweak the beard of the mighty Spanish king, what wonders *couldn't* they perform? As a starter, they laid claim to the whole of Spanish North America above Florida, and named it Virginia. Sir Humphrey Gilbert and Sir Walter Raleigh had failed to plant colonies there, but nothing could stop the English now!

It is Christmastime, 1606. James I of England has granted two stock companies the right to make trading and colonizing expeditions to Virginia (provided the Crown gets a healthy share of any profits). Three ships in the service of the London Company—the *Goodspeed,* the *Sarah Constant* and the *Discovery*—are just about to set sail for the New World.

The ships swarm with gentleman adventurers, many of them down on their luck, eagerly looking forward to the trip. They expect to find gold, discover a "Northwest Passage" to the Pacific, and otherwise make their fortunes in America. One of their leaders is a certain Captain John Smith.

The cocky spirits and extravagant hopes of these men as they set forth are captured in the following verses, written during this time of enthusiastic departures.

BRITONS, YOU STAY TOO LONG

from "Ode to the Virginian Voyage"
by Michael Drayton

Britons, you stay too long,
Quickly aboard bestow you,
And with a merry Gale
Swell your stretch'd Sail
With Vows as strong
As the Winds that blow you.

*　*　*

And cheerfully at Sea,
Success you still entice,
To get the Pearl and Gold,
And ours to hold,
VIRGINIA,
Earth's only Paradise.

* * *

When as the luscious smell
Of that delicious Land—
Above the Sea that flows,
The clear Wind throws—
Your Hearts to swell,
Approaching that dear Strand.

In kenning of the Shore
(Thanks to God first given)
O you the happy'st men,
Be frolic then,
Let Cannons roar,
Frighting the wide Heaven . . .

* * *

The cannons roared in May, 1607, when the three ships dropped anchor in the James River of Virginia. Men poured ashore, all set to rake in the "Pearl and Gold." Their rude settlement of Jamestown became the first permanent English colony in the New World. A year later—in what is now Canada—Champlain claimed the rock of Quebec for France. The year after *that,* Henry Hudson, in the service of the Dutch, explored the river which bears his name. Thus, the basis for three contending American empires—English, French and Dutch—was laid.

Now we come to the Pilgrims and a different kind of American dream. Up to the sail-ing of the *Mayflower,* most men had come to the New World seeking treasure, easy profits —expecting to reap without having to sow. However, the Pilgrims didn't want to *take* from the New World; they came to plant their roots there. They were a group of English farmers and workmen, who had separated from the official Church of England. They believed that a congregation had the right to choose its own form of worship, free from the authority of bishops and established ritual. The religious intolerance of the day caused them to flee to Holland. After some years there, they decided to emigrate to America, where they hoped to build a new life, free from persecution . . . Other ships had brought men and swords to America; the *Mayflower* carried families and tools.

LANDING OF THE PILGRIM FATHERS

by Felicia Dorothea Hemans

The breaking waves dashed high
On a stern and rock-bound coast;
And the woods against a stormy sky,
Their giant branches tossed;
And the heavy night hung dark
The hills and waters o'er—
When a band of exiles moored their bark
On a wild New England shore.

Not as the conqueror comes,
They, the true-hearted, came;—
Not with the roll of stirring drums,
And the trumpets that sing of fame;—
Not as the flying come,
In silence and in fear;

They shook the depths of the
    desert's gloom
With their hymns of lofty cheer.

Amidst the storm they sang,
And the stars heard, and the sea!
And the sounding aisles of the
    dim woods rang
To the anthem of the free;
The ocean eagle soared
From his nest by the white wave's foam,
And the rocking pines of the
    forest roared:—
This was their welcome home!

There were men with hoary hair
Amidst that pilgrim band;
Why had they come to wither there,
Away from their childhood's land?

There was woman's fearless eye,
Lit by her deep love's truth;
There was manhood's brow
    serenely high,
And the fiery heart of youth.

What sought they thus afar?
Bright jewels of the mine?
The wealth of seas? the spoils of war?
They sought a faith's pure shrine!
Ay, call it holy ground,
The soil where first they trod!
They left unstained what there
    they found
Freedom to worship God!

The Pilgrims established Plymouth Colony in 1620. Other Englishmen set up scattered trading and fishing posts along the

coasts of New Hampshire, Maine and Massachusetts. Then, in 1630, a second persecuted religious group left England for America. They were Puritans—close to a thousand of them, aboard a fleet of seventeen ships.

These weren't just simple yeomen and working people like the Pilgrims. They included scholars, gentry, wealthy merchants, servants, artisans—a whole society in miniature. The Puritans planned literally to found a New World in the wilderness— a Commonwealth ruled by the laws of the Bible, far from the vices of the Old World. Their leaders—hard-headed men of affairs as well as visionaries—founded Massachusetts Bay Colony. They quickly built Boston and other towns into both thriving centers of commerce and pious Cities of God.

Now more and more ships began arriving in America, all up and down the Eastern Seaboard. The men and women aboard them settled both North and South. They came from a variety of backgrounds, and they dreamed a variety of dreams . . .

SOUTHERN SHIPS AND SETTLERS

(1606-1732)

by Stephen Vincent Benét

O, where are you going, "Goodspeed" and "Discovery"?
With meek "Susan Constant" to make up the three?
We're going to settle the wilds of Virginia,
For gold and adventure we're crossing the sea.

And what will you find there? Starvation and fever.
We'll eat of the adder and quarrel and rail.
All but sixty shall die of the first seven hundred,
But a nation begins with the voyage we sail.

O, what are you doing, my handsome Lord Baltimore?
Where are you sending your "Ark" and your "Dove"?
I'm sending them over the ocean to Maryland
To build up a refuge for people I love.

Both Catholic and Protestant there may find harbor,
Though I am a Catholic by creed and by prayer.
The South is Virginia, the North is New England.
I'll go in the middle and plant my folk there.

O, what do you seek, "Carolina" and "Albemarle,"
Now the Stuarts are up and the Roundheads are down?
We'll seek and we'll find, to the South of Virginia,
A site by two rivers and name it Charles Town.

And, in South Carolina, the cockfighting planters
Will dance with their belles by a tropical star.
And, in North Carolina, the sturdy Scotch-Irish

Will prove at King's Mountain the metal they are.

O, what are you dreaming, cock-hatted James Oglethorpe?
And who are the people you take in the "Anne"?
They're poor English debtors whom hard laws imprison,
And poor, distressed Protestants, fleeing a ban.

I'll settle them pleasantly on the Savannah,
With Germans and Highlanders, thrifty and strong.
They shall eat Georgia peaches in huts of palmetto,
And their land shall be fertile, their days shall be long.

All:
We're the barques and the sailors, the bread on the waters,
The seed that was planted and grew to be tall,
And the South was first won by our toils and our dangers,
So remember our journeys. Remember us all.

It's not likely we'll forget the pioneers who made our country possible. They arrived here hoping to achieve the Good Life. When they didn't find it waiting for them, they rolled up their sleeves and started to build it. But first, there was a wilderness to tame . . .

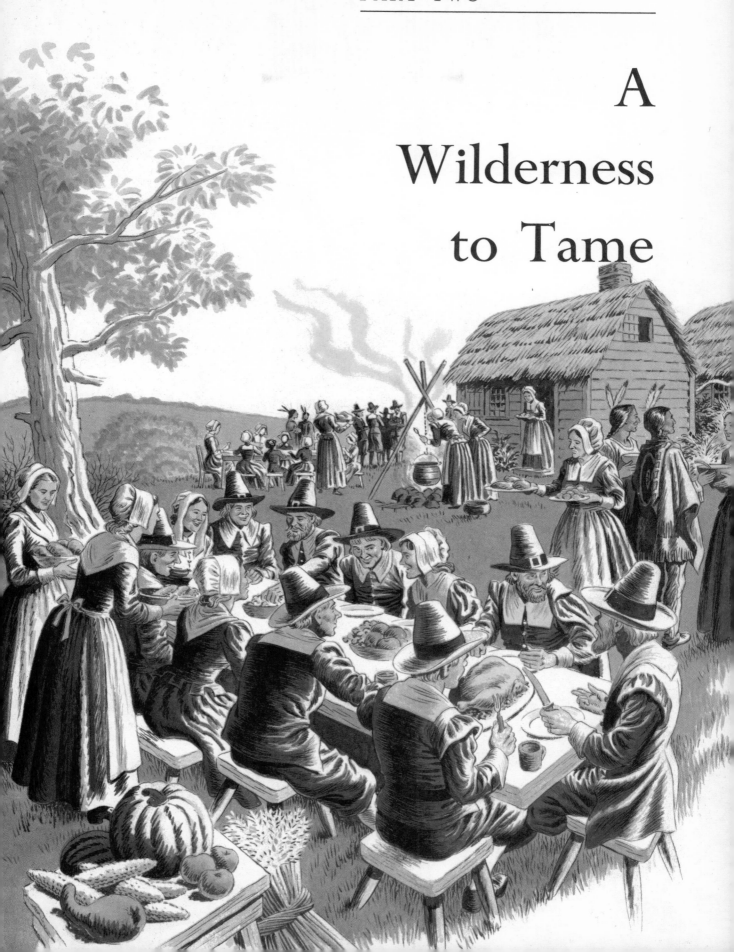

PART TWO

A Wilderness to Tame

THE early settlers arrived on the shores of Virginia and New England as uninvited guests. Their puzzled and curious hosts, the Indians, had long since worked out a way of life that suited them. Braves hunted, fished, and gained manly "virtue" by showing skill and courage in battles against other tribes. Squaws raised corn, made clothes out of deerskin, and tended children, wigwam and campfire.

Suddenly—strange palefaces appear. They invade hunting grounds, frighten game away with loud noises from guns, make general nuisances of themselves. Why don't they go back where they came from? *Still — those wonderfully shiny beads they bring . . . and those guns . . . marvelous weapons . . . much better than bows and arrows . . . like to find out how to use them . . . If palefaces have such powerful weapons, maybe they'd make fine allies against our enemies . . .*

Torn by these conflicting attitudes, the Indians were highly unpredictable. Sometimes they'd help the colonists, but they were just as likely to attack them as intruders. John Smith's experience was typical. Gifted with charm as well as enterprise, he managed to talk the Indians into bringing corn and other food to the starving Jamestown settlers. But even he had his troubles. According to his own account, he was surprised and captured by some Indians while explor-

15

ing in the woods one day (1608). They brought him before their ruler, Powhatan, who ordered him slain. It it hadn't been for Powhatan's daughter—but why not let the hero tell his own story? Here is Captain Smith's version of the famous Pocahontas incident, no less fascinating for being told in the third person.

JOHN SMITH AND POCAHONTAS

from "The Generall Historie of Virginia"
by John Smith

At last they brought [Captain Smith] to Werowocomoco, where was Powhatan, their emperor. Here more than two hundred of those grim courtiers stood wondering at him, as he had been a monster, till Powhatan and his train had put themselves in their greatest braveries. Before a fire upon a seat like a bedstead [Powhatan] sat covered with a great robe, made of raccoon skins, and all the tails hanging by. On either hand did sit a young wench of sixteen or eighteen years, and along on each side the house, two rows of men, and behind them as many women, with all their heads and shoulders painted red, many of their heads bedecked with the white down of birds, but every one with something, and a great chain of white beads about their necks. At [Captain Smith's] entrance before the king, all the people gave a great shout. The queen of Appamatuck was appointed to bring him water to wash his hands, and another brought him a bunch of feathers, instead of a towel, to dry them. Having feasted him after their best barbarous manner they could, a long consultation was held, but the conclusion was two great stones were brought before Powhatan: then as many as could laid hands on [Captain Smith], dragged him to them, and thereon laid his head, and being ready with their clubs to beat out his brains, Pocahontas, the king's dearest daughter, when no entreaty could prevail, got his head in her arms, and laid her own upon his to save his from death: whereat the emperor was contented he should live to make him hatchets, and her bells, beads, and copper; for they thought him as well of all occupations as themselves. For the king himself will make his own robes, shoes, bows, arrows, pots; plant, hunt, or do anything so well as the rest.

Two days after, Powhatan having disguised himself in the most fearfulest manner he could, caused Captain Smith to be brought forth to a great house in the woods, and there upon a mat by the fire to be left alone. Not long after, from behind a mat that divided the house, was made the most dolefulest noise he ever heard; then Powhatan, more like a devil than a man, with some two hundred more as black as himself, came unto him and told him now they were friends, and presently he should go to Jamestown, to send him two great guns and a grindstone, for which he would give him the county of Capahowosick and for ever esteem him as his son Nantaquoud.

Pocahontas later married John Rolfe, another Jamestown settler. Wedding bells proved to be great peacemakers, and the Indian and the white man entered one of their tragically brief periods of harmony.

It was Rolfe who managed to turn the

growing and exporting of a certain Indian weed into the gold mine the Virginians had failed to find. The weed's name was tobacco, and the Indian habit of smoking it had been taken up by the English. They not only smoked it—they chewed it and sniffed and sneezed it in the form of snuff. Most seventeenth century Englishmen, therefore, would have seen eye to eye with the author of our next poem.

TOBACCO!

by George F. Jones

What is it soothes my weary brain,
And takes away all mental pain,
Which comes across me, when at night
I ponder o'er the long day's fight?
    Tobacco!

What is it makes me care forget,
When Sal (my wife) begins to fret,
Because I can't afford to pay
For chignon and for dresses gay?
    Tobacco!

What is it makes me pass from this,
Into a world of perfect bliss,
Where money is as thick as bees
In swarming time, upon the trees?
    Tobacco!

What is it that I hope to see,
When nothing else is left to me,
When bankrupt through the world I roam,
Without a spot to call my home?
    Tobacco!

As plantations spread out along the James River, Virginia became more and more thickly settled. In 1619, the wheels of democracy started rolling in Virginia with the election of the first representative assembly in America. In the same year, the first Negro slaves were introduced. The opposing ideas of democratic freedom and slavery would one day tear the country in two.

While tobacco planters thrived, life was difficult over in New England. The *Mayflower* had actually been heading for sunny Virginia but had been blown off course by a storm, and was forced to anchor off the shore of icy Cape Cod. Here, the Pilgrims drew up the famous Mayflower Compact, which established temporary government by majority will. They disembarked at the worst possible time—the beginning of a bleak New England winter. Governor Bradford has left us an unforgettable record of their arrival.

THE LANDING

from "History of Plymouth Plantation"
by William Bradford

And for the season, it was winter, and they that know the winters of that country know them to be sharp and violent, and subject to cruel and fierce storms, dangerous to travel to known places, much more to search an unknown coast. Besides, what could they see but a hideous and desolate wilderness full of wild beasts and wild men? . . . If they looked behind them, there was the mighty ocean which they had passed, and was now as a main bar and gulf to separate them from all the civil parts of the world. . . . What could now sustain them but the spirit of God and His grace?

17

During that first terrible winter, half the colonists died. The rest might have joined them had not friendly Indians shown them how to catch fish and plant corn, pumpkins and other native vegetables. They gathered their first harvest in the fall of 1621, and at the same time a relief ship arrived from England. In November, Governor Bradford proclaimed a great feast of Thanksgiving, which was to become a national holiday. However, the colony still had to struggle hard to survive. Around 1630, an unknown settler expressed mixed feelings about his adopted land. Here is what he wrote:

OUR FOREFATHERS' SONG

Anonymous

New England's annoyances you that would
    know them,
Pray ponder these verses which briefly doth
    show them.

The place where we live is a wilderness
    wood,
Where grass is much wanting that's fruit-
    ful and good:
Our mountains and hills and our valleys
    below,
Being commonly covered with ice and with
    snow;
And when the north-west wind with violence
    blows,
Then every man pulls his cap over his nose:
But if any's so hardy and will it withstand,
He forfeits a finger, a foot or a hand.

But when the Spring opens we then take the
    hoe,
And make the ground ready to plant and to
    sow;

Our corn being planted and seed being sown,
The worms destroy much before it is grown;
And when it is growing some spoil there is
    made,
By birds and by squirrels that pluck up the
    blade;
And when it is come to full corn in the ear,
It is often destroyed by raccoon and by deer.

If fresh meat be wanting, to fill up our dish,
We have carrots and turnips as much as we
    wish;
And is there a mind for a delicate dish
We repair to the clam-banks, and there we
    catch fish.
Instead of pottage and puddings, and cus-
    tards and pies,
Our pumpkins and parsnips are common
    supplies;
We have pumpkins at morning, and pump-
    kins at noon,
If it was not for pumpkins we should be un-
    done.

If barley be wanting to make into malt,
We must be contented, and think it no fault;
For we can make liquor to sweeten our lips,
Of pumpkins and parsnips and walnut tree
    chips.

Now while some are going let others be
    coming,
For while liquor's boiling it must have a
    scumming;
But I will not blame them, for birds of a
    feather,
By seeking their fellows are flocking to-
    gether.

But you whom the Lord intends hither to
    bring,
Foresake not the honey for fear of the sting;
But bring both a quiet and contented mind,
And all needful blessings you surely will find.

They griped; but in spite of freezing winters, Indian attacks and wild beasts, they
cleared their fields and built their towns. Yet
they were neither saints nor supermen. It
was as though the promise of the New World
pulled out of them a stubborn resolve to
persevere that they didn't know they had.
. . . *So what if it is a wilderness? Axes can
chop down trees, can't they? And there's lots
of game to shoot—those wonderful fat tur-
keys, for instance . . . And enough land for
everybody—think of that! Remember how
it was in the Old World? Practically every
square foot owned by somebody else. But
here—just pick your spot . . .* Thoughts like
these must have inspired Thomas Morton,
who first came to Massachusetts in the
1620s, to write the following:

IF THIS LAND BE NOT RICH

by Thomas Morton

And while our houses were building, I did
endeavor to take a survey of the country; the
more I looked, the more I liked it . . . For so
many goodly groves of trees; dainty, fine,
round, rising hillocks; delicate, fair, large
plains; sweet crystal fountains, and clear running streams . . . Contained within the volume of the land, fowls in abundance; fish in
multitude; and discovered besides, millions
of turtle doves on the green boughs, which
sat pecking of the full, ripe, pleasant grapes,
that were supported by the lusty trees . . .
which made the land to me seem paradise,
for in mine eye it was Nature's masterpiece
. . . *If this land be not rich, then is the whole
world poor.*

The author of this description was so carried away that he set up a colony in Massachusetts called Merry Mount, where young
men spent most of their time feasting, singing, and dancing around a Maypole. Un-
fortunately, they also traded guns to the Indians, who promptly used them on other settlers. To the sober Pilgrims nearby—already convinced that Morton and his merry-
makers were doing the Devil's work—this
was the last straw. They descended in force
on Merry Mount and ended the fun and
games for good.

You couldn't really blame the Pilgrims;
pushing back the wilderness was no laughing
matter. In order for settlements to survive,
men had to conform to the highest standards
of self-discipline, courage and cooperation.
As the frontier slowly retreated, the character of America's first folk hero was forged:
the pioneer.

THE SETTLER

by *Alfred B. Street*

His echoing axe the settler swung
  Amid the sea-like solitude,
And rushing, thundering, down were flung
  The Titans of the wood;
Loud shrieked the eagle as he dashed
From out his mossy nest, which crashed
  With its supporting bough,
And the first sunlight, leaping, flashed
  On the wolf's haunt below.

Rude was the garb, and strong the frame
  Of him who plied his ceaseless toil;
To form that garb, the wild-wood game
  Contributed their spoil;
The soul that warmed that frame disdained
The tinsel, gaud and glare, that reigned
  Where men their crowds collect;
The simple fur, untrimmed, unstained,
  This forest tamer decked.

* * *

His roof adorned, a pleasant spot:
  'Mid the black logs, green glowed the
    grain;
And herbs and plants the woods knew
    not,
  Throve in the sun and rain.
The smoke-wreath curling o'er the dell,
The low—the bleat—the tinkling bell,
  All made a landscape strange,
Which was the living chronicle
  Of deeds that wrought the change.

The violet sprung at Spring's first tinge,
  The rose of Summer spread its glow,
The maize hung on its Autumn fringe,
  Rude Winter brought his snow;
And still the settler labored there,

His shout and whistle woke the air,
  As cheerily he plied
His garden spade, or drove his share
  Along the hillock's side.

He marked the fire-storm's blazing flood,
  Roaring and crackling on its path,
And scorching earth and melting wood
  Beneath its greedy wrath;
He marked the rapid whirlwind shoot,
Trampling the pine tree with its foot,
  And darkening thick the day
With streaming bough and severed root,
  Hurled whizzing on its way.

His gaunt hound yelled, his rifle flashed,
  The grim bear hushed its savage growl,
In blood and foam the panther gnashed
  Its fangs with dying howl;
The fleet deer ceased its flying bound,
Its snarling wolf foe bit the ground,
  And with its moaning cry,
The beaver sank beneath the wound,
  Its pond-built Venice by.

Humble the lot, yet his the race,
  When Liberty sent forth her cry,
Who thronged in Conflict's deadliest place,
  To fight, to bleed, to die!

* * *

England didn't provide the only settlers
for the early frontier. France and Holland
were busy carving their own slices out of the
rich American pie. By the middle of the seventeenth century, the enterprising Dutch had
established New Netherland in what are now
the states of New York and New Jersey.
They brought their customs and traditions

with them. Red-cheeked Dutch peasants did chores on neat little "boueries" or farms. Wealthy "patroons" built magnificent estates on the Hudson, where they lorded it over their tenants in fine feudal style. In the bustling seaport town of New Amsterdam, stout Dutch burghers puffed solemnly on long clay pipes while discussing the latest profits in the fur or tobacco trade . . .

The Dutch made better businessmen than colonial administrators. Holland neglected its American colony, which was governed by a succession of corrupt or inept officials. The colonists became so indifferent to who ruled them that when the English decided to take over New Netherland in 1664, nobody would back up "peg-leg" Peter Stuyvesant (the current governor) in making a fight of it. He was forced to surrender, and without bloodshed, New Amsterdam turned into New York City. That's the official record. Here's a legendary version which makes up in color what it may lack in truth.

WHY SPUYTEN DUYVIL IS SO NAMED

from "Myths and Legends of Our Own Land"
by Charles M. Skinner

The tidewater creek that forms the upper boundary of Manhattan Island is known to dwellers in tenements round about as "Spittin' Divvle." The proper name of it is Spuyten Duyvil, and this, in turn, is the compression of a celebrated boast by Anthony Van Corlaer. This redoubtable gentleman, famous for fat, long wind, and long whiskers, was trumpeter for the garrison at New Amsterdam, which his countryman had just bought for twenty-four dollars, and he sounded the brass so sturdily that in the fight between the Dutch and Indians at the Dey Street peach orchard his blasts struck more terror into the red men's hearts than did the matchlocks of his comrades. William the Testy vowed that Anthony and his trumpet were garrison enough for all Manhattan Is-

21

land, for he argued that no regiment of Yankees would approach near enough to be struck with lasting deafness, as must have happened if they came when Anthony was awake.

Peter Stuyvesant—Peter the Headstrong—showed his appreciation of Anthony's worth by making him his esquire, and when he got news of an English expedition on its way to seize his unoffending colony, he at once ordered Anthony to rouse the villages along the Hudson with a trumpet call to war. The esquire took a hurried leave of six or eight ladies, each of whom delighted to believe that his affections were lavished on her alone, and bravely started northward, his trumpet hanging on one side, a stone bottle, much heavier, depending from the other. It was a stormy evening when he arrived at the upper end of the island, and there was no ferryman in sight, so, after fuming up and down the shore, he swallowed a mighty draught of Dutch courage—for he was as accomplished a performer on the horn as on the trumpet—and swore with ornate and voluminous oaths that he would swim the stream "in spite of the devil" [En spuyt den Duyvil].

He plunged in, and had gone halfway across when the Evil One, not to be spited, appeared as a huge moss-bunker, vomiting boiling water and lashing a fiery tail. This dreadful fish seized Anthony by the leg; but the trumpeter was game, for, raising his instrument to his lips, he exhaled his last breath through it in a defiant blast that rang through the woods for miles and made the devil himself let go for a moment. Then he was dragged below, his nose shining through the water more and more faintly, until, at last,

all sight of him was lost. The failure of his mission resulted in the downfall of the Dutch in America, for, soon after, the English won a bloodless victory, and St. George's cross flaunted from the ramparts where Anthony had so often saluted the setting sun. But it was years, even then, before he was hushed, for in stormy weather it was claimed that the shrill of his trumpet could be heard near the creek that he had named, sounding above the deeper roar of the blast.

The Dutch flavor has contributed richly to the American brew. Many regions of New York City—Harlem, the Bowery, and others—still retain their Dutch names. A single Dutch family—the Roosevelts—has given two great Presidents to the United States.

After New Netherland was absorbed by England, in 1664, France emerged as England's main contender for control of the continent. While English settlers spread out along the Eastern Seaboard during the seventeenth and eighteenth centuries, the French were creating a huge fur-trading empire up north in Canada. Their string of trading posts and forts extended up and down the St. Lawrence River, and as far west as the region of the Great Lakes. The main source of wealth was beaver, which had become quite the fashion in Europe. Indians trapped them in great numbers and were happy to exchange glossy pelts for cheap trinkets and goods. (Cheap to the French, precious to the Indians; it's all relative.) Washington Irving has left us a vivid account of Indians arriving in Montreal, beaver in their canoes and trading on their minds . . .

FUR-BEARING INDIANS COME TO TOWN

from "Astoria" by Washington Irving

Every now and then a large body of Ottawas, Hurons, and other tribes who hunted the countries bordering on the great lakes, would come down in a squadron of light canoes, laden with beaver skins and other spoils of their year's hunting. The canoes would be unladen, taken on shore, and their contents disposed in order. A camp of birch bark would be pitched outside of the town, and a kind of primitive fair opened with that grave ceremonial so dear to the Indians. An audience would be demanded of the governor-general, who would hold the conference with becoming state, seated in an elbow chair, with the Indians ranged in semicircles before him, seated on the ground, and silently smoking their pipes. Speeches would be made, presents exchanged, and the audience would break up in universal good humor.

Now would ensue a brisk traffic with the merchants, and all Montreal would be alive with naked Indians running from shop to shop, bargaining for arms, kettles, knives, axes, blankets, bright-colored cloths, and other articles of use or fancy; upon all which, says an old French writer, the merchants were sure to clear at least two hundred per cent. There was no money used in this traffic, and, after a time, all payment in spirituous liquors was prohibited, in consequence of the frantic and frightful excesses and bloody brawls which they were apt to occasion.

Their wants and caprices being supplied, they would take leave of the governor, strike their tents, launch their canoes, and ply their way up the Ottawa to the lakes.

The fur trade created a colorful class of Frenchmen known as bush-rangers. They became experts in the lore of the woods and guided trading expeditions that wished to contact remote tribes. Many bush-rangers grew to like Indian ways so much that they adopted them for themselves, living up to the following description.

FRENCH BUSH-RANGERS GO "NATIVE"

*from "History of the Conspiracy of Pontiac"
by Francis Parkman*

In many a squalid [Indian] camp among the plains and forests of the west, the traveller would have encountered men owning the blood and speaking the language of France, yet, in their wild and swarthy visages and barbarous costume, seeming more akin to those with whom they had cast their lot. The renegade of civilization caught the habits and imbibed the prejudices of his chosen associates. He loved to decorate his long hair with eagle feathers, to make his face hideous with vermilion, ochre and soot, and to adorn his greasy hunting frock with horsehair fringes. His dwelling, if he had one, was a wigwam. He lounged on a bear-skin while his squaw boiled his venison and lighted his pipe. In hunting, in dancing, in singing, in taking a scalp, he rivalled the genuine Indian. His mind was tinctured with the superstitions of the forest. He had faith in the magic drum

23

of the conjurer; he was not sure that a thunder-cloud could not be frightened away by whistling at it through the wing bone of an eagle; he carried the tail of a rattlesnake in his bullet-pouch by way of amulet; and he placed implicit trust in the prophetic truth of his dreams.

While the French often went "native" and generally dealt with Indians according to a "live and let live" code, the English attitude was quite different. They tended to see Indians by unrealistic extremes: as either Devilish Barbarians or Noble Savages. The truth lay somewhere in between. Indians undeniably raided, scalped, and burned prisoners at the stake. But white Puritans hanged innocent women as witches, and frontiersmen butchered Indians with as little concern as if they were animal pests. It was a cruel age, and the struggle for the wilderness was bound to produce violence—just as the Indians were bound to lose. They slowly became a confused and frustrated people. The introduction of white men's whiskey, guns and bright gewgaws undermined their traditional way of life, while settlers gradually pushed them out of their ancient hunting grounds. If they tried to adapt to white society and white ways, they were generally treated as inferiors and became misfits, living a shadowy existence between two worlds, belonging to neither.

Sometimes Indians would try to reverse the process. Since "If you can't lick 'em— join 'em" didn't seem to work, they would attempt to adapt the white man to *their* ways. In 1755, a pioneer named James Smith was captured by some Delaware Indians, who took him to their town of Tullihas and made him a member of their tribe. Here is his own account of the adoption ceremony.

A WHITE MAN IS FORCED TO BECOME AN INDIAN

from "Account of the Remarkable Occurrences in the Life and Travels of Colonel James Smith"

The day after my arrival at the aforesaid town, a number of Indians collected about me, and one of them began to pull the hair out of my head. He had some ashes on a piece of bark in which he frequently dipped his fingers in order to take the firmer hold, and so he went on, as if he had been plucking a turkey, until he had all the hair clean out of my head, except a small spot about three or four inches square on my crown; this they cut off with a pair of scissors, excepting three locks, which they dressed up in their own mode. Two of these they wrapped round with a narrow beaded garter made by themselves for that purpose, and the other they plaited at full length and then stuck it full of silver brooches. After this they bored my nose and ears, and fixed me off with earrings and nose jewels; then they ordered me to strip off my clothes and put on a breechclout, which I did; then they painted my head, face, and body in various colors. They put a large belt of wampum on my neck, and silver bands on my hands and right arm; and so an old chief led me out in the street and gave the alarm halloo, *oo-wigh,* several times repeated quick, and on this, all that were in the town came running and stood round the old chief, who held me by the hand in the midst.

As I at that time knew nothing of their mode of adoption . . . I made no doubt but they were about putting me to death in some cruel manner. The old chief, holding me by the hand, made a long speech, very loud, and when he had done he handed me to three young squaws, who led me by the hand down the bank into the river until the water was up to our middle. The squaws then made signs to me to plunge myself into the water, but I did not understand them; I thought that the result of the council was that I should be drowned, and that these young ladies were to be the executioners. They all three laid violent hold of me, and I for some time opposed them with all my might, which occasioned loud laughter by the multitude that were on the bank of the river. At length, one of the squaws made out to speak a little English (for I believe they began to be afraid of me) and said, "No hurt you"; on this, I gave myself up to their ladyships, who were as good as their word, for though they plunged me under water and washed and rubbed me severely, I could not say they hurt me much.

These young women then led me up to the council house, where some of the tribe were ready with new clothes for me. They gave me a new, ruffled shirt, which I put on, also a pair of leggings done off with ribbons and beads, likewise a pair of moccasins, and garters dressed with beads, porcupine quills, and red hair—also a tinsel-laced cap. They again painted my head and face with various colors, and tied a bunch of red feathers to one of these locks they had left on the crown of my head, which stood up five or six inches. They seated me on a bearskin, and gave me a pipe, tomahawk, and polecatskin pouch, which had been skinned pocket fashion, and contained tobacco, killegenico or dry sumach leaves, which they mix with their tobacco, also spunk, flint, and steel. When I was thus seated, the Indians came in dressed and painted in their grandest manner. As they came in they took their seats and for a considerable time there was a profound silence; every one was smoking, but not a word was spoken among them. At length one of the chiefs made a speech which was delivered to me by an interpreter, and was as followeth: "My son, you are now flesh of our flesh and bone of our bone."

Smith was a reluctant adopted son for four years, before escaping from his tribal "brothers." Meanwhile, the French and Indian War was raging. This was a local reflection of a great world-wide struggle between contending British and French empires. For about a hundred years, friction had been growing between settlers of the two nationalities in North America. The British Hudson's Bay Company competed for the fur trade in areas claimed by French Canadians. The French, on the other hand, moved into regions of Ohio claimed by the British. The French and Indian War would settle things for good.

Both sides used different Indian tribes as irregular troops, raiding enemy settlements and forts. The Indians hoped to get great advantages by siding with the winner, but they were merely pawns. Some of them realized it. "You and the French," said one to an Englishman, "are like the two edges of a pair of shears, and we are the cloth which is cut to pieces between them." In the first part of the war, however, it was the English who were cut to pieces, because of the stubbornness of British General Braddock. On his way through the wilderness to attack Fort Duquesne (now Pittsburgh), in 1755, he insisted on marching his men in erect close order—as though they were on the parade ground. In spite of the warning of a shrewd Colonial named Ben Franklin (who supplied his wagons), he expected the enemy to "stand up and fight" in the accepted European military tradition. Instead, the French and Indians hid behind trees and slaughtered his smart-stepping, red-coated Regulars like sitting ducks. Braddock himself was killed. Among the few Englishmen who distinguished themselves was a certain colonel of Virginia Militia named George Washington.

The French had the best of it for years. Then, in 1759, a young British general named Wolfe marched his army in a bold attack on the fortress city of Quebec. The French commander was Montcalm. The resulting struggle took both their lives. Historian Francis Parkman has left us a stirring picture of this battle which decided the outcome of the war.

THE BATTLE FOR QUEBEC

from "History of the Conspiracy of Pontiac"
by Francis Parkman

The sun rose, and, from the ramparts of Quebec, the astonished people saw the Plains of Abraham glittering with arms, and the dark-red lines of the English forming in array of battle. Breathless messengers had borne the evil tidings to Montcalm, and far and near his wide-extended camp resounded with the rolling of alarm drums and the din of startled preparation . . . "They have got to the weak side of us at last," he is reported to have said, "and we must crush them with our numbers." With headlong haste, his troops were pouring over the bridge of the St. Charles, and gathering in heavy masses under the western ramparts of the town. Could numbers give assurance of success, their triumph would have been secure; for five French battalions and the armed colonial peasantry amounted in all to more than seven thousand five hundred men. Full in sight before them stretched the long, thin lines of the British forces—the half-wild Highlanders, the steady soldiery of England, and the hardy levies of the provinces—less than five thousand in number, but all inured to battle, and strong in the full assurance of success . . .

It was nine o'clock, and the adverse armies stood motionless, each gazing on the other. The clouds hung low, and, at intervals, warm, light showers descended, besprinkling both alike. The coppice and cornfields in front of the British troops were filled with French sharpshooters, who kept up a distant, spattering fire. Here and there a soldier fell in the ranks, and the gap was filled in silence.

At a little before ten, the British could see that Montcalm was preparing to advance, and, in a few moments, all his troops appeared in rapid motion. They came on in three divisions, shouting after the manner of their nation, and firing heavily as soon as they came within range. In the British ranks, not a trigger was pulled, not a soldier stirred; and their ominous composure seemed to damp the spirits of the assailants. It was not till the French were within forty yards that the fatal word was given. At once, from end to end of the British line, the muskets rose to the level, as if with the sway of some great machine, and the whole blazed forth at once in one crashing explosion. Like a ship at full career, arrested with sudden ruin on a sunken rock, the columns of Montcalm staggered, shivered, and broke before that wasting storm of lead. The smoke, rolling along the field, for a moment shut out the view; but when the white wreaths were scattered on the wind, a wretched spectacle was disclosed;

men and officers tumbled in heaps, columns resolved into a mob, order and obedience gone; and when the British muskets were levelled for a second volley, the masses were seen to cower and shrink with uncontrollable panic. For a few minutes, the French regulars stood their ground, returning a sharp and not ineffectual fire. But now, echoing cheer on cheer, redoubling volley on volley, trampling the dying and the dead, and driving the fugitives in crowds, the British troops advanced and swept the field before them. The ardour of the men burst all restraint. They broke into a run, and with unsparing slaughter chased the flying multitude to the very gates of Quebec. Foremost of all, the light-footed Highlanders dashed along in furious pursuit, hewing down the Frenchmen with their broadswords, and slaying many in the very ditch of the fortifications. Never was victory more quick or more decisive . . .

Townshend and Murray, the only general officers who remained unhurt, passed to the head of every regiment in turn, and thanked the soldiers for the bravery they had shown; yet the triumph of the victors was mingled with sadness, as the tidings went from rank to rank that Wolfe had fallen.

In the heat of the action, as he advanced at the head of the grenadiers of Louisburg, a bullet shattered his wrist; but he wrapped his handkerchief about the wound, and showed no sign of pain. A moment more, and a ball pierced his side. Still he pressed forward, waving his sword and cheering his soldiers to the attack, when a third shot lodged deep within his breast. He paused, reeled, and, staggering to one side, fell to the earth. Brown, a lieutenant of the grenadiers, Hen-

derson, a volunteer, an officer of artillery, and a private soldier raised him together in their arms, and, bearing him to the rear, laid him softly on the grass. They asked if he would have a surgeon; but he shook his head, and answered that all was over with him. His eyes closed with the torpor of approaching death, and those around sustained his fainting form. Yet they could not withhold their gaze from the wild turmoil before them, and the charging ranks of their companions rushing through fire and smoke. "See how they run," one of the officers exclaimed, as the French fled in confusion before the levelled bayonets. "Who run?" demanded Wolfe, opening his eyes like a man aroused from sleep. "The enemy, sir," was the reply; "they give way everywhere." "Then," said the dying general, "tell Colonel Burton to march Webb's regiment down to Charles River, to cut off their retreat from the bridge. Now, God be praised, I will die in peace," he murmured; and, turning on his side, he calmly breathed his last.

Almost at the same moment fell his great adversary, Montcalm, as he strove, with useless bravery, to rally his shattered ranks. Struck down with a mortal wound, he was placed upon a litter and borne to the General Hospital on the banks of the St. Charles. The surgeons told him that he could not recover. "I am glad of it," was his calm reply. He then asked how long he might survive, and was told that he had not many hours remaining. "So much the better," he said; "I am happy that I shall not live to see the surrender of Quebec." Officers from the garrison came to his bedside to ask his orders and instructions. "I will give no more orders," replied the defeated soldier; "I have much business that must be attended to, of greater moment than your ruined garrison and this wretched country. My time is very short; therefore, pray leave me." The officers withdrew, and none remained in the chamber but his confessor and the Bishop of Quebec. To the last, he expressed his contempt for his own mutinous and half-famished troops, and his admiration for the disciplined valour of his opponents. He died before midnight, and was buried at his own desire in a cavity of the earth formed by the bursting of a bombshell.

The victorious army encamped before Quebec and pushed their preparations for the siege with zealous energy; but before a single gun was brought to bear, the white flag was hung out, and the garrison surrendered. On the eighteenth of September, 1759, the rock-built citadel of Canada passed forever from the hands of its ancient masters.

A year later, Montreal surrendered. In 1763, the Treaty of Paris officially ended the war. France had lost an empire.

FRENCH PIONEERS

(1534-1759)

by Stephen Vincent Benét

New France, New Spain, New England,
Which will it be?
Who will win the new land?
The land across the sea?

They came here, they toiled here,
They broke their hearts afar,
Normandy and Brittany,
Paris and Navarre.

They lost here, at last here,
It wasn't so to be.
Let us still remember them,
Men from oversea.

Marquette and Joliet,
Cartier, La Salle,
Priest, corsair, gentleman,
Gallants one and all.

France was in their quick words,
France was in their veins.
They came here, they toiled here.
They suffered many pains.

Lake and river, stream and wood,
Seigneurs and dames—
They lived here, they died here,
They left singing names.

England received from France: Canada, Nova Scotia, Cape Breton, and all of eastern Louisiana except New Orleans (which was currently owned by Spain, along with western Louisiana). She traded Havana to Spain, in return for Florida. It was a real estate transfer on a truly gigantic scale. But the British Empire would come out on the short end of another deal in a few years when a Revolution would deprive her of thirteen fat colonies . . .

Meanwhile, more and more settlers were arriving, all through the eighteenth century. Wars, Indian struggles—nothing stopped them from embarking for the Promised Land. They were of many nationalities besides English—Scotch, Irish, German, Swedish. Many religious groups—Swiss Mennonites, Jews, Quakers—were also finding haven in America. The intolerance of Puritans and others toward different religions had begun to soften, possibly because the country was so big that communities with opposing views didn't have to tread on each other's toes. Pennsylvania, in particular, practiced tolerance and encouraged immigration. People too poor to pay their way over could arrive as indentured servants. This was a form of short-term slavery which was cruel, yet had its practical side. Our next selection, written from personal observation in the middle of the eighteenth century, is a graphic description of what poor immigrants were willing to go through in order to get to America.

INDENTURED SERVANTS FOR SALE

from "Gottlieb Mittelberger's Journey to Pennsylvania in the Year 1750"

When the ships have landed at Philadelphia after their long voyage, no one is permitted to leave them except those who pay for their passage or can give good security; the others, who cannot pay, must remain on board the ships till they are purchased and are released from the ships by their purchasers. The sick always fare the worst, for the healthy are naturally preferred and purchased first; and so the sick and wretched must often remain on board in front of the city for two or three weeks, and frequently die, whereas many a one, if he could pay his debt and were permitted to leave the ship immediately, might recover and remain alive.

The sale of human beings in the market on board the ship is carried on thus: Every day Englishmen, Dutchmen, and High German people come from the city of Philadel-

phia and other places, in part from a great distance, say twenty, thirty, or forty hours away, and go on board the newly arrived ship that has brought and offers for sale passengers from Europe, and select among the healthy persons such as they deem suitable for their business, and bargain with them how long they will serve for their passage money, which most of them are still in debt for. When they have come to an agreement, it happens that adult persons bind themselves in writing to serve three, four, five, or six years for the amount due by them, according to their age and strength. But very young people, from ten to fifteen years, must serve till they are twenty-one years old.

Many parents must sell and trade away their children like so many head of cattle, for if their children take the debt upon themselves, the parents can leave the ship free and unrestrained; but as the parents often do not know where and to what people their children are going, it often happens that such parents and children, after leaving the ship, do not see each other again for many years, perhaps no more in all their lives.

It often happens that whole families, husband, wife, and children, are separated by being sold to different purchasers, especially when they have not paid any part of their passage money.

When a husband or wife has died at sea, when the ship has made more than half of her trip, the survivor must pay or serve not only for himself or herself, but also for the deceased. When both parents have died over halfway at sea, their children, especially when they are young and have nothing to pawn or to pay, must stand for their own and their parents' passage, and serve till they are twenty-one years old. When one has served his or her term, he or she is entitled to a new suit of clothes at parting; and if it has been so stipulated, a man gets in addition a horse, a woman, a cow.

Work and labor in this new and wild land are very hard and manifold, and many a one who came there in his old age must work very hard to his end for his bread. I will not speak of young people. Work mostly consists in cutting wood, felling oak trees, rooting out, or as they say there, clearing large tracts of forest. Such forests, being cleared, are then laid out for fields and meadows. From the best hewn wood, fences are made around the new fields; for there all meadows, orchards, and fruit fields are surrounded and fenced in with planks made of thickly split wood, laid one above the other, as in zigzag lines, and within such inclosures horses, cattle, and sheep are permitted to graze. Our Europeans who are purchased must always work hard, for new fields are constantly laid out; and so they learn that stumps of oak trees are in America certainly as hard as in Germany.

It was hard, but if the immigrant endured through his term of service, he had the chance to build a life for himself and his children that he never would have dared hoped for in the Old Country. He might head for the frontier, which was spilling over the Appalachian Mountains into the rich Ohio Valley, and carve out a farm for himself. He might never get rich, but he would have the satisfaction of owning his own land. He would probably leave his heirs such a color-

ful assortment of frontier necessities as described in the following verses, written in 1731.

FATHER ABBEY'S WILL

by John Seccomb

To my dear wife,
My joy and life,
I freely now do give her,
My whole estate,
With all my plate,
Being just about to leave her.

My tub of soap,
A long cart rope,
A frying pan and kettle,
An ashes pail,
A threshing flail,
An iron wedge and beetle.

Two painted chairs,
Nine warden pears,
A large old dripping platter,
This bed of hay,
On which I lay,
An old saucepan for batter.

A little mug,
A two quart jug,
A bottle full of brandy,
A looking glass
To see your face,
You'll find it very handy.

A musket true,
As ever flew,
A pound of shot and wallet,
A leather sash,
My calabash,
My powder horn and bullet.

An old sword blade,
A garden spade,
A hoe, a rake, a ladder,
A wooden can,
A close-stool pan,
A clyster-pipe and bladder.

A greasy hat,
My old ram cat,
A yard and half of linen,
A woollen fleece,
A pot of grease,
In order for your spinning.

A small tooth comb,
An ashen broom,
A candlestick and hatchet,
A coverlid,
Strip'd down with red,
A bag of rags to patch it.

A ragged mat,
A tub of fat,
A book put out by Bunyan,
Another book,
By Robin Cook,
A skein or two of spunyarn.

An old black muff,
Some garden stuff,
A quantity of borage,
Some devil's weed,
And burdock seed,
To season well your porridge.

A chafing dish,
With one salt fish,
If I am not mistaken,
A leg of pork,

A broken fork,
And half a flitch of bacon.

A spinning wheel,
One peck of meal,
A knife without a handle,
A rusty lamp,
Two quarts of samp,
And half a tallow candle.

My pouch and pipes,
Two oxen tripes,
An oaken dish well carved,
My little dog,
And spotted hog,
With two young pigs just starved.

This is my store,
I have no more,
I heartily do give it,
My years are spun,
My days are done,
And so I think to leave it.

* * *

If he was a more ambitious sort, our immigrant might become the hero of this typical American success story. (Although written during the 1790s, these verses apply as well to Colonial times.)

ROUND OF AMERICAN LIFE— FROM GREENFIELD HILL

by Timothy Dwight

In this New World, life's changing round,
In three descents, is often found.
The first, firm, busy, plodding, poor,
Earns, saves, and daily swells, his store;
By farthings first, and pence, it grows;

In shillings next, and pounds, it flows;
Then spread his widening farms, abroad;
His forests wave; his harvests nod;
Fattening, his numerous cattle play,
And debtors dread his reckoning day.
Ambitious then t'adorn with knowledge
His son, he places him at college;
And sends, in smart attire, and neat,
To travel, thro' each neighboring state;
Builds him a handsome house, or buys,
Sees him a gentleman, and dies.

*   *   *

The poet goes on to suggest that the next two generations come to no good, but he's in a pessimistic mood. The point is: the father an immigrant—and the son a *gentleman!* That kind of a leap upward would have been impossible in almost every part of the world save America. Some of America's most successful families were started by hard-working indentured servants.

Let's take up the son now. Maybe he develops a yen for the Southern way of life and buys a stately plantation in Virginia, the Carolinas or Georgia. His hands will raise tobacco, rice, indigo or cotton for him, while he enjoys the pleasures of polite society. These include gaming, dancing, riding to the hunt—with an occasional duel to pep things up.

He might prefer to become a shipbuilder or merchant fleet owner in Boston . . . a banker in New York . . . a lawyer or printer in Philadelphia. As a substantial citizen, he might be elected to a provincial congress. The costume of such a fully arrived gentleman would resemble the fashion plate described below.

A COLONIAL BEAU BRUMMEL

from "The Life of Elbridge Gerry"
by James T. Austin

A gentleman, who paid any attention to his toilet, would have his hair combed out, powdered and tied in a long queue, a plaited white stock, a shirt ruffled at the bosom and over the hands, and fastened at the wrist with gold sleeve buttons, a peach bloom coat and white buttons, lined with white silk, and standing off at the skirts with buckram, a figured silk vest divided at the bottom, so that the pockets extended on the thighs, black silk small clothes with large gold or silver knee buckles, white cotton or silk stockings, large shoes with short quarters and buckles to match. This dress, sketched from the

33

wardrobe of a member, was not peculiarly appropriate to occasions of ceremony, but assumed with more or less exactness by the fashionable gentlemen of the day.

A far cry from an immigrant's rags or a pioneer's coonskin cap! Safely removed from the log cabin frontier, Colonial society preened its feathers and developed its customs and manners.

Meanwhile, most Americans were busy rolling up their sleeves and getting ahead. Their essential character was that of a self-made people, proud of having shaped thriving towns and enterprises out of the wilderness with their own hands. When England, in 1763, started to enforce laws designed to severely control and tax Colonial commerce, Americans naturally resented it. Especially since much of the tax revenue went toward the support of British troops in the Colonies. "Why should *we* pay for *your* Redcoats?" was the American attitude. "To protect you from the Indians," the English answered. "Besides, you're our children, part of the British Empire, and must help pay for its upkeep. Mama knows best." "We're no children! Where was the British Empire when we were chopping down trees? We're responsible men, with our own militia to protect us and our own Colonial legislatures to pass necessary laws. Who needs taxation without representation?" Feeling they were being treated as second-class citizens, the Colonials sent Benjamin Franklin to London, in 1757, to plead their cause. At this point, they still thought of themselves as loyal Englishmen with a legitimate beef. The following verses, written by Franklin while he was in England, illustrate this.

THE MOTHER COUNTRY

by Benjamin Franklin

We have an old mother that peevish is
    grown;
She snubs us like children that scarce walk
    alone;
She forgets we're grown up, and have sense
    of our own;
        Which nobody can deny, deny,
        Which nobody can deny.

If we don't obey orders, whatever the case,
She frowns, and she chides, and she loses all
    pati-
Ence, and sometimes she hits us a slap in
    the face;
        Which nobody can deny, deny,
        Which nobody can deny.

Her orders so odd are, we often suspect
That age has impaired her sound intellect;
But still an old mother should have due re-
    spect;
        Which nobody can deny, deny,
        Which nobody can deny.

Let's bear with her humors as well as we can;
But why should we bear the abuse of her
    man?
When servants make mischief, they earn the
    rattan;
        Which nobody can deny, deny,
        Which nobody can deny.

Know, too, ye bad neighbors, who aim to
    divide
The sons from the mother, that still she's our
    pride;
And if ye attack her, we're all of her side;
        Which nobody can deny, deny,
        Which nobody can deny.

We'll join in her law-suits, to baffle all those
Who, to get what she has, will be often her
   foes;
For we know it must all be our own, when
   she goes;
   Which nobody can deny, deny,
      Which nobody can deny.

"We know it must all be our own, when she goes . . ." The writing of these words showed Franklin's shrewd grasp of things to come. He managed to help talk the British into repealing the hated Stamp Act, but in 1767, they passed the even more unpopular Townshend Acts, which imposed duties on many new items of Colonial commerce. His mission a failure, Franklin returned to an America that was seething with discontent and anger. Verses began to appear in handbills and newspapers, with sentiments like these:

How sweet are the labors that freemen
   endure
That they shall enjoy all the profit secure,
No more such sweet labors Americans know,
If Britons shall reap what Americans sow.

King George III had ignored Colonial petitions, and seemed heartily in favor of disciplining his disobedient "children." His officials took power away from Colonial legislatures and gave it to royal governors. British troops were quartered on American towns. The popular hatred of Redcoats in Boston, whose citizens refused to provide quarters for them, led to the violence of the Boston Massacre in 1770. The pot was starting to boil over. Revolutionary organizations like the Sons of Liberty were gaining recruits.

Then join hand in hand brave Americans all,
By uniting we stand, by dividing we fall . . .

In 1772, a mob burned a British revenue boat. By 1773, most colonies were discussing possible courses of action through Committees of Correspondence. In that year, the growing mood of popular defiance was expressed by some Bostonians who disguised themselves as Indians and threw a shipload of British tea into Boston Harbor. Here is an eyewitness account by one of the rebellious "Indians."

THE BOSTON TEA PARTY

from "A Retrospect of the Boston Tea-Party"
by George Hewes

The tea destroyed was contained in three ships, lying near each other, at what was called at that time Griffin's wharf, and [they] were surrounded by armed ships of war; the commanders of which had publicly declared, that if the rebels, as they were pleased to style the Bostonians, should not withdraw their opposition to the landing of the tea before a certain day, the 17th day of December, 1773, they should on that day force it on shore, under the cover of their cannon's mouth. On the day preceding the seventeenth, there was a meeting of the citizens of the county of Suffolk, convened at one of the churches in Boston, for the purpose of consulting on what measures might be considered expedient to prevent the landing of the tea, or secure the people from the collection of the duty. At that meeting a committee was appointed to wait on Governor Hutchinson, and request him to inform them whether he would take any measures to satisfy the people on the object of the meeting. To the first application of this committee, the Governor told them he would give them a definite answer by five o'clock in the afternoon. At the hour appointed, the committee again repaired to the Governor's house, and on inquiry found he had gone to his country seat at Milton, a distance of about six miles. When the committee returned and informed the meeting of the absence of the Governor, there was a confused murmur among the members, and the meeting was immediately dissolved, many of them crying out, "Let every man do his duty, and be true to his country"; and there was a general huzza for Griffin's wharf. It was now evening, and I immediately dressed myself in the costume of an Indian, equipped with a small hatchet, which I and my associates denominated the tomahawk, with which, and a club, after having painted my face and hands with coal dust in the shop of a blacksmith, I repaired to Griffin's wharf, where the ships lay that contained the tea. When I first appeared in the street, after being thus disguised, I fell in with many who were dressed, equipped, and painted as I was, and who fell in with me, and marched in order to the place of our destination. When we arrived at the wharf, there were three of our number who assumed an authority to direct our operations, to which we readily submitted. They divided us into three parties, for the purpose of boarding the three ships which contained the tea at the same time. The name of him who commanded the division to which I was assigned was Leonard Pitt. The names of the other commanders I never knew. We were immediately ordered by the respective commanders to board all the ships at the same time, which we promptly obeyed. The commander of the division to which I belonged, as soon as we were on board the ship, appointed me boatswain, and ordered me to go to the captain and demand of him the keys to the hatches and a dozen candles. I made the demand accordingly, and the captain promptly replied, and delivered the articles; but requested me at the same time to do no damage to the ship or rigging. We then were ordered by our commander to open the hatches, and take out all the chests of tea and throw them overboard, and we immediately proceeded to execute his orders; first cutting and splitting the chests with our tomahawks, so as thoroughly to expose them to the effects of the water. In about three hours from the time we went on board, we had thus broken and thrown overboard every tea chest to be found in the ship, while those in the other ships were disposing of the tea in the same way, at the same time. We were surrounded by British armed ships, but no attempt was made to resist us. We then quietly retired to our several places of residence, without having any conversation with each other, or taking any measures to discover who were our associates; nor do I recollect of our having had the knowledge of the name of a single individual concerned in that affair, except that of Leonard Pitt, the commander of my division, whom I have mentioned. There appeared to be an understanding that each individual should volunteer his services, keep his own secret, and risk the consequences for himself. No disorder took place during that transaction, and it was observed at that time, that the stillest night ensued that Boston had enjoyed for many months.

During the time we were throwing the tea overboard, there were several attempts made by some of the citizens of Boston and its vicinity to carry off small quantities of it for their family use. To effect that object, they would watch their opportunity to snatch up a handful from the deck, where it became plentifully scattered, and put it into their pockets. One Captain O'Connor, whom I well knew, came on board for that purpose, and when he supposed he was not noticed, filled his pockets, and also the lining of his coat. But I had detected him, and gave information to the captain of what he was doing. We were ordered to take him into custody, and just as he was stepping from the vessel, I seized him by the skirt of his coat, and in attempting to pull him back, I tore it off; but springing forward, by a rapid effort, he made his escape. He had, however, to run a gauntlet through the crowd upon the wharf; each one, as he passed, giving him a kick or a stroke.

Another attempt was made to save a little tea from the ruins of the cargo by a tall, aged man who wore a large cocked hat and white wig, which was fashionable at that time. He had sleightly slipped a little into his pocket, but being detected, they seized him, and taking his hat and wig from his head, threw them, together with the tea, of which they had emptied his pockets, into the water. In consideration of his advanced age, he was permitted to escape, with now and then a slight kick.

The next morning, after we had cleared the ships of the tea, it was discovered that very considerable quantities of it were floating upon the surface of the water; and to prevent the possibility of any of its being saved for use, a number of small boats were manned by sailors and citizens, who rowed them into those parts of the harbor wherever the tea was visible, and by beating it with oars and paddles, so thoroughly drenched it, as to render its entire destruction inevitable.

In punishment for the "tea party," the British promptly closed the Port of Boston, and

deprived the colonists of even more of their rights. The situation swiftly approached a point of no return. In September, 1774, colonies sent representatives to the First Continental Congress at Philadelphia. An aggressive Declaration of Rights and Grievances was drawn up, under the guidance of Samuel Adams and others. The explosive emotions of the day were funneled toward revolution by such fiery orators as Patrick Henry. Here is the famous closing passage from his speech delivered in the Virginia Convention, March 23, 1775.

PATRICK HENRY FANS THE FLAMES

Quoted by William Wirt in "Sketches of the Life and Character of Patrick Henry"

They tell us, sir, that we are weak—unable to cope with so formidable an adversary. But when shall we be stronger? Will it be the next week or the next year? Will it be when we are totally disarmed, and when a British guard shall be stationed in every house? Shall we gather strength by irresolution and inaction? Shall we acquire the means of effectual resistance by lying supinely on our backs, and hugging the delusive phantom of hope, until our enemies shall have bound us hand and foot? Sir, we are not weak, if we make a proper use of those means which the God of nature hath placed in our power. Three millions of people, armed in the holy cause of Liberty, and in such a country as that which we possess, are invincible by any force which our enemy can send against us.

Besides, sir, we shall not fight our battles alone. There is a just God, who presides over the destinies of nations, and who will raise up friends to fight our battles for us. The battle, sir, is not to the strong alone; it is to the vigilant, the active, the brave. Besides, sir, we have no election. If we were base enough to desire it, it is now too late to retire from the contest. There is no retreat but in submission and slavery! Our chains are forged. Their clanking may be heard on the plains of Boston! The war is inevitable—and let it come! I repeat it, sir, let it come!

It is vain, sir, to extenuate the matter. The gentlemen may cry, Peace, peace! but there is no peace. The war has actually begun! The next gale that sweeps from the north will bring to our ears the clash of resounding arms! Our brethren are already in the field! Why stand we here idle? What is it that the gentlemen wish? What would they have? Is life so dear or peace so sweet as to be purchased at the price of chains and slavery? Forbid it, Almighty God. I know not what course others may take, but as for me, give me liberty or give me death!

Farmers began to put away their plows and take up their guns. In Massachusetts, the Minutemen were formed, and military supplies for their use were stored at the town of Concord. On April 18, 1775, a column of British soldiers left Boston under cover of night, on the way to destroy those stores. The next day's action at Lexington-Concord —occurring less than a month after Patrick Henry's cry for Liberty—sparked the beginning of the Revolutionary War.

PART THREE

Give Me Liberty or Give Me Death!

IT is midnight, April 18–19, 1775: the eve of the Revolution. As British regulars march toward Concord, they expect to surprise farmers in bed, seize illegal military supplies, and squelch this "rebellion nonsense" for good. However, unknown to them, two men are galloping through the night ahead of them, ready to spread the word that the Redcoats are coming. One of these hard-riding horsemen is a certain silversmith, political cartoonist, and former leader of the Boston Tea Party. This night's work will make him immortal. Come along now, as Longfellow takes us on the midnight ride of Paul Revere . . .

PAUL REVERE'S RIDE

by Henry Wadsworth Longfellow

Listen, my children, and you shall hear
Of the midnight ride of Paul Revere,
On the eighteenth of April, in Seventy-five;
Hardly a man is now alive
Who remembers that famous day and year.

He said to his friend, "If the British march
By land or sea from the town tonight,
Hang a lantern aloft in the belfry arch
Of the North Church tower as a signal
    light,—
One, if by land, and two, if by sea;

41

And I on the opposite shore will be,
Ready to ride and spread the alarm
Through every Middlesex village and farm,
For the country folk to be up and to arm."

Then he said, "Good night!" and with muf-
    fled oar
Silently rowed to the Charlestown shore,
Just as the moon rose over the bay,
Where swinging wide at her moorings lay
The *Somerset,* British man-of-war;
A phantom ship, with each mast and spar
Across the moon like a prison bar,
And a huge black hulk, that was magnified
By its own reflection in the tide.

Meanwhile, his friend through alley and
    street
Wanders and watches, with eager ears,
Till in the silence around him he hears
The muster of men at the barrack door,
The sound of arms, and the tramp of feet,
And the measured tread of the grenadiers,
Marching down to their boats on the shore.

Then he climbed the tower of the Old North
    Church,
By the wooden stairs, with stealthy tread,
To the belfry-chamber overhead,
And startled the pigeons from their perch
On the sombre rafters, that round him
    made
Masses and moving shapes of shade,—
By the trembling ladder, steep and tall,
To the highest window in the wall,
Where he paused to listen and look down
A moment on the roofs of the town
And the moonlight flowing over all.

Beneath, in the churchyard, lay the dead,
In their night-encampment on the hill,
Wrapped in silence so deep and still
That he could hear, like a sentinel's tread,
The watchful night-wind, as it went
Creeping along from tent to tent,
And seeming to whisper, "All is well!"
A moment only he feels the spell
Of the place and the hour, and the secret
    dread
Of the lonely belfry and the dead;
For suddenly all his thoughts are bent
On a shadowy something far away,
Where the river widens to meet the bay,—
A line of black that bends and floats
On the rising tide, like a bridge of boats.

Meanwhile, impatient to mount and ride,
Booted and spurred, with a heavy stride
On the opposite shore walked Paul Revere.
Now he patted his horse's side,
Now gazed at the landscape far and near,
Then impetuous, stamped the earth,
And turned and tightened his saddle girth;
But mostly he watched with eager search
The belfry's tower of the Old North Church,
As it rose above the graves on the hill,
Lonely and spectral and sombre and still.
And lo! as he looks, on the belfry height
A glimmer, and then a gleam of light!
He springs to the saddle, the bridle he turns,
But lingers and gazes, till full on his sight
A second lamp in the belfry burns!

A hurry of hoofs in a village street,
A shape in the moonlight, a bulk in the dark,
And beneath, from the pebbles, in passing,
    a spark
Struck out by a steed flying fearless and fleet;

That was all! And yet, through the gloom
   and the light,
The fate of a nation was riding that night;
And the spark struck out by that steed, in his
   flight,
Kindled the land into flame with its heat.

He has left the village and mounted the steep,
And beneath him, tranquil and broad and
   deep,
Is the Mystic, meeting the ocean tides;
And under the alders that skirt its edge,
Now soft on the sand, now loud on the
   ledge,
Is heard the tramp of his steed as he rides.

It was twelve by the village clock,
When he crossed the bridge into Medford
   town.
He heard the crowing of the cock,
And the barking of the farmer's dog,
And he felt the damp of the river fog,
That rises after the sun goes down.

It was one by the village clock,
When he galloped into Lexington.
He saw the gilded weathercock
Swim in the moonlight as he passed,
And the meeting-house windows, blank and
   bare,
Gaze at him with a spectral glare,
As if they already stood aghast
At the bloody work they would look upon.

It was two by the village clock,
When he came to the bridge in Concord
   town.
He heard the bleating of the flock,
And the twitter of birds among the trees,

And felt the breath of the morning breeze
Blowing over the meadows brown.
And one was safe and asleep in his bed
Who at the bridge would be first to fall,
Who that day would be lying dead,
Pierced by a British musket-ball.

You know the rest. In books you have read,
How the British Regulars fired and fled,—
How the farmers gave them ball for ball,
From behind each fence and farmyard wall,
Chasing the redcoats down the lane,
Then crossing the fields to emerge again
Under the trees at the turn of the road,
And only pausing to fire and load.
So through the night rode Paul Revere;
And so through the night went his cry of
   alarm
To every Middlesex village and farm,—
A cry of defiance, and not of fear,
A voice in the darkness, a knock at the door,
And a word that shall echo for evermore!
For, borne on the night-wind of the Past,
Through all our history, to the last,
In the hour of darkness and peril and need,
The people will waken and listen to hear
The hurrying hoof-beats of that steed,
And the midnight message of Paul Revere.

The patriots who responded to Paul Revere's message were only farmers with guns, but they gave a good account of themselves —first at Lexington, then at Concord bridge. The British managed to destroy some stores, but were forced to retreat to Boston, leaving many dead behind. The Minutemen's stand captured the imagination of America, and tribute was paid to it many years afterward, in these famous verses.

CONCORD HYMN

by Ralph Waldo Emerson

Sung at the completion of the Battle Monument,
April 19, 1886

By the rude bridge that arched the flood,
   Their flag to April's breeze unfurled,
Here once the embattled farmers stood,
   And fired the shot heard round the world.

The foe long since in silence slept;
   Alike the conqueror silent sleeps;
And Time the ruined bridge has swept
   Down the dark stream which seaward
      creeps.

On this green bank, by this soft stream,
   We set today a votive stone;
That memory may their deed redeem,
   When, like our sires, our sons are gone.

Spirit, that made those spirits dare
   To die, and leave their children free,
Bid Time and Nature gently spare
   The shaft we raise to them and thee.

The firing of the "shot heard round the world" meant that the war was definitely on. At the beginning, there was no American army as such—just groups of loosely organized militia. One of these groups was the Green Mountain Boys of Vermont. Their loyalties—typical of the time—placed Vermont first, America second. They were as ready to squabble with neighboring New York and New Hampshire over land rights as to fight the British. What they lacked in military discipline, however, they made up for in pugnacious spirit.

THE SONG OF THE VERMONTERS

Anonymous

Ho—all to the borders! Vermonters, come
   down,
With your breeches of deer-skin, and jackets
   of brown;
With your red woolen caps, and your moccasins, come,
To the gathering summons of trumpet and
   drum.

Come down with your rifles!—let grey wolf
   and fox
Howl on in the shade of their primitive rocks;
Let the bear feed securely from pig-pen and
   stall;
Here's a two-legged game for your powder
   and ball.

* * *

Speaking of "powder and ball," Americans were woefully short of enough of both to fight a large-scale war. But there were plenty of military supplies inside British Fort Ticonderoga, over in northeastern New York. A Vermont firebrand named Ethan Allen managed to talk the Green Mountain Boys into forgetting their local quarrels long enough to march—together with men from Connecticut and Massachusetts—in a surprise attack on the fort. In May, 1775, they took it—less than a month after Lexington and Concord. (Also serving with the American forces was Benedict Arnold, a brilliant general, who later sold out to the British.) But this was mainly Ethan Allen's victory, and here is his own account of it.

THE CAPTURE OF TICONDEROGA

from "Narrative of Captivity" by Ethan Allen

Ever since I arrived at the state of manhood, and acquainted myself with the general history of mankind, I have felt a sincere passion for liberty. The history of nations doomed to perpetual slavery in consequence of yielding up to tyrants their natural-born liberties, I read with a sort of philosophical horror; so that the first systematical and bloody attempt, at Lexington, to enslave America, thoroughly electrified my mind, and fully determined me to take part with my country. And, while I was wishing for an opportunity to signalize myself in its behalf, directions were privately sent to me from the then colony (now State) of Connecticut, to raise the Green Mountain Boys, and, if possible, with them to surprise and take the fortress of Ticonderoga. This enterprise I cheerfully undertook; and, after first

guarding all the several passes that led thither, to cut off all intelligence between the garrison and the country, made a forced march from Bennington, and arrived at the lake opposite to Ticonderoga, on the evening of the 9th day of May, 1775, with two hundred and thirty valiant Green Mountain Boys; and it was with the utmost difficulty that I procured boats to cross the lake. However, I landed eighty-three men near the garrison, and sent the boats back for the rear guard, commanded by Colonel Seth Warner; but the day began to dawn, and I found myself under the necessity to attack the fort, before the rear could cross the lake; and, as it was viewed hazardous, I harangued the officers and soldiers in the manner following:

"Friends and fellow soldiers, you have, for a number of years past, been a scourge and terror to arbitrary power. Your valor has been famed abroad, and acknowledged, as appears by the advice and orders to me, from the General Assembly of Connecticut, to sur-

45

prise and take the garrison now before us. I now propose to advance before you, and, in person, conduct you through the wicket gate; for we must this morning either quit our pretensions to valor, or possess ourselves of this fortress in a few minutes; and, inasmuch as it is a desperate attempt, which none but the bravest of men dare undertake, I do not urge it on any contrary to his will. You that will undertake voluntarily, poise your firelocks."

The men being, at this time, drawn up in three ranks, each poised his firelock. I ordered them to face to the right, and, at the head of the center file, marched them immediately to the wicket gate aforesaid, where I found a sentry posted, who instantly snapped his fusee at me; I ran immediately toward him, and he retreated through the covered way into the parade within the garrison, gave a halloo, and ran under a bombproof. My party, who followed me into the fort, I formed on the parade in such a manner as to face the two barracks which faced each other.

The garrison being asleep, except the sentries, we gave three huzzas, which greatly surprised them. One of the sentries made a pass at one of my officers with a charged bayonet and slightly wounded him. My first thought was to kill him with my sword; but, in an instant, I altered the design and fury of the blow to a slight cut on the side of the head, upon which he dropped his gun and asked quarter, which I readily granted him, and demanded of him the place where the commanding officer kept. He showed me a pair of stairs in the front of a barrack, on the west part of the garrison, which led up to a second story in said barrack, to which I immediately repaired, and ordered the commander, Cap-

tain de la Place, to come forth instantly, or I would sacrifice the whole garrison; at which the Captain came immediately to the door, with his breeches in his hand. When I ordered him to deliver me the fort instantly, he asked me by what authority I demanded it. I answered him, *"In the name of the great Jehovah and the Continental Congress."* The authority of the Congress being very little known at that time, he began to speak again; but I interrupted him, and with my drawn sword over his head, again demanded an immediate surrender of the garrison; with which he then complied, and ordered his men to be forthwith paraded without arms, as he had given up the garrison. In the meantime some of my officers had given orders, and in consequence thereof, sundry of the barrack doors were beat down, and about one-third of the garrison imprisoned, which consisted of the said commander, a Lieutenant Feltham, a conductor of artillery, a gunner, two sergeants, and forty-four rank and file; about one hundred pieces of cannon, one thirteen-inch mortar, and a number of swivels. This surprise was carried into execution in the gray of the morning of the 10th of May, 1775. The sun seemed to rise that morning with a superior luster, and Ticonderoga and its dependencies smiled to its conquerors, who tossed about the flowing bowl and wished success to Congress, and the liberty and freedom of America.

Two days later, the American Seth Warner captured Crown Point. Meanwhile the Second Continental Congress met. They still didn't know whether the goal of the war should be complete independence or not, but they *did* know they'd better get a unified army together or the slow-starting British would make short work of them. They needed a strong commander to organize things. In June, 1775, they appointed George Washington, who had distinguished himself during the French and Indian Wars. It was an excellent choice. The confidence Americans had in their new commander-in-chief is illustrated by this ballad, written at the beginning of the American Revolution.

WAR AND WASHINGTON

Anonymous

Vain BRITONS, boast no longer with proud
    indignity,
By land your conqu'ring legions, your match-
    less strength at sea,
Since we, your braver sons incens'd, our
    swords have girded on,
Huzza, huzza, huzza, huzza, for WAR and
    WASHINGTON.

Mysterious, unexampled! incomprehensi-
    ble!
The blund'ring schemes of Britain, their
    folly, pride, and zeal,
Like lions how ye growl and threat! mere
    asses have you shown,
And ye shall share an ass's fate, and drudge
    for WASHINGTON!

Great Heav'n! is this the nation whose
    thund'ring arms were hurl'd,
Thro' EUROPE, AFRIC, INDIA? whose NAVY
    rul'd a WORLD?
The lustre of your former deeds, whole ages
    of renown,
Lost in a moment, or transferr'd to us and
    WASHINGTON!

Should GEORGE, too, choice of Britons, to
    foreign realms apply,
And madly arm half EUROPE, yet still we
    would defy
Turk, Hessian, Jew, and Infidel, or all those
    pow'rs in one,
While ADAMS guides our senate, our camp
    great WASHINGTON!

Should warlike weapons fail us, disdain-
    ing slavish fears,
To swords we'll beat our ploughshares, our
    pruning-hooks to spears,
And rush, all desp'rate! on our foe, nor
    breathe 'till battle won,
Then shout, and shout AMERICA! and con-
    qu'ring WASHINGTON!

A less emotional tribute to Washington's qualities as a leader has been left us by a contemporary. He was John Marshall, who later became a great Chief Justice of the United States Supreme Court.

WASHINGTON

by John Marshall

He made no pretensions to that vivacity which fascinates, or to that wit which dazzles, and frequently imposes on the understanding. More solid than brilliant, judgment rather than genius constituted the most prominent feature of his character . . . As a military man, he was brave, enterprising, and cautious . . . Inferior to his adversary in the numbers, in the equipment, and in the discipline of his troops, it is evidence of real merit that no great or decisive advantages were ever obtained over him, and that the opportunity to strike an important blow never passed away unused.

Two days after Washington's appointment, the Battle of Bunker Hill (actually fought on Breed's Hill) occurred outside of British-held Boston. The Americans lost the hill, but only after they ran out of gun powder. The spunk displayed by their small force, which inflicted heavy losses on the British, won more people over to the Revolutionaries' cause. True, there were still many colonials—often men of substance and principle—who remained loyal to the king, but public opinion was turning against them. One of these "Tories" was attorney general of New York, whose rebellious citizens forced him to flee aboard a British man-of-war in the harbor (early in 1776). The ship's name was the *Asia,* and soon Attorney General Kemp was welcoming another fleeing Tory onto its deck with the following bit of verse. (The "Whigs" here are the Revolutionaries.)

WELCOME, WELCOME, BROTHER TORY

by John Tabor Kemp

Welcome, welcome, brother Tory,
  To this merry floating place;
I came here a while before you;
  Coming here is no disgrace.
Freedom finds a safe retreat here,
  On the bosom of the waves;
You she now invites to meet her.
  Welcome, then, thou Tory brave.

As you serve, like us, the King, sir,
  In a hammock you must lay;
Better for 'tis so to swing, sir,
  Than to swing another way.

* * *

Should vile Whigs come here to plunder,
  Quick we'd send them whence they came;
They'd soon hear the Asia thunder,
  And the Phoenix in a flame.
Neptune's gallant sons befriend us,
  While at anchor here we ride;
Britain's wooden walls defend us,
  Britain's glory and her pride.

Britain's glory and pride fared badly at Boston (which Americans took over after a siege) but did all right at Quebec (holding firm against an American thrust into Canada). The first year of the war, neither side won a really decisive victory. Many Americans were halfhearted about the whole thing anyway, wishing that *both* sides would go away so that "business as usual" could be resumed. Farmers who joined up with the Continental Army were full of spit and vinegar but often had a quaint idea of military discipline. They expected to serve for a few days, weeks, or—at the most—months, then to return home for the spring plowing. It's a remarkable testament to Washington's leadership, and that of his fellow officers, that they were able to mold an effective army at all. They were helped in 1776 by the appearance of Tom Paine's brilliant pamphlet *Common Sense,* which rallied Americans to liberty's cause with arguments like these.

TOM PAINE ON THE AMERICAN CAUSE

from "Common Sense" by Thomas Paine

The sun never shone on a cause of greater worth. 'Tis not the affair of a city, a county, a province, or a kingdom, but of a continent —of at least one-eighth part of the habitable globe . . . Now is the seedtime of continental union, faith and honor . . .

I have heard it asserted by some, that as America has flourished under her former connection with Great Britain, the same connection is necessary towards her future happiness, and will always have the same effect . . . We may as well assert that because a child has thrived upon milk, that it is never to have meat, or that the first twenty years of our lives is to become a precedent for the next twenty.

But even this is admitting more than is true, for I answer roundly that America would have flourished as much, and probably much more, had no European power taken any notice of her. The articles of commerce by which she has enriched herself are the necessaries of life, and will always have a market while eating is the custom of Europe . . .

As Europe is our market for trade, we ought to form no partial connection with any part of it . . . and whenever a war breaks out between England and any foreign power, the trade of America goes to ruin, because of her connection with Britain . . . Everything that is right or natural pleads for separation. The blood of the slain, the weeping voice of nature cries, " 'Tis time to part!" Even the distance at which the Almighty hath placed England and America is a strong and natural proof that the authority of the one over the other was never the design of Heaven.

Common Sense, which sold over 100,000 copies, pushed opinion in the thirteen rebellious colonies toward the idea of complete separation from England. On June 7, 1776, at Philadelphia, Richard Henry Lee introduced a resolution in Congress stating that "these United Colonies are and of right ought to be free and independent States." A Congressional committee asked Thomas Jefferson to prepare a declaration of independence. He did so. Revisions were made by Ben Franklin, John Adams, and others. On July 4, Congress was still debating whether or not to sign the document in its current form. Outside, in the streets of Philadelphia, the people waited . . .

INDEPENDENCE BELL —JULY 4, 1776

Anonymous

There was a tumult in the city
In the quaint old Quaker town,
And the streets were rife with people
Pacing restless up and down—
People gathering at corners,
Where they whispered each to each,

49

And the sweat stood on their temples
With the earnestness of speech.

As the bleak Atlantic currents
Lash the wild Newfoundland shore,
So they beat against the State House,
So they surged against the door;
And the mingling of their voices
Made the harmony profound,
Till the quiet street of Chestnut
Was all turbulent with sound.

"Will they do it?" "Dare they do it?"
"Who is speaking?" "What's the news?"
"What of Adams?" "What of Sherman?"
"Oh, God grant they won't refuse!"
"Make some way there!" "Let me nearer!"
"I am stifling!" "Stifle then!
When a nation's life's at hazard,
We've no time to think of men!"

So they surged against the State House,
While all solemnly inside,
Sat the Continental Congress,
Truth and reason for their guide,
O'er a simple scroll debating,
Which, though simple it might be,
Yet should shake the cliffs of England
With the thunders of the free.

Far aloft in that high steeple
Sat the bellman, old and gray,
He was weary of the tyrant
And his iron-sceptered sway;
So he sat, with one hand ready
On the clapper of the bell,
When his eye could catch the signal,
The long-expected news to tell.

See! See! The dense crowd quivers
Through all its lengthy line,
As the boy beside the portal
Hastens forth to give the sign!
With his little hands uplifted,
Breezes dallying with his hair,
Hark! with deep, clear intonation,
Breaks his young voice on the air.

Hushed the people's swelling murmur,
Whilst the boy cries joyously;
"Ring!" he shouts, "Ring! Grandpapa,
Ring! oh, ring for Liberty!"
Quickly, at the given signal,
The old bellman lifts his hand,
Forth he sends the goods news, making
Iron music through the land.

How they shouted! What rejoicing!
How the old bell shook the air,
Till the clang of freedom ruffled
The calmly gliding Delaware!
How the bonfires and the torches
Lighted up the night's repose,
And from the flames, like fabled Phoenix,
Our glorious liberty arose!

That old State House bell is silent,
Hushed is now its clamorous tongue;
But the spirit it awakened
Still is living—ever young;
And when we greet the smiling sunlight
On the fourth of each July,
We will ne'er forget the bellman
Who, betwixt the earth and sky,
Rung out, loudly, "Independence";
Which, please God, shall never die!

Fifty-six men signed the Declaration of Independence. They were lawyers, bankers, planters, merchants, printers; but by this historic act, they all dedicated themselves to becoming *Americans,* free and clear.

IN CONGRESS, JULY 4, 1776.

The unanimous Declaration of the thirteen united States of America,

When in the Course of human events, it becomes necessary for one people to dissolve the political bands which have connected them with another, and to assume among the powers of the earth, the separate and equal station to which the Laws of Nature and of Nature's God entitle them, a decent respect to the opinions of mankind requires that they should declare the causes which impel them to the separation.

We hold these truths to be self-evident, that all men are created equal, that they are endowed by their Creator with certain unalienable Rights, that among these are Life, Liberty and the pursuit of Happiness. — That to secure these rights, Governments are instituted among Men, deriving their just powers from the consent of the governed, — That whenever any Form of Government becomes destructive of these ends, it is the Right of the People to alter or to abolish it, and to institute new Government, laying its foundation on such principles and organizing its powers in such form, as to them shall seem most likely to effect their Safety and Happiness. Prudence, indeed, will dictate that Governments long established should not be changed for light and transient causes; and accordingly all experience hath shewn, that mankind are more disposed to suffer, while evils are sufferable, than to right themselves by abolishing the forms to which they are accustomed. But when a long train of abuses and usurpations, pursuing invariably the same Object evinces a design to reduce them under absolute Despotism, it is their right, it is their duty, to throw off such Government, and to provide new Guards for their future security. — Such has been the patient sufferance of these Colonies; and such is now the necessity which constrains them to alter their former Systems of Government. The history of the present King of Great Britain is a history of repeated injuries and usurpations, all having in direct object the establishment of an absolute Tyranny over these States. To prove this, let Facts be submitted to a candid world.

He has refused his Assent to Laws, the most wholesome and necessary for the public good.

He has forbidden his Governors to pass Laws of immediate and pressing importance, unless suspended in their operation till his Assent should be obtained; and when so suspended, he has utterly neglected to attend to them.

He has refused to pass other Laws for the accommodation of large districts of people, unless those people would relinquish the right of Representation in the Legislature, a right inestimable to them and formidable to tyrants only.

He has called together legislative bodies at places unusual, uncomfortable, and distant from the depository of their public Records, for the sole purpose of fatiguing them into compliance with his measures.

He has dissolved Representative Houses repeatedly, for opposing with manly firmness his invasions on the rights of the people.

He has refused for a long time, after such dissolutions, to cause others to be elected; whereby the Legislative powers, incapable of Annihilation, have returned to the People at large for their exercise; the State remaining in the mean time exposed to all the dangers of invasion from without, and convulsions within.

He has endeavoured to prevent the population of these States; for that purpose obstructing the Laws for Naturalization of Foreigners; refusing to pass others to encourage their migrations hither, and raising the conditions of new Appropriations of Lands.

He has obstructed the Administration of Justice, by refusing his Assent to Laws for establishing Judiciary powers.

He has made Judges dependent on his Will alone, for the tenure of their offices, and the amount and payment of their salaries.

He has erected a multitude of New Offices, and sent hither swarms of Officers to harrass our people, and eat out their substance.

He has kept among us, in times of peace, Standing Armies without the Consent of our legislatures.

He has affected to render the Military independent of and superior to the Civil power.

He has combined with others to subject us to a jurisdiction foreign to our constitution, and unacknowledged by our laws; giving his Assent to their Acts of pretended Legislation:

For Quartering large bodies of armed troops among us:

For protecting them, by a mock Trial, from punishment for any Murders which they should commit on the Inhabitants of these States:

For cutting off our Trade with all parts of the world:

For imposing Taxes on us without our Consent:

For depriving us in many cases, of the benefits of Trial by Jury:

For transporting us beyond Seas to be tried for pretended offences

For abolishing the free System of English Laws in a neighbouring Province, establishing therein an Arbitrary government, and enlarging its Boundaries so as to render it at once an example and fit instrument for introducing the same absolute rule into these Colonies:

For taking away our Charters, abolishing our most valuable Laws, and altering fundamentally the Forms of our Governments:

For suspending our own Legislatures, and declaring themselves invested with power to legislate for us in all cases whatsoever.

He has abdicated Government here, by declaring us out of his Protection and waging War against us.

He has plundered our seas, ravaged our Coasts, burnt our towns, and destroyed the lives of our people.

He is at this time transporting large Armies of foreign Mercenaries to compleat the works of death, desolation and tyranny, already begun with circumstances of Cruelty & perfidy scarcely paralleled in the most barbarous ages, and totally unworthy the Head of a civilized nation.

He has constrained our fellow Citizens taken Captive on the high Seas to bear Arms against their Country, to become the executioners of their friends and Brethren, or to fall themselves by their Hands.

He has excited domestic insurrections amongst us, and has endeavoured to bring on the inhabitants of our frontiers, the merciless Indian Savages, whose known rule of warfare, is an undistinguished destruction of all ages, sexes and conditions.

In every stage of these Oppressions We have Petitioned for Redress in the most humble terms: Our repeated Petitions have been answered only by repeated injury. A Prince, whose character is thus marked by every act which may define a Tyrant, is unfit to be the ruler of a free people.

Nor have We been wanting in attentions to our Brittish brethren. We have warned them from time to time of attempts by their legislature to extend an unwarrantable jurisdiction over us. We have reminded them of the circumstances of our emigration and settlement here. We have appealed to their native justice and magnanimity, and we have conjured them by the ties of our common kindred to disavow these usurpations, which, would inevitably interrupt our connections and correspondence. They too have been deaf to the voice of justice and of consanguinity. We must, therefore, acquiesce in the necessity, which denounces our Separation, and hold them, as we hold the rest of mankind, Enemies in War, in Peace Friends.

We, therefore, the Representatives of the united States of America, in General Congress, Assembled, appealing to the Supreme Judge of the world for the rectitude of our intentions, do, in the Name, and by Authority of the good People of these Colonies, solemnly publish and declare, That these United Colonies are, and of Right ought to be Free and Independent States; that they are Absolved from all Allegiance to the British Crown, and that all political connection between them and the State of Great Britain, is and ought to be totally dissolved; and that as Free and Independent States, they have full Power to levy War, conclude Peace, contract Alliances, establish Commerce, and to do all other Acts and Things which Independent States may of right do. And for the support of this Declaration, with a firm reliance on the protection of divine Providence, we mutually pledge to each other our Lives, our Fortunes and our sacred Honor.

John Hancock

Button Gwinnett
Lyman Hall
Geo Walton.

Wm Hooper
Joseph Hewes,
John Penn

Edward Rutledge.
Thos. Heyward Junr.
Thomas Lynch Junr.
Arthur Middleton

Samuel Chase
Wm. Paca
Thos. Stone
Charles Carroll of Carrollton

George Wythe
Richard Henry Lee
Th Jefferson
Benja. Harrison
Thos. Nelson jr.
Francis Lightfoot Lee
Carter Braxton

Robt Morris
Benjamin Rush
Benja. Franklin
John Morton
Geo Clymer
Jas. Smith.
Geo. Taylor
James Wilson
Geo. Ross
Caesar Rodney
Geo Read
Tho McKean

Wm Floyd
Phil. Livingston
Frans. Lewis
Lewis Morris

Richd. Stockton
Jno Witherspoon
Fras. Hopkinson
John Hart
Abra Clark

Josiah Bartlett
Wm Whipple
Saml Adams
John Adams
Robt Treat Paine
Elbridge Gerry
Step Hopkins
William Ellery
Roger Sherman
Saml Huntington
Wm Williams
Oliver Wolcott
Matthew Thornton

America now had a glorious ideal to live up to: "We hold these truths to be self-evident, that all men are created equal, that they are endowed by their Creator with certain unalienable Rights, that among these are Life, Liberty and the pursuit of Happiness . . ."

However, liberty at this point existed only on paper. There was still a hard war to be won, and things were not going at all well. The Americans lost the Battle of Long Island, and Washington was forced to retreat from New York (which was taken by the British). By late fall, the Continental Army had been pushed back across New Jersey into Pennsylvania. Men were deserting by the hundreds. On December 18, Washington wrote ". . . if every nerve is not strained to the utmost to recruit the new army with all possible expedition, I think the game is pretty nearly up." The very next day, Tom Paine reignited the fading spark of defiance with the publication of his *The Crisis*. Washington caused it to be read before all his troops. You will see why, when you read the following excerpts:

THE TIMES THAT TRY MEN'S SOULS

from "The Crisis" by Thomas Paine

These are the times that try men's souls. The summer soldier and the sunshine patriot will, in this crisis, shrink from the service of their country; but he that stands it *now*, deserves the love and thanks of man and woman. Tyranny, like hell, is not easily conquered; yet we have this consolation with us, that the harder the conflict, the more glorious the triumph . . . Heaven knows how to put a proper price upon its goods; and it would be strange indeed if so celestial an article as FREEDOM should not be highly rated. Britain, with an army to enforce her tyranny, has declared that she has a right *(not only to* TAX*)* but "to BIND *us* in CASES WHATSOEVER," and if being *bound in that manner,* is not slavery, then there is not such a thing as slavery upon earth . . .

I once felt all that kind of anger, which a man ought to feel, against the mean principles which are held by the Tories: a noted one who kept a tavern at Amboy was standing at his door, with as pretty a child in his hand, about eight or nine years old, as ever I saw, and after speaking his mind as freely as he thought was prudent, finished with this unfatherly expression, *"Well! give me peace in my day."* Not a man lives on the continent but fully believes that a separation must sometime or other finally take place, and a generous parent should have said, *"If there must be trouble, let it be in my day, that my child may have peace";* and this single reflection, well applied, is sufficient to awaken every man to duty . . .

Inspired by the words of Paine, hungry for a victory, Washington's troops crossed the Delaware on December 26, surprised and defeated the Hessians at Trenton, and later won the battle of Princeton (January, 1777). In June '77, Francis Hopkinson arranged thirteen red and white stripes together with thirteen white stars (to represent the thirteen original states) on a blue background. Betsy Ross is believed to have got-

ten busy with her needle, and soon Old Glory was unfurled for the first time. America not only had a Declaration of Independence—it had a flag!

THE FLAG GOES BY

by Henry Holcomb Bennett

Hats off!
Along the street there comes
A blare of bugles, a ruffle of drums,
A flash of color beneath the sky:
Hats off!
The flag is passing by!

Blue and crimson and white it shines,
Over the steel-tipped, ordered lines.
Hats off!
The colors before us fly;
But more than the flag is passing by:

Sea-fights and land-fights, grim and great,
Fought to make and to save the State;
Weary marches and sinking ships;
Cheers of victory on dying lips;

Days of plenty and years of peace;
March of a strong land's swift increase;
Equal justice, right and law,
Stately honor and reverend awe;

Sign of a nation great and strong
To ward her people from foreign wrong;
Pride and glory and honor,—all
Live in the colors to stand or fall.

Hats off!
Along the street there comes
A blare of bugles, a ruffle of drums;
And loyal hearts are beating high:
Hats off!
The flag is passing by!

America may not have had a national anthem to go with its flag, but it had a *song*—one with several hundred verses . . . A British army surgeon is believed to have composed *Yankee Doodle* (based on an old English tune) in mockery of raw Colonial troops. But Americans took it up, added words that struck their fancy, and made it very much their own. Here are a few of its many verses. Try to imagine the tattered Continental Army singing them to keep their spirits up as they march along, accompanied by fife and drum.

YANKEE DOODLE

Anonymous

Father and I went down to camp,
    Along with Captain Gooding,
And there we see the men and boys,
    As thick as hasty pudding.

Chorus:

Yankee Doodle, keep it up,
    Yankee Doodle, dandy,
Mind the music and the step,
    And with the girls be handy.

There was Captain Washington,
    Upon a slapping stallion,
A giving orders to his men—
    I guess there was a million.

And then the feathers on his hat,
    They look'd so tarnal fina,
I wanted pockily to get
    To give to my Jemima.

And there they'd fife away like fun,
    And play on cornstalk fiddles,
And some had ribbons red as blood,
    All wound about their middles.

The troopers, too, would gallop up,
    And fire right in our faces;
It scar'd me almost half to death,
    To see them run such races.

But I can't tell you half I see,
    They kept up such a smother;
So I took my hat off, made a bow,
    And scamper'd home to mother.

Yankee Doodle, keep it up,
    Yankee Doodle, dandy,
Mind the music and the step,
    And with the girls be handy.

Yankee Doodle won a battle in August '77, lost two in September and was chased out of Philadelphia by the British. And then, the seesaw swung again. British General "Gentleman Johnny" Burgoyne had marched an army down from Canada with the intention of occupying the Hudson Valley. It was part of a pincer maneuver designed to cut the colonies in two. But the Americans squelched the plan by winning the second battle of Bemis Heights, and the defeated General Burgoyne was forced to surrender his entire army to American General Gates at Saratoga.

Saratoga was to prove the turning point in the war, but its effects wouldn't make themselves known until later. Meanwhile, fortune suddenly seemed to reverse itself again and to frown on the American cause. Washington lost the battle of Germantown, and the British gained control of the Delaware. As winter of '77-'78 approached, Washington was forced to hole up with his dwindling, rag-tag army at Valley Forge. Yankee Doodle was in bad shape. Listen to the following comments of a French volunteer who visited Valley Forge during that cruel winter.

THE SHOELESS ARMY OF VALLEY FORGE

by the Chevalier de Pontgibaud

Soon I came in sight of the camp. My imagination had pictured an army with uniforms, the glitter of arms, standards, etc., in short, military pomp of all sorts. Instead of the imposing spectacle I expected, I saw, grouped together or standing alone, a few militiamen, poorly clad, and for the most part without shoes—many of them badly armed, but all well supplied with provisions, and I noticed that tea and sugar formed part of their rations. . . . In passing through the camp I also noticed soldiers wearing cotton nightcaps under their hats, and some having for cloaks or greatcoats coarse woolen blankets, exactly like those provided for the patients in our French hospitals. I learned afterwards that these were the officers and generals.

Such, in strict truth, was, at the time I came amongst them, the appearance of this armed mob, the leader of whom was the man who has rendered the name of Washington famous; such were the colonists—unskilled warriors who learned in a few years how to conquer the finest troops that England could send against them. Such also, at the beginning of the War of Independence, was the state of want in the insurgent army, and such was the scarcity of money, and the poverty of that government, now so rich, powerful, and prosperous, that its notes, called Continental paper money, were nearly valueless.

Amazingly, the American army emerged from Valley Forge tougher, better disciplined, and more determined than ever before. Partially, this was due to the efforts of foreign volunteers in the cause of liberty— Von Steuben, De Kalb, Lafayette, etc.—who had worked throughout the winter to turn raw recruits into an efficient fighting force. However, it had been a long, cold winter, and men were grateful for anything that could cheer them up. A welcome laugh was provided by the famous Battle of the Kegs.

Certain Americans had sent kegs charged with gunpowder floating down the Delaware to annoy British shipping at Philadelphia. This threw the enemy into such a trigger-happy panic that they proceeded to fire off their cannon at everything that floated on the water. Francis Hopkinson lost no time in having fun at British expense with the following verses.

THE BATTLE OF THE KEGS

by Francis Hopkinson

Gallants attend and hear a friend,
  Trill forth harmonious ditty,
Strange things I'll tell which late befell
  In Philadelphia city.

'Twas early day, as poets say,
  Just when the sun was rising,
A soldier stood on a log of wood,
  And saw a thing surprising.

As in amaze he stood to gaze,
  The truth can't be denied, sir,
He spied a score of kegs or more
  Come floating down the tide, sir.

55

A sailor too in jerkin blue,
  This strange appearance viewing,
First damn'd his eyes, in great surprise,
  Then said, "Some mischief's brewing.

"These kegs, I'm told, the rebels hold,
  Pack'd up like pickled herring;
And they're come down t' attack the town,
  In this new way of ferrying."

The soldier flew, the sailor too,
  And scar'd almost to death, sir,
Wore out their shoes, to spread the news,
  And ran till out of breath, sir.

Now up and down throughout the town,
  Most frantic scenes were acted;
And some ran here, and others there,
  Like men almost distracted.

Some fire cry'd, which some denied,
  But said the earth had quaked;
And girls and boys, with hideous noise,
  Ran thro' the streets half naked.

* * *

"Arise, arise," Sir Erskine cries,
  "The rebels—more's the pity,
Without a boat are all afloat,
  And rang'd before the city.

"The motley crew, in vessels new,
  With Satan for their guide, sir,
Pack'd up in bags, or wooden kegs,
  Come driving down the tide, sir.

"Therefore prepare for bloody war,
  These kegs must all be routed,
Or surely we despised shall be,
  And British courage doubted."

The royal band now ready stand
  All rang'd in dread array, sir,
With stomach stout to see it out,
  And make a bloody day, sir.

The cannons roar from shore to shore,
  The small arms make a rattle;
Since wars began I'm sure no man
  E'er saw so strange a battle.

The rebel dales, the rebel vales,
  With rebel trees surrounded;
The distant woods, the hills and floods,
  With rebel echoes sounded.

The fish below swam to and fro,
  Attack'd from ev'ry quarter;
Why sure, thought they, the devil's to pay,
  'Mongst folks above the water.

The kegs, 'tis said, tho' strongly made,
  Of rebel staves and hoops, sir,
Could not oppose their powerful foes,
  The conq'ring British troops, sir.

From morn to night these men of might
  Display'd amazing courage;
And when the sun was fairly down,
  Retir'd to sup their porrage.

An hundred men with each a pen,
  Or more upon my word, sir,
It is most true would be too few,
  Their valour to record, sir.

Such feats did they perform that day,
  Against these wicked kegs, sir,
That years to come, if they get home,
  They'll make their boasts and brags, sir.

Things began to look up for America. Impressed by the victory at Saratoga, the French finally came in as allies (February, 1778). The British promptly offered their rebellious colonies a generous peace, but were turned down. Independence or nothing! The British were forced to evacuate Philadelphia, and their army was defeated in New Jersey by Washington, at the Battle of Monmouth. A French fleet arrived. George Rogers Clark conquered the Northwest for the Americans. Spain entered the war against England. John Paul Jones gave the American Navy its first victory. Meanwhile, the British decided to concentrate on conquering the Southern states. (By now, the Articles of Confederation had turned the colonies into the United States of America.)

By 1780, the main English army, under Cornwallis, was centered in Virginia and the Carolinas. Cornwallis brought his army to Yorktown, Virginia. A French fleet entered Chesapeake Bay and bottled him up from the sea. A combined American-French army, led by Washington and Rochambeau, sealed off Yorktown by land. After a siege of less than three weeks, Cornwallis, his position hopeless, surrendered (October 19, 1781).

Yankee Doodle had won the war.

Here is a description of the surrender, as witnessed by a surgeon in the Continental Army.

57

THE BRITISH SURRENDER AT YORKTOWN

from "Military Journal during the American Revolution" by James Thacher

At about twelve o'clock, the combined army was arranged and drawn up in two lines, extending more than a mile in length. The Americans were drawn up in a line on the right side of the road, and the French occupied the left. At the head of the former, the great American commander, mounted on his noble courser, took his station, attended by his aides. At the head of the latter was posted the excellent Count Rochambeau and his suite. . . . The Americans, though not all in uniform nor their dress so neat, yet exhibited an erect, soldierly air, and every countenance beamed with satisfaction and joy. The concourse of spectators from the country was prodigious, in point of numbers was probably equal to the military, but universal silence and order prevailed. It was about two o'clock when the captive army advanced through the line formed for their reception. Every eye was prepared to gaze on Lord Cornwallis, the object of peculiar interest and solicitude, but he disappointed our anxious expectations; pretending indisposition, he made General O'Hara his substitute as the leader of his army. This officer was followed by the conquered troops in a slow and solemn step, with shouldered arms, colors cased, and drums beating a British march.

The British played the following song at their surrender. It seemed appropriate.

THE WORLD TURNED UPSIDE DOWN

Anonymous

If buttercups buzz'd after the bee,
If boats were on land, churches on sea,
If ponies rode men, and if grass ate the cows,
And cats should be chased into holes by the
    mouse;

If the mamas sold their babies to the gypsies
    for half a crown,
If summer were spring, and the other way
    'round:
Then all the world would be upside down.

The world must have appeared upside down indeed. The child of the mother country had refused to be spanked. Instead, it threw off its swaddling clothes and revealed itself as a lusty, brawling young giant . . .

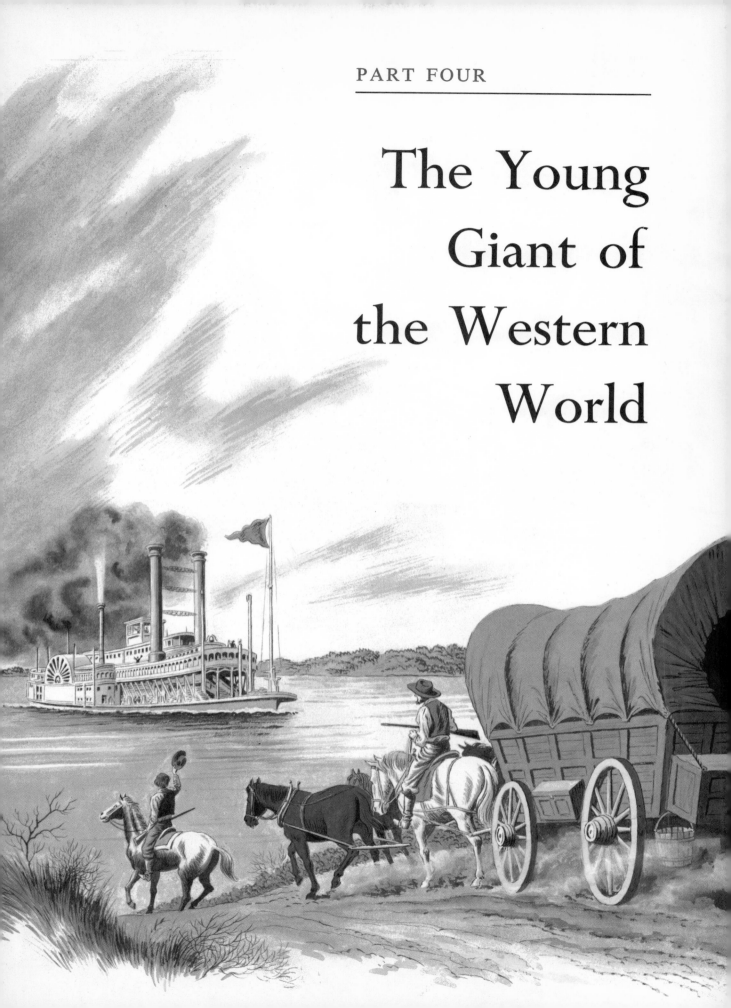

PART FOUR

The Young Giant of the Western World

As the curtain dropped on the Revolutionary War, Independence became not only a ringing Declaration but a hard-won reality. Who could blame the newborn country for kicking up its heels in the following manner?

A MERRY ODE COMPOSED
FOR THE FOURTH OF JULY

by Royall Tyler

Squeak the fife, and beat the drum
Independence Day is come!
Let the roasting pig be bled.
Quick twist off the cockerel's head.
Quickly rub the pewter platter,
Heap the nutcakes fried in butter.

Set the cups and beaker glass,
The pumpkin and the apple sauce,
Send the keg to shop for brandy;
Maple sugar we have handy . . .

Sal, put on your russel skirt,
Jotham, get your *boughten* shirt,
Today we dance to tiddle diddle.
—Here comes Sambo with his fiddle;
Sambo, take a dram of whiskey,
And play up Yankee Doodle frisky.
Moll, come leave your witched tricks,
And let us have a reel of six.

* * *

—Thus we drink and dance away,
This glorious INDEPENDENT DAY!

What was he really like—this bumptious Yankee Doodle Dandy who had dared twist the tail of the British lion? His official language was English, but one observer of the early American scene wrote of a man "whose grandfather was an Englishman, whose wife was Dutch, whose son married a French woman, and whose present four sons have now four wives of different nations . . . Here individuals of all nations are melted into a new race of men . . ."

A new race of men. An idea, a potential that captured the imagination of the world. Read what a French enthusiast wrote while the Revolutionary War was still touch and go.

THE PROMISE OF AMERICA

from "Letter to Dr. Price, 1778" by Turgot

This people is the hope of the human race. It may become the model. It ought to show the world, by facts, that men can be free and yet peaceful, and may dispense with the chains in which tyrants and knaves of every color have presumed to bind them, under pretext of the public good. The American should be an example of political, religious, commercial and industrial liberty. The asylum they offer to the oppressed of every nation, the avenue of escape they open, will compel governments to be just and enlightened; and the rest of the world in due time will see through the empty illusions in which policy is conceived. But to obtain these ends for us, America must secure them to herself; and must not become . . . a mass of divided powers, contending for territory and trade, cementing the slavery of peoples by their own blood.

A bright hope—and a warning. The warning was well put; for during the years 1783–1787, immediately after the war, America threatened indeed to become a "mass of divided powers." With the common enemy defeated, the states fell back to bickering amongst themselves over rights to western lands, tariff laws, etc., as though they were thirteen separate and quarrelsome little countries. Fortunately, far-thinking men like Alexander Hamilton and James Madison managed to convince the majority of states that in unity alone there was strength. A stronger central government was needed than that provided for in the Articles of Confederation—one with the authority to regulate commerce and justice, raise necessary revenue, conduct foreign relations, handle emergencies, protect the rights of all citizens . . .

In May, 1787, a group of representatives from twelve of the states met in Philadelphia. Out of their efforts, arguments and compromises came the Constitution and the balanced form of republican government we enjoy today.

In June, 1788, the new Constitution of the United States of America was ratified by a majority of the states. It outlined the basic organization of the new national government, which was divided into three departments with different functions: *legislative* (the U.S. Senate and House of Representatives), *executive* (the President, Vice-President and Cabinet), and *judiciary* (the Supreme Court and "such inferior courts as the Congress may from time to time ordain and establish"). The Constitution defined the powers this federal government had, the rela-

We the People

of the United States, in order to form a more perfect Union, establish Justice, insure domestic Tranquility, provide for the common defence, promote the general Welfare, and secure the Blessings of Liberty to ourselves and our Posterity, do ordain and establish this Constitution for the United States of America.

Article. I.

Section. 1. All legislative Powers herein granted shall be vested in a Congress of the United States, which shall consist of a Senate and House of Representatives.

Section. 2. The House of Representatives shall be composed of Members chosen every second Year by the People of the several States, and the Electors in each State shall have the Qualifications requisite for Electors of the most numerous Branch of the State Legislature.

No Person shall be a Representative who shall not have attained to the Age of twenty five Years, and been seven Years a Citizen of the United States, and who shall not, when elected, be an Inhabitant of that State in which he shall be chosen.

Representatives and direct Taxes shall be apportioned among the several States which may be included within this Union, according to their respective Numbers, which shall be determined by adding to the whole Number of free Persons, including those bound to Service for a Term of Years, and excluding Indians not taxed, three fifths of all other Persons. The actual Enumeration shall be made within three Years after the first Meeting of the Congress of the United States, and within every subsequent Term of ten Years, in such Manner as they shall by Law direct. The Number of Representatives shall not exceed one for every thirty Thousand, but each State shall have at Least one Representative; and until such enumeration shall be made, the State of New Hampshire shall be entitled to chuse three, Massachusetts eight, Rhode Island and Providence Plantations one, Connecticut five, New York six, New Jersey four, Pennsylvania eight, Delaware one, Maryland six, Virginia ten, North Carolina five, South Carolina five, and Georgia three.

When vacancies happen in the Representation from any State, the Executive Authority thereof shall issue Writs of Election to fill such Vacancies.

The House of Representatives shall chuse their Speaker and other Officers; and shall have the sole Power of Impeachment.

Section. 3. The Senate of the United States shall be composed of two Senators from each State, chosen by the Legislature thereof, for six Years; and each Senator shall have one Vote.

Immediately after they shall be assembled in Consequence of the first Election, they shall be divided as equally as may be into three Classes. The Seats of the Senators of the first Class shall be vacated at the Expiration of the second Year, of the second Class at the Expiration of the fourth Year, and of the third Class at the Expiration of the sixth Year, so that one third may be chosen every second Year; and if Vacancies happen by Resignation, or otherwise, during the Recess of the Legislature of any State, the Executive thereof may make temporary Appointments until the next Meeting of the Legislature, which shall then fill such Vacancies.

No Person shall be a Senator who shall not have attained to the Age of thirty Years, and been nine Years a Citizen of the United States, and who shall not, when elected, be an Inhabitant of that State for which he shall be chosen.

The Vice President of the United States shall be President of the Senate, but shall have no Vote, unless they be equally divided.

The Senate shall chuse their other Officers, and also a President pro tempore, in the Absence of the Vice President, or when he shall exercise the Office of President of the United States.

The Senate shall have the sole Power to try all Impeachments. When sitting for that Purpose, they shall be on Oath or Affirmation. When the President of the United States is tried, the Chief Justice shall preside: And no Person shall be convicted without the Concurrence of two thirds of the Members present.

Judgment in Cases of Impeachment shall not extend further than to removal from Office, and disqualification to hold and enjoy any Office of honor, Trust or Profit under the United States: but the Party convicted shall nevertheless be liable and subject to Indictment, Trial, Judgment and Punishment, according to Law.

Section. 4. The Times, Places and Manner of holding Elections for Senators and Representatives, shall be prescribed in each State by the Legislature thereof; but the Congress may at any time by Law make or alter such Regulations, except as to the Places of chusing Senators.

The Congress shall assemble at least once in every Year, and such Meeting shall be on the first Monday in December, unless they shall by Law appoint a different Day.

Section. 5. Each House shall be the Judge of the Elections, Returns and Qualifications of its own Members, and a Majority of each shall constitute a Quorum to do Business; but a smaller Number may adjourn from day to day, and may be authorized to compel the Attendance of absent Members, in such Manner, and under such Penalties as each House may provide.

Each House may determine the Rules of its Proceedings, punish its Members for disorderly Behaviour, and, with the Concurrence of two thirds, expel a Member.

Each House shall keep a Journal of its Proceedings, and from time to time publish the same, excepting such Parts as may in their Judgment require Secrecy; and the Yeas and Nays of the Members of either House on any question shall, at the Desire of one fifth of those Present, be entered on the Journal.

Neither House, during the Session of Congress, shall, without the Consent of the other, adjourn for more than three days, nor to any other Place than that in which the two Houses shall be sitting.

Section. 6. The Senators and Representatives shall receive a Compensation for their Services, to be ascertained by Law, and paid out of the Treasury of the United States. They shall in all Cases, except Treason, Felony and Breach of the Peace, be privileged from Arrest during their Attendance at the Session of their respective Houses, and in going to and returning from the same; and for any Speech or Debate in either House, they shall not be questioned in any other Place.

No Senator or Representative shall, during the Time for which he was elected, be appointed to any civil Office under the Authority of the United States, which shall have been created, or the Emoluments whereof shall have been increased during such time; and no Person holding any Office under the United States, shall be a Member of either House during his Continuance in Office.

Section. 7. All Bills for raising Revenue shall originate in the House of Representatives; but the Senate may propose or concur with Amendments as on other Bills.

Every Bill which shall have passed the House of Representatives and the Senate, shall, before it become a Law, be presented to the President of the

THE ADVENTURE OF AMERICA

tionships among its three departments, and the relationship between the federal government and the states. The Constitution also provided for its own amendment—thus making it a flexible instrument, capable of growth and change as conditions and needs changed. The first ten amendments, adopted in 1791, composed the Bill of Rights.

The Constitution of the United States would prove to be so effective a guide to enlightened government that, in years to come, it would influence the federal systems of Brazil, Argentina and Switzerland, among other countries.

Overwhelming choice for first President was George Washington. On April 24, 1789, a ship conducted him to the temporary capital, New York City, where he was due to take the oath of office six days later. As the vessel approached the harbor, it touched off a high-spirited demonstration, which proved beyond a doubt that the President-elect was "first in the hearts of his countrymen." A member of Washington's own shipboard party described the welcome in a letter written the next day to his wife. Here are some excerpts.

GEORGE WASHINGTON
SAILS INTO THE PRESIDENCY

from Elias Boudinot's Letter to His Wife

Soon after we opened the bay, General Knox and several generals in a large barge presented themselves, with their splendid colors. Boat after boat and sloop after sloop, added to our train, gaily dressed in all their naval ornaments, made a most splendid appearance. Before we got to Bedloe Island, a large sloop came with full sail on our starboard bow, when there stood up about twenty gentlemen and ladies and with most excellent voices sang an elegant ode prepared for the purpose, to the tune of "God Save the King," welcoming their great chief to the seat of government. On the conclusion, we gave them our hats, and then they with the surrounding boats gave us three cheers. . . .

As we approached the harbor, our train increased, and the huzzaing and shouts of joy seemed to add life to this lively scene. At this moment a number of porpoises came playing amongst us, as if they had risen up to know what was the cause of all this joy. We now discovered the shores covered with thousands of people—men, women, and children—nay, I might venture to say tens of thousands. From the fort to the place of landing, although near half a mile, you could see little else along the shores—in the streets and aboard every vessel—but heads standing as thick as ears of corn before the harvest. . . .

We soon arrived at the ferry stairs, where there were many thousands of the citizens waiting with all the eagerness of expectation to welcome our excellent patriot to that shore, which he had regained from a powerful enemy by his valor and good conduct. We found the stairs covered with carpeting and the rails hung with crimson. The President, being preceded by the committee, was received by the Governor and citizens in the most brilliant manner. . . .

Under Washington and his successor, John Adams, the country began to gain momentum. The Bill of Rights was added to the Constitution, Alexander Hamilton got the country's financial house in order, the Mississippi River was navigated . . . The first political parties made their debut, with Hamilton's Federalists (supporting businessmen, high tariffs, and a strong central government) opposed by Jefferson's Republicans (later Democrats, they championed farmers' rights, low tariffs, and a limited central government). Foreign affairs got off to a shaky start as friction developed with England and with France, whose Revolution followed the American one but was eventually taken over by Napoleon's dreams of glory and empire.

Young America made mistakes and stumbled a bit as it groped its way forward, but the nineteenth century approached in an over-all atmosphere of expansion and progress. Eli Whitney invented the cotton gin, and the first textile mills were built in New England, bringing the factory system and industrial revolution to America. The symbol of the eighteenth century — old-fashioned Colonial man—was on the way out. His many virtues had helped lay the foundations for a new country, but his horizons had tended to be local, his imagination limited. The age to come would remember him with affectionate nostalgia, while leaving him far behind.

As the nineteenth century succeeded the eighteenth, America got a new capital (Washington, D.C.) and a President whose energy, will power, and varied interests symbolized a dynamic new era. He was Thomas Jefferson—author of the Declaration of Independence, defender of religious liberty, architect, inventor, patron of arts and sciences, etc., etc.

Jefferson thought that just about any problem could be solved by individual initiative. He had great confidence in the average American. He believed that in this country of fresh beginnings, exciting discoveries, great natural resources, expanding horizons of land, knowledge and freedom—nobody was actually "born without a chance."

BORN WITHOUT A CHANCE

by Edmund Vance Cooke

THE TIME: *Napoleonic in Europe, Jeffersonian in America.*
THE SCENE: *An outlying border state sometimes called "the dark and bloody ground."*
THE EXACT DATE: *February 12, 1809.*

A squalid village set in wintry mud.
A hub-deep oxcart slowly groans and creaks.
A horseman hails and halts. He shifts his cud
And speaks:
   "Well, did you hear? Tom Lincoln's wife today.
The devil's luck for folk as poor as they!
   Poor Tom! poor Nance!
Poor youngun born without a chance!

"A baby in that Godforsaken den,
That worse than cattle pen!
Well, what are they but cattle? Cattle? Tut!
A critter is beef, hide and tallow, but
Who'd swap one for the critters of that hut?
   White trash! small fry!
Whose only instincts are to multiply!
   They're good at that,
And so, today, God wot! another brat!

"Another squawking, squalling, red-faced good-for-naught
Spilled on the world, heaven only knows for what.
   Better if he were black,
For then he'd have a shirt upon his back,

65

And something in his belly, as he grows.
More than he's like to have, as I suppose.
   Yet there be those
Who claim 'equality' for this new brat,
   And that damned democrat
Who squats today where Washington once
    sat,

He'd have it that this Lincoln cub might be
Of even value in the world with you and me!

"Yes, Jefferson, Tom Jefferson, who but he?
Who even hints that black men should be
   free.
That featherheaded fool would tell you
   maybe
A president might lie in this new baby!
In this new squawker born without a rag
To hide himself! Good God, it makes me gag!
   This human spawn
Born for the world to wipe its feet upon
   A few years hence, but now
More helpless than the litter of a sow,
And—Oh, well! send the womenfolks to see
    to Nance.

"Poor little devil! born without a chance!"

We'll meet this poor, unfortunate "Lincoln cub" later on in our story, but meanwhile, Jefferson, that energetic egghead president, was keeping things lively. The major accomplishment of his two terms in office (1801–1809) was the Louisiana Purchase from Napoleon, who decided—much to Jefferson's relief—that he was less interested in an American empire than in money to continue his European wars. The Purchase—negotiated by Secretary of State James Madison in 1803—more than doubled the size of the United States, adding vast stretches of land west of the Mississippi, all the way to the Rockies. The cost? A little over $27,000,000—or about four cents an acre. Not a bad bargain. The third President also had the foresight to send Lewis and Clark blazing a trail to the far west, as far as Oregon. Jefferson spent his last years helping found the University of Virginia. If he hadn't died at the age of eighty-three, who knows what his next project would have been?

THOMAS JEFFERSON
(1743-1826)

by *Stephen Vincent Benét*

Thomas Jefferson,
What do you say
Under the gravestone
Hidden away?

"I was a giver,
I was a molder,
I was a builder
With a strong shoulder."

Six feet and over,
Large-boned and ruddy,
The eyes grey-hazel
But bright with study.

The big hands clever
With pen and fiddle
And ready, ever,
For any riddle.

From buying empires
To planting 'taters,
From Declarations
To trick dumb-waiters.

"I liked the people,
The sweat and crowd of them,
Trusted them always
And spoke aloud of them.

"I liked all learning
And wished to share it
Abroad like pollen
For all who merit.

"I liked fine houses
With Greek pilasters,
And built them surely,
My touch a master's.

"I liked queer gadgets
And secret shelves,
And helping nations
To rule themselves.

"Jealous of others?
Not always candid?
But huge of vision
And open-handed.

67

"A wild-goose chaser?
Now and again.
Build Monticello,
You little men!

"Design my plow, sirs,
They use it still,
Or found my college
At Charlottesville.

"And still go questing
New things and thinkers,
And keep as busy
As twenty tinkers.

"While always guarding
The people's freedom—
You need more hands, sir?
I didn't need 'em.

"They call you rascal?
They called me worse.
You'd do grand things, sir,
But lack the purse?

"I got no riches.
I died a debtor.
I died free-hearted
And that was better.

"For life was freakish
But life was fervent,
And I was always
Life's willing servant.

"Life, life's too weighty?
Too long a haul, sir?
I lived past eighty.
I liked it all, sir."

Jefferson helped choose his successor, President Madison, who probably wasn't too grateful for the package of headaches he inherited. These led to the War of 1812, which really grew out of the Napoleonic Wars being waged between England and France at the time.

As part of its struggle to survive, England had thrown a naval blockade around Napoleonic Europe. She wasn't very happy about the shipowners of neutral America, who insisted that freedom of the seas included getting rich supplying the French. The English expressed their annoyance by the stopping and searching of American ships, confiscation, and impressment of seamen believed to be deserters from the harsh British Navy. American "war hawks" inflamed public opinion on the general theme of "Are we going to let the Big Bad British Bully push us around?"

Actually, men of good will in both countries were working toward a peaceful solution, but the "war hawks"—Henry Clay, John C. Calhoun and others—were simply looking for an excuse to conquer Canada and West Florida (controlled by the British). They believed the British in America were holding back the "natural" westward expansion of the United States by inciting Indians to violence against settlers. (They cited the Shawnee uprising led by Chief Tecumseh in 1811 as a prime example.) After a bitter fight, the "war hawks" gained control of Congress, and on June 18, 1812, war was declared.

The immediate attempt to conquer Canada was a dismal failure. However, the tiny American navy gave a good account of itself with victories achieved by such commanders as Stephen Decatur, Isaac Hull, Oliver Perry. These were the days of "wooden ships and iron men," when battles were fought at close quarters between fast, square-rigged frigates with forty or fifty guns . . .

AN OLD-TIME SEA-FIGHT

from "Song of Myself" by Walt Whitman

Would you hear of an old-time sea-fight?
Would you learn who won by the light of the
    moon and stars?
List to the yarn, as my grandmother's father
    the sailor told it to me.

Our foe was no skulk in his ship I tell you,
    (said he,)
His was the surly English pluck, and there is
    no tougher or truer, and never was, and
    never will be;
Along the lower'd eve he came horribly rak-
    ing us.

We closed with him, the yards entangled, the
    cannon touch'd,
My captain lash'd fast with his own hands.

We had receiv'd some eighteen pound shots
    under the water,
On our lower-gun-deck two large pieces had
    burst at the first fire, killing all around
    and blowing up overhead.

Fighting at sun-down, fighting at dark,
Ten o'clock at night, the full moon well up,
    our leaks on the gain, and five feet of
    water reported,

The master-at-arms loosing the prisoners
    confined in the after-hold to give them
    a chance for themselves.

The transit to and from the magazine is now
    stopt by the sentinels,
They see so many strange faces they do not
    know whom to trust.

Our frigate takes fire,
The other asks if we demand quarter?
If our colors are struck and the fighting
    done?

Now I laugh content, for I hear the voice of
   my little captain,
We have not struck, he composedly cries, *we
   have just begun our part of the fighting.*

Only three guns are in use,
One is directed by the captain himself against
   the enemy's main-mast,
Two well serv'd with grape and canister silence his musketry and clear his decks.

The tops alone second the fire of this little
   battery, especially the main-top,
They hold out bravely during the whole of
   the action.

Not a moment's cease,
The leaks gain fast on the pumps, the fire
   eats toward the powder-magazine.

One of the pumps has been shot away, it is
   generally thought we are sinking.

Serene stands the little captain,
He is not hurried, his voice is neither high
   nor low,
His eyes give more light to us than our battle-
   lanterns.

Toward twelve there in the beams of the
   moon they surrender to us.

   One of the most famous sea fights of the
war occurred off Newfoundland when the
forty-four-gun frigate *Constitution,* commanded by Isaac Hull, defeated the British
Guerrière (August 19, 1812). Eighteen years
later, when "Old Ironsides" was about to be
junked, Oliver Wendell Holmes wrote the
following poem, which aroused public feeling and saved the ship.

OLD IRONSIDES

by Oliver Wendell Holmes

Ay, tear her tattered ensign down!
   Long has it waved on high,
And many an eye has danced to see
   That banner in the sky;
Beneath it rung the battle-shout,
   And burst the cannon's roar:
The meteor of the ocean air
   Shall sweep the clouds no more!

Her deck, once red with heroes' blood,
   Where knelt the vanquished foe,
When winds were hurrying o'er the flood
   And waves were white below,
No more shall feel the victor's tread,
   Or know the conquered knee:
The harpies of the shore shall pluck
   The eagle of the sea!

O better that her shattered hulk
   Should sink beneath the wave!
Her thunders shook the mighty deep,
   And there should be her grave:
Nail to the mast her holy flag,
   Set every threadbare sail,
And give her to the god of storms,
   The lightning and the gale!

   As the War of 1812 turned into the War
of 1813 and '14, the superior (in numbers)
British navy managed to bottle up most of
the American ships. A British army landed
on the Virginia coast. It defeated an American force, caused President Madison and his
Cabinet to flee into the Virginia woods, and
captured and burned Washington, D.C. Arriving at the abandoned White House to destroy it, a group of hungry British soldiers

had the following pleasant surprise, described here by a British veteran of the day.

MR. MADISON'S UNINVITED GUESTS

from "A Narrative of the Campaigns of the British Army" by George Robert Gleig

When the detachment sent out to destroy Mr. Madison's house entered his dining parlor, they found a dinner table spread and covers laid for forty guests . . . whilst in the kitchen . . . spits, loaded with joints of various sorts, turned before the fire; pots, saucepans, and other culinary utensils stood upon the grate; and all the other requisites for an elegant and substantial repast were exactly in a state which indicated that they had been lately and precipitately abandoned.

You will readily imagine that these preparations were beheld by a party of hungry soldiers with no indifferent eye. An elegant dinner, even though considerably overdressed, was a luxury to which few of them, at least for some time back, had been accustomed, and which, after the dangers and fatigues of the day, appeared peculiarly inviting. They sat down to it, therefore, not indeed in the most orderly manner, but with countenances which would not have disgraced a party of aldermen at a civic feast, and, having satisfied their appetites . . . and partaken pretty freely of the wines, they finished by setting fire to the house which had so liberally entertained them.

The victorious British marched on Baltimore in September, 1814, but were stopped by the American defenders of Fort McHenry,

outside the city. An American attorney and poet, Francis Scott Key, was detained by the British fleet while it bombarded Fort McHenry through a long night. The fort had withstood fantastic punishment; surely dawn would reveal the lowered flag of surrender! What Key saw—and felt—at dawn, he set down in a stirring poem, which later became the words to the American national anthem.

THE STAR-SPANGLED BANNER

by Francis Scott Key

Oh, say, can you see, by the dawn's early
    light,
    What so proudly we hailed at the twilight's
      last gleaming,
Whose broad stripes and bright stars through
    the perilous fight,
    O'er the ramparts we watched were so gallantly streaming?
And the rockets' red glare, the bombs bursting in air,
Gave proof thro' the night that our flag was
    still there.
Oh, say, does that star-spangled banner yet
    wave
O'er the land of the free, and the home of the
    brave!

On the shore, dimly seen thro' the mists of
    the deep,
    Where the foe's haughty host in dread silence reposes,
What is that which the breeze o'er the towering steep,
    As it fitfully blows, half conceals, half discloses?

Now it catches the gleam of the morning's
    first beam,
In full glory reflected, now shines on the
    stream.
'Tis the star-spangled banner; oh, long may
    it wave
O'er the land of the free, and the home of the
    brave!

And where is that band who so vauntingly
    swore
    That the havoc of war and the battle's con-
      fusion
A home and a country should leave us no
    more?
    Their blood has washed out their foul
      footsteps' pollution.
No refuge could save the hireling and slave
From the terror of flight, or the gloom of the
    grave:
And the star-spangled banner in triumph
    doth wave
O'er the land of the free, and the home of the
    brave!

Oh, thus be it ever when freemen shall stand
    Between their loved homes and the war's
      desolation;
Blest with victory and peace, may the
    heaven-rescued land
    Praise the power that hath made and pre-
      served us a nation!
Then conquer we must, when our cause it is
    just,
And this be our motto: "In God is our trust!"
And the star-spangled banner in triumph
    doth wave,
O'er the land of the free, and the home of the
    brave!

After the British were halted at Fort Mc-
Henry, an invading fleet of theirs was defeated at Plattsburg. Both sides began to get
tired of the indecisive war, and peace nego-
tiations began. Meanwhile, however, a British force under Sir Edward Packenham
made the mistake of attacking New Orleans
when it was commanded by "Old Hickory"
Andrew Jackson. New Orleans was famous
for its wealth and its lovely Creole women.
Sir Edward promised his troops "Booty and
Beauty." Instead, they received a hail of
American lead that mowed down Sir Edward
and two other generals, and caused two thousand casualties in all. The Americans lost
thirteen dead, which indicates they must
have been the better shots. (They were.
Jackson's small army contained Kentucky
hunters—famous for their deadly skill with
the rifle.)

The Battle of New Orleans was fought on
January 8, 1815—ironically, over two weeks
after the war officially ended with the sign-
ing of the Treaty of Ghent in London. (News
traveled slowly in the days before the telegraph and Atlantic Cable.)

Although the war had gained America
nothing concrete, it did win her respect as a
nation willing to fight for her rights. Meanwhile, Napoleon was defeated, and American success inspired the revolt of Spanish
colonies in Latin America. The concept that
European nations should leave the American hemisphere alone to develop in its own
way would lead, in 1823, to the Monroe
Doctrine.

Yankee Doodle rebuilt Washington bigger
and better than before, turned his back on
Europe, and faced westward. This was the

direction of the future—from the fertile Mississippi Valley to the great rolling prairies . . . from the Great Lakes to the Rocky Mountains and the Pacific coast beyond . . . a vast, rich, practically untouched country calling for new pioneers to come and conquer it . . .

THE COMING AMERICAN

by Sam Walter Foss

Bring me men to match my mountains,
Bring me men to match my plains,
And new eras in their brains.
Bring me men to match my prairies,
Men to match my inland seas,
Men whose thoughts shall pave a highway
Up to ampler destinies,
Pioneers to cleanse thought's marshlands,
   And to cleanse old error's fen;
Bring me men to match my mountains—
   Bring me men!

Bring me men to match my forests,
Strong to fight the storm and beast,
Branching toward the skyey future,
Rooted on the futile past.
Bring me men to match my valleys,
   Tolerant of rain and snow,
Men within whose fruitful purpose
   Time's consummate blooms shall grow,
Men to tame the tigerish instincts
   Of the lair and cave and den,
Cleanse the dragon slime of nature—
   Bring me men!

Bring me men to match my rivers,
   Continent cleansers, flowing free,
Drawn by eternal madness,

To be mingled with the sea—
Men of oceanic impulse,
   Men whose moral currents sweep
Toward the wide, infolding ocean
   Of an undiscovered deep—
Men who feel the strong pulsation
   Of the central sea, and then
Time their currents by its earth throbs—
   Bring me Men.

And they came; not only men, but women, children, whole families pulling up stakes, heading west with all they owned piled high on carts, wagons, or even strapped to their backs . . . Why did they do it? One reason was the promise of good, cheap land. It was hard wresting crops from the thin, rocky soil of New England, and other parts of the East were becoming thickly settled and industrialized. But a man could trade a hundred dollars for eighty acres in the great Federal-owned western reserves. All he had to do was go settle them himself.

Another reason for the trek westward was the age-old dream that life is better, somehow, and golden opportunity waits, beyond the distant horizon. The same dream had sent the restless Norsemen a-roving in the age of Leif Ericson, had driven those who followed Columbus across the sea in little wooden ships. The nineteenth-century emigrant thought of the unknown West as "God's country," in the same way that seventeenth-century Englishmen, yearning to improve their lot, had labeled as "Earth's only Paradise" a Virginia they had never even seen. Now let's roll with one of these streams of migration as it heads toward the Ohio River in 1817. This is an actual account.

AMERICA ROLLS WESTWARD

from "Notes on a Journey in America"
by Morris Birkbeck

We have now fairly turned our backs on the old world and find ourselves in the very stream of emigration. Old America seems to be breaking up and moving westward. We are seldom out of sight, as we travel on this grand track towards the Ohio, of family groups, behind and before us, some with a view to a particular spot, close to a brother, perhaps, or a friend who has gone before and reported well of the country. Many, like ourselves, when they arrive in the wilderness, will find no lodge prepared for them.

A small wagon (so light that you might almost carry it, yet strong enough to bear a good load of bedding, utensils and provisions, and a swarm of young citizens, and to sus-

tain marvelous shocks in its passage over these rocky heights) with two small horses, sometimes a cow or two, comprises their all, excepting a little store of hard-earned cash for the land office of the district, where they may obtain a title for as many acres as they possess half-dollars, being one-fourth of the purchase money. The wagon has a tilt, or cover, made of a sheet or perhaps a blanket. The family are seen before, behind, or within the vehicle, according to the road or weather or perhaps the spirits of the party.

The New Englanders, they say, may be known by the cheerful air of the women advancing in front of the vehicle, the Jersey people by their being fixed steadily within it, whilst the Pennsylvanians creep lingering behind, as though regretting the homes they have left. A cart and single horse frequently afford the means of transfer, sometimes a horse and packsaddle. Often the back of the poor pilgrim bears all his effects, and his wife follows, naked-footed, bending under the hopes of the family. . . .

To give an idea of the internal movements of this vast hive, about twelve thousand wagons passed between Baltimore and Philadelphia in the last year, with from four to six horses, carrying from thirty-five to forty hundredweight. . . . Add to these the numerous stages, loaded to the utmost, and the innumerable travelers on horseback, on foot, and in light wagons, and you have before you a scene of bustle and business, extending over a space of three hundred miles, which is truly wonderful.

As the century advanced, the frontier advanced with it, pouring over the Alleghenies, filling up the Ohio and Mississippi Valleys and the Great Lakes region, eventually

crossing the prairies, the great plains, the Rockies . . .

Always ranging out ahead of the farmers and town builders were the solitary trailblazers. Sometimes these were explorers—like Lewis and Clark—and land surveyors, sent out by the Government. But, more often, they were the raw-boned misfits of society, restless hunters and woodsmen who believed that the trappings of civilization cramped a man's style. Perennial Huckleberry Finns, they might be hobos or hermits in today's world. However, we owe them a vote of thanks for opening up the frontier, simply because they sought room to be free in.

Frontiersmen were deadly riflemen—they *had* to be. In the wilderness, a poor shot didn't eat very well. One of the most famous riflemen of all was Daniel Boone (1734–1820). In our next selection, the renowned American bird painter, John James Audubon, recalls an exhibition he witnessed of Old Dan'l's skill at bringing home the bacon (in this case, squirrels).

DANIEL BOONE HAS HIM A SQUIRREL SHOOT

from "Kentucky Sports" by John James Audubon

Barking off squirrels is delightful sport, and in my opinion requires a greater degree of accuracy than any other. I first witnessed this manner of procuring squirrels whilst near the town of Frankfort. The performer was the celebrated Daniel Boone. We walked out together and followed the rocky margins of the Kentucky River until we reached a piece of flat land thickly covered with black walnuts, oaks, and hickories. . . .

My companion, a stout, hale, and athletic man, dressed in a homespun hunting-shirt, bare-legged and moccasined, carried a long and heavy rifle, which, as he was loading it, he said had proved efficient in all his former undertakings, and which he hoped would not fail on this occasion, as he felt proud to show me his skill. The gun was wiped, the powder measured, the ball patched with six-hundred-thread linen, and the charge sent home with a hickory rod.

We moved not a step from the place, for the squirrels were so numerous that it was unnecessary to go after them. Boone pointed to one of these animals, which had observed us, and was crouched on a branch about fifty paces distant, and bade me mark well the spot where the ball should hit. He raised his piece gradually, until the *bead* (that being the name given by the Kentuckians to the *sight*) of the barrel was brought to a line with the spot which he intended to hit. The whiplike report resounded through the woods and along the hills in repeated echoes. Judge

of my surprise when I perceived that the ball had hit the piece of the bark immediately beneath the squirrel, and shivered it into splinters, the concussion produced by which had killed the animal and sent it whirling through the air, as if it had been blown up by explosion of a powder magazine. Boone kept up his firing, and before many hours had elapsed we had procured as many squirrels as we wished; for you must know that to load a rifle requires only a moment, and that if it is wiped once after each shot, it will do duty for hours. Since that first interview with our veteran Boone I have seen many other individuals perform the same feat. . . .

After what I have said you may easily imagine with what ease a Kentuckian procures game or dispatches an enemy, more especially when I tell you that everyone in the state is accustomed to handle the rifle from the time when he is first able to shoulder it until near the close of his career.

As important and basic a piece of frontier equipment as the rifle was the axe. It cleared the land, helped build cabins, fences, stock enclosures, houses. The country couldn't have been settled without it.

THE AXE LEAPS!

from "Song of the Broad-Axe" by Walt Whitman

The axe leaps!
The solid forest gives fluid utterances,
They tumble forth, they rise and form,
Hut, tent, landing, survey,
Flail, plough, pick, crowbar, spade,
Shingle, rail, prop, wainscot, jamb, lath,
    panel, gable . . .

*   *   *

The shapes arise!
Shapes of the using of axes anyhow, and the
    users and all that neighbors them,
Cutters down of wood and haulers of it to
    the Penobscot or Kennebec,
Dwellers in cabins among the Californian
    mountains or by the little lakes, or on
    the Columbia . . .

* * *

Wielder of both rifle and axe, the frontiers-
man looms as a uniquely colorful figure in
American history. Here is a balanced, keenly
observed sketch of him, written in the early
nineteenth century.

PORTRAIT OF A FRONTIERSMAN

from "Recollections of the Last Ten Years"
by Timothy Flint

The gentlemen of the towns, even here,
speak often with a certain contempt and horror of the backwoodsmen. It is true there are
worthless people here; it is true there are
gamblers and gougers and outlaws; but there
are fewer of them than, from the nature of
things and the character of the age and the
world, we ought to expect. But the backwoodsman of the West, as I have seen him,
is generally an amiable and virtuous man.
His general motive for coming here is to be
a freeholder, to have plenty of rich land, and
to be able to settle his children about him.
It is a most virtuous motive. And I fully believe that nine in ten of the emigrants have
come here with no other motive. You find,
in truth, that he has vices and barbarisms peculiar to his situation. His manners are
rough. He wears, it may be, a long beard.
He has a great quantity of bear- or deerskins

wrought into his household establishment,
his furniture and dress. He carries a knife or
a dirk in his bosom, and when in the woods
has a rifle on his back and a pack of dogs at
his heels. An Atlantic stranger, transferred
directly from one of our cities to his door,
would recoil from a rencounter with him.
But remember that his rifle and his dogs are
among his chief means of support and profit.
Remember that all his first days here were
passed in dread of the savages. Remember
that he still encounters them, still meets bears
and panthers. Enter his door and tell him
you are benighted and wish the shelter of his
cabin for the night. The welcome is indeed
seemingly ungracious: "I reckon you can
stay," or "I suppose we must let you stay."
But this apparent ungraciousness is the har-
binger of every kindness that he can bestow
and every comfort that his cabin can afford.
Good coffee, corn bread and butter, venison,
pork, wild and tame fowls, are set before you.
His wife, timid, silent, reserved, but constantly attentive to your comfort, does not sit
at the table with you, but, like the wives of
the patriarchs, stands and attends on you.
You are shown to the best bed which the
house can afford. . . . And when you depart
and speak about your bill, you are most commonly told with some slight mark of resentment that they do not keep tavern. Even the
flaxen-headed urchins will turn away from
your money. . . .

I have found the backwoodsmen to be
such as I have described—a hardy, adventurous, hospitable, rough, but sincere and up-
right race of people.

Modesty was definitely *not* a virtue of the
early frontier. Unlike the tall-in-the-saddle,

soft-spoken cowboy hero of the later West, the backwoodsman believed in letting the world know (with plenty of lung-power) just how good he was. Humorous and extravagant boasting became a highly developed art, and the teller of especially mighty brags was esteemed as a "ring-tailed roarer." One of the most accomplished of these was coonskin-capped Davy Crockett—although, like many of his breed, his accomplishments weren't too far behind his claims. A legend in his own day, he emerged from the woods of Tennessee to serve two terms in Congress, and died heroically in defense of the Alamo. The following speech, attributed to him—although probably fictional—is a good example of the ring-tailed roarer in action.

SPEECH OF COLONEL CROCKETT IN CONGRESS

from "Davy Crockett's Almanac, of Wild Sports in the West, Life in the Backwoods, & Sketches of Texas"

Mr. Speaker.

Who — Who — Whoop — Bow — Wow — Wow — Yough. I say, Mr. Speaker; I've had a speech in soak this six months, and it has swelled me like a drowned horse; if I don't deliver it I shall burst and smash the windows. The gentleman from Massachusetts [Mr. Everett] talks of summing up the merits of the question, but I'll sum up my own. In one word I'm a screamer, and have got the roughest racking horse, the prettiest sister, the surest rifle and the ugliest dog in the district. I'm a leetle the savagest crittur

you ever *did see*. My father can whip any man in Kentucky, and I can lick my father. I can outspeak any man on this floor, and give him two hours start. I can run faster, dive deeper, stay longer under, and come out drier, than any *chap* this side the big *Swamp*. I can outlook a panther and outstart a flash of lightning, tote a steamboat on my back and play at rough and tumble with a lion, and an occasional kick from a *zebra*. To sum up all in one word *I'm a horse*. Goliah was a pretty hard colt but I could choke him. I can take the rag off—frighten the old folks—astonish the natives—and beat the Dutch all to smash—make nothing of sleeping under a blanket of snow—and don't mind being frozen more than a rotten apple.

Congress allows *lemonade* to the members and has it charged under the head of stationery—I move also that *whiskey* be allowed under the item of *fuel*. For *bitters* I can suck away at a noggin of aquafortis, sweetened with brimstone, stirred with a lightning rod, and skimmed with a hurricane. I've soaked my head and shoulders in Salt River, so much that I'm always corned. I can walk like an ox, run like a fox, swim like an eel, yell like an Indian, fight like a devil, spout like an earthquake . . .

. . . and so forth. Another kind of trail blazer was the "mountain man"—the fur trapper or trader. Many of them were recruited by the American Fur Company, which made its founder, John Jacob Astor (1763–1848), the richest American of the early nineteenth century. Trappers swarmed over the Rockies and the Columbia River region, looking mainly for beaver pelts. Like the French "bush-rangers," they often solved the problem of loneliness by going native . . .

I SAW THE MARRIAGE OF THE TRAPPER

from "Song of Myself" by Walt Whitman

I saw the marriage of the trapper in the open
    air in the far west, the bride was a red
    girl,
Her father and his friends sat near cross-
    legged and dumbly smoking, they had
    moccasins to their feet and large thick
    blankets hanging from their shoulders,
On a bank lounged the trapper, he was drest
    mostly in skins, his luxuriant beard and
    curls protected his neck, he held his
    bride by the hand,
She had long eyelashes, her head was bare,
    her coarse straight locks descended
    upon her voluptuous limbs and reach'd
    to her feet.

*   *   *

While the men who trapped the fur lived like savages, the pelts themselves were sent back East to make elegant and fashionable beaver hats. However, it wasn't easy to become a lady of fashion. Oliver Wendell Holmes describes what his aunt had to go through.

MY AUNT

by Oliver Wendell Holmes

(excerpts)

Her father—Grandpapa! forgive
  This erring lip its smiles—
Vowed she should make the finest girl

Within a hundred miles;
He sent her to a stylish school;
  'Twas in her thirteenth June;
And with her, as the rules required,
  "Two towels and a spoon."

They braced my aunt against a board,
  To make her straight and tall;
They laced her up, they starved her down,
  To make her light and small;
They pinched her feet, they singed her hair,
  They screwed it up with pins—
O never mortal suffered more
  In penance for her sins.

Frontier women had no time for the fripperies or civilized tortures of fashion. They were too busy raising children, feeding stock, cooking—keeping one hand free to grab a rifle in case a hungry Indian or bear should wander too close to the cabin. They inspired their share of tall tales, which paid humorous tribute to their "sand," "grit," and general, all-round toughness.

A LADY RING-TAILED ROARER

from "Harry Macarthy, the Arkansas Comedian"

My first sweetheart gave me this description of herself:

"You just ought to see me rigged out in my best. My bonnet is a hornet's nest, garnished with wolves' tails and eagles' feathers. My gown's made of a whole bear's hide, with the tail for a train. I can drink from the branch without a cup, shoot a wild goose flying, wade the Mississippi without getting wet, outscream a catamount, and jump over my

THE ERIE CANAL

Anonymous

We were forty miles from Albany,
Forget it I never shall!
What a terrible storm we had one night
On the E-ri-ee Canal!

Chorus:
The E-ri-ee was a-risin',
The gin was a-gittin' low,
And I scarcely think we'll git a drink
Till we git to Buffalo,
Till we git to Buffalo.

Our captain he came up on deck
With a spy glass in his hand,
And the fog it was so tarnal'd thick
That he couldn't spy the land.

Our cook she was a grand ol' gal,
She had a ragged dress.
We hoisted her upon a pole
As a signal of distress.

The captain he got married,
And the cook she went to jail,
And I'm the only son-of-a-gun
That's left to tell the tale.

The E-ri-ee was a-risin',
The gin was a-gittin' low,
And I scarcely think we'll git a drink
Till we git to Buffalo,
Till we git to Buffalo.

own shadow. I've good, strong horse sense, and know a woodchuck from a skunk. I can dance down any fellow in Arkansas, and cut through the bushes like a pint of whisky among forty men. Your Sal."

In the settling of the West, waterways, as well as land routes, played an important part. One of the most famous was man-made. In 1825, the 352-mile-long Erie Canal, connecting the Hudson River with Lake Erie, was opened to traffic. The settlement of Michigan, Illinois and Wisconsin owes a lot to commerce along the Canal, where great barges were towed by mules and horses plodding along the bank. The bargemen had their own songs to relieve the monotony of the trip. Here's one of them . . .

Other legendary types of men were the keelboatmen and raftsmen who handled the commerce on the great Mississippi River be-

80

fore the steamboats took over. Here they are, vividly described by the most famous riverman of them all.

MARK TWAIN RECOLLECTS MISSISSIPPI RAFTSMEN

from "Life on the Mississippi" by Mark Twain

The river's earliest commerce was in great barges—keelboats, broadhorns. They floated and sailed from the upper rivers to New Orleans, changed cargoes there, and were tediously warped and poled back by hand. A voyage down and back sometimes occupied nine months. In time this commerce increased until it gave employment to hordes of rough and hardy men; rude, uneducated, brave, suffering terrific hardships with sailor-like stoicism; heavy drinkers, coarse frolickers in moral sties like the Natchez-under-the-hill of that day, heavy fighters, reckless fellows, everyone, elephantinely jolly, foul-witted, profane, prodigal of their money, bankrupt at the end of the trip, fond of barbaric finery, prodigious braggarts; yet, in the main, honest, trustworthy, faithful to promises and duty, and often picturesquely magnanimous.

By and by the steamboat intruded. Then, for fifteen or twenty years, these men continued to run their keelboats downstream, and the steamers did all of the up-stream business, the keelboatmen selling their boats in New Orleans, and returning home as deck-passengers in the steamers.

But after a while the steamboats so increased in number and in speed that they were able to absorb the entire commerce; and then keelboating died a permanent death. The keelboatman became a deck-hand, or a mate, or a pilot on the steamer; and when steamer-berths were not open to him, he took a berth on a Pittsburgh coal-flat, or on a pine raft constructed in the forests up toward the sources of the Mississippi.

In the heyday of the steamboating prosperity, the river from end to end was flaked with coal-fleets and timber-rafts, all managed by hand, and employing hosts of the rough characters whom I have been trying to describe. I remember the annual processions of mighty rafts that used to glide by Hannibal when I was a boy—an acre or so of white, sweet-smelling boards in each raft, a crew of two dozen men or more, three or four wigwams scattered about the raft's vast level space for storm-quarters—and I remember the rude ways and the tremendous talk of their big crews, the ex-keelboatmen and their admiringly patterning successors; for we used to swim out a quarter or a third of a mile and get on these rafts and have a ride.

As the age of the keelboats and rafts faded, steamboats took over. They had been navigating Eastern waters as far back as the first successful demonstration in 1787. The most famous of them was Robert Fulton's 150-foot-long *Clermont,* launched in 1807. Four years later came the debut of the first steamboat on western waters: the stern-wheeler *New Orleans.* Over the next few years, steamboats became the undisputed rulers of the Mississippi, forging majestically upstream, great paddlewheels churning, black smoke belching from tall stacks, fed by wood-burning furnaces below. Captains

took great pride in the speed and perform-
ance of their crafts. Races between river-
boats were common, sometimes ending in
collision and fiery death.

The stubborn American will to be first
sometimes blundered headlong into tragedy, but it was that same will power and
drive that tamed the wilderness and pushed
the frontier ever westward . . . As the tide of
emigration swelled across Ohio, Indiana, Illinois, Missouri—during the first half of the
nineteenth century—it came eventually to
the vast, rolling prairies, stretching westward
from the Ohio River to the plains region.

THE PRAIRIES

by William Cullen Bryant

These are the gardens of the Desert,
  these
The unshorn fields, boundless and beauti-
  ful,
For which the speech of England has no
  name—
The Prairies. I behold them for the first,
And my heart swells, while the dilated sight
Takes in the encircling vastness. Lo! they
  stretch,
In airy undulations, far away,
As if the ocean, in his gentlest swell,
Stood still, with all his rounded billows fixed,
And motionless forever . . .

* * *

Still this great solitude is quick with life.
Myriads of insects, gaudy as the flowers
They flutter over, gentle quadrupeds,
And birds, that scarce have learned the fear
  of man,

Are here, and sliding reptiles of the ground,
Startlingly beautiful. The graceful deer
Bounds to the wood at my approach. The
  bee,
A more adventurous colonist than man,
With whom he came across the eastern deep,
Fills the savannas with his murmurings,
And hides his sweets, as in the golden age,
Within the hollow oak. I listen long
To his domestic hum, and think I hear
The sound of that advancing multitude
Which soon shall fill these deserts. From the
  ground
Comes up the laugh of children, the soft
  voice
Of maidens, and the sweet and solemn hymn
Of Sabbath worshippers. The low of herds
Blends with the rustling of the heavy grain
Over the dark brown furrows. All at once
A fresher wind sweeps by, and breaks my
  dream,
And I am in the wilderness alone.

Land-hungry farmers poured into the
empty prairies of Ohio, Illinois, Indiana and
other regions through the 1830s, '40s and
'50s. Soon, the prairie grass began to be replaced with sun-burnished fields of wheat.

THE SHEAVES

by Edwin Arlington Robinson

Where long the shadows of the wind had
  rolled,
Green wheat was yielding to the change as-
  signed,
And as by some vast magic undivined
The world was turning slowly into gold.
Like nothing that was ever bought or sold

It waited there, the body and the mind;
And with a mighty meaning of a kind
That tells the more the more it is not told.

So in a land where all days are not fair,
Fair days went on till on another day
A thousand golden sheaves were lying there,
Shining and still, but not for long to stay—
As if a thousand girls with golden hair
Might rise from where they slept and go
      away.

The richness of the soil out west—especially in river valley regions—made for a variety of abundant crops. It was also responsible for many such "slight" exaggerations as in the following description of the perils of farming in Arkansas around 1840.

PLANTING IN ARKANSAS IS DANGEROUS

from "The Big Bear of Arkansas" by T. B. Thorpe

"Such timber, and such bottom land, why you can't preserve anything natural you plant in it unless you pick it young, things thar will grow out of shape so quick. I once planted in those diggins a few potatoes and beets: they took a fine start, and after that an ox team couldn't have kept them from growing. About that time I went off to old Kentuck on bisiness, and did not hear from them things in three months, when I accidentally stumbled on a fellow who had stopped at my place, with an idea of buying me out. 'How did you like things?' said I. 'Pretty well,' said he; 'the cabin is convenient, and the timber land is good; but that bottom land ain't worth the first red cent.' 'Why?' said I.

'Cause it's full of cedar stumps and Indian mounds,' said he, *'and it can't be cleared.'* 'Lord,' said I, 'them ar "cedar stumps" is beets, and them ar "Indian mounds" ar tater hills.' As I expected, the crop was overgrown and useless: the sile is too rich, *and planting in Arkansaw is dangerous.* I had a good-sized sow killed in that same bottom land. The old thief stole an ear of corn, and took it down where she slept at night to eat. Well, she left a grain or two on the ground, and lay down on them: before morning the corn shot up, and the percussion killed her dead. . . ."

When the settler of a new farm had his claim staked out on the expanding western frontier, he built a dwelling for his family out of whatever materials were handiest. A common type on the large, treeless prairies was a shanty with a sod roof.

THE LITTLE OLD SOD SHANTY

Anonymous

I'm looking rather seedy now while holding
    down my claim;
My vittles are not always of the best,
And the mice play shyly round me as I nes-
    tle down to rest
In my little old sod shanty on the plain.

    Oh, the hinges are of leather and the win-
        dows have no glass,
    The boards, they let the howling blizzard
        in.
    You can see the hungry coyote as he
        sneaks up through the grass
    To my little old sod shanty on the claim.

I rather like the novelty of living in this way,
Though my bill of fare isn't always of the best,
But I'm happy as a clam on the land of Uncle Sam
In my little old sod shanty in the West.

* * *

While some settlers moved on to a new dream of "God's country," others put their roots down. The sod shanty was replaced by a substantial house, and the traditional American sentiment for home, mother and apple pie was born.

HOME, SWEET HOME

by John Howard Payne

'Mid pleasures and palaces though we may roam,
Be it ever so humble, there's no place like home;
A charm from the sky seems to hallow us there,
Which, seek through the world, is ne'er met with elsewhere.
Home, home, sweet, sweet home!
There's no place like home, oh, there's no place like home!

An exile from home, splendor dazzles in vain;
Oh, give me my lowly thatched cottage again!
The birds singing gayly, that came at my call—
Give me them—and the peace of mind, dearer than all!
Home, home, sweet, sweet home!
There's no place like home, oh, there's no place like home!

I gaze on the moon as I tread the drear wild,
And feel that my mother now thinks of her child,
As she looks on that moon from our own cottage door
Thro' the woodbine, whose fragrance shall cheer me no more.
Home, home, sweet, sweet home!
There's no place like home, oh, there's no place like home!

How sweet 'tis to sit 'neath a fond father's smile,
And the caress of a mother to soothe and beguile!
Let others delight 'mid new pleasure to roam,
But give me, oh, give me, the pleasures of home.
Home, home, sweet, sweet home!
There's no place like home, oh, there's no place like home!

To thee I'll return, overburdened with care;
The heart's dearest solace will smile on me there;
No more from that cottage again will I roam;
Be it ever so humble, there's no place like home.
Home, home, sweet, sweet home!
There's no place like home, oh, there's no place like home!

Home, Sweet Home was actually a song in a drama written by Payne in 1823. The drama became part of the repertoire of a touring American acting family, the Jeffersons. They and other troupers roamed the West as early as the 1830s, playing in tents, halls, barns—whatever was available—bringing the magic of theatre to people who had only occasional square dances, church socials or corn-husking parties for entertainment. Thought of as gypsies in greasepaint, they were often forced to combat puritanical prejudice, as well as the difficulties of climate, geography and primitive conditions. Actors who complain about road conditions today might well read this reminiscence of a tour through Illinois in 1837.

SHOW BUSINESS HAS TROUBLE IN THE WEST

from "The Autobiography of Joseph Jefferson"

After a short season in Chicago, with the varying success which in those days always attended the drama, the company went to Galena for a short season [1837], traveling in open wagons over the prairie. . . .

We traveled from Galena to Dubuque on the frozen river in sleighs—smoother work than the roughly rutted roads of the prairie, but it was a perilous journey, for a warm spell had set in and made the ice sloppy and unsafe. We would sometimes hear it crack and see it bend under our horses' feet—now a long-drawn breath of relief as we passed some dangerous spot, then a convulsive grasping of our nearest companion as the ice groaned and shook beneath us. Well, the passengers arrived safe, but, horror to relate! the sleigh containing the baggage, private and public, with the scenery and properties, green curtain and drop, broke through the ice and tumbled into the Mississippi. My poor mother was in tears, but my father was in high spirits at his good luck, as he called it

—because there was a sand bar where the sleigh went in! So the things were saved at last, though in a forlorn condition. The opening had to be delayed in order to dry the wardrobe and smooth the scenery.

The halls of the hotel were strung with clotheslines, and costumes of all nations festooned the doors of the bedrooms, so that when an unsuspicious boarder came out suddenly into the entry he was likely to run his head into a damp Roman shirt or perhaps have the legs of a soaking pair of red tights dangling round his neck. Mildew filled the air. The gilded pasteboard helmets fared the worst. They had succumbed to the softening influences of the Mississippi and were as battered and out of shape as if they had gone through the pass of Thermopylae. Limp leggings of scale armor hung wet and dejected from the lines; low-spirited cocked hats were piled up in a corner; rough-dried court coats stretched their arms out as if in the agony of drowning, as though they would say, "Help me, Cassius, or I sink." Theatrical scenery at its best looks pale and shabby in the daytime, but a well-worn set after a six hours' bath in a river presents the most woebegone appearance that can well be imagined; the sky and water of the marine had so mingled with each other that the horizon line had quite disappeared. My father had painted the scenery, and he was not a little crestfallen as he looked upon the ruins: a wood scene had amalgamated with a Roman street painted on the back of it and had so run into stains and winding streaks that he said it looked like a large map of South America; and pointing out the Andes with his cane, he humorously traced the

Amazon to its source. Of course this mishap on the river delayed the opening for a week. In the meantime, the scenery had to be re-painted and the wardrobe put in order; many of the things were ruined, and the helmets defied repair.

After a short, and, I think, a good season at Dubuque, we traveled along the river to the different towns just springing up in the west — Burlington, Quincy, Peoria, Pekin, and Springfield. In those primitive days, I need scarcely say, we were often put to severe shifts for a theater.

In Quincy the courthouse was fitted up, and it answered admirably. In one town a large warehouse was utilized, but in Pekin we were reduced to the dire necessity of act-ing in a pork house. This establishment was a large frame building, stilted up on piles about two feet from the ground, and situated in the open prairie just at the edge of the town. The pigs were banished from their comfortable quarters and left to browse about on the common during the day, taking shelter under their former abode in the eve-ning. After undergoing some slight repairs in the roof and submitting to a thorough scouring and whitewashing, the building pre-sented quite a respectable appearance. The opening play was *Clari, the Maid of Milan.* This drama was written by John Howard Payne, and his song of *Home, Sweet Home* belongs to the play. My mother, on this oc-casion, played the part of Clari and sang the touching ballad.

Now it is a pretty well-established fact in theatrical history that if an infant has been smuggled into the theater under the shawl of its fond mother, however dormant it may

have been during the unimportant scenes of the play, no sooner is an interesting point ar-rived at, where the most perfect stillness is required, than the dear little innocent will break forth in lamentation loud and deep. On this occasion no youthful humanity dis-turbed the peace, but the animal kingdom, in the shape of the banished pigs, asserted its right to a public hearing. As soon as the song *Home, Sweet Home* commenced, they began by bumping their backs up against the beams, keeping anything but good time to the music; and as my mother plaintively chanted the theme "sweet, sweet home," real-izing their own cruel exile, the pigs squealed most dismally. Of course the song was ruined, and my mother was in tears at the failure. My father, however, consoled her by saying that though the grunting was not quite in harmony with the music, it was in perfect sympathy with the sentiment.

Springfield being the capital of Illinois, it was determined to devote the entire season to the entertainment of the members of the Legislature. Having made money for several weeks previous to our arrival here, the man-agement resolved to hire a lot and build a theater. This sounds like a large undertak-ing, and perhaps with their limited means it was a rash step. I fancy that my father rather shrank from this bold enterprise, but the sen-ior partner (McKenzie) was made of sterner stuff, and his energy being quite equal to his ambition, the ground was broken and the temple erected. . . .

In the midst of our rising fortunes a heavy blow fell upon us. A religious revival was in progress at the time, and the fathers of the church not only launched forth against us in their sermons, but by some political maneuver got the city to pass a new law enjoining a heavy license against our unholy calling; I forget the amount, but it was large enough to be prohibitory. Here was a terrible condition of affairs: all our available funds invested, the Legislature in session, the town full of people, and we by a heavy license denied the privilege of opening the new theater!

In the midst of their trouble a young lawyer called on the managers. He had heard of the injustice and offered, if they would place the matter in his hands, to have the license taken off, declaring that he only desired to see fair play, and he would accept no fee whether he failed or succeeded. The case was brought up before the council. The young lawyer began his harangue. He handled the subject with tact, skill, and humor, tracing the history of the drama from the time when Thespis acted in a cart to the stage of today. He illustrated his speech with a number of anecdotes and kept the council in a roar of laughter; his good humor prevailed, and the exorbitant tax was taken off.

This young lawyer was very popular in Springfield, and was honored and beloved by all who knew him. His name was Abraham Lincoln!

We saw Lincoln "born without a chance" —well, now, in the 1830s, he's a rising young lawyer. We'll meet him again, later on.

As the nation spread out from the Eastern seaboard to the Western frontier, it produced enormous crops of American children. They ate turkey on Thanksgiving, set off fireworks on the Fourth of July, and, in the heat of summer, shucked off their clothes to dive into the old swimming hole . . .

THE OLD SWIMMIN'-HOLE

by James Whitcomb Riley

Oh! the old swimmin'-hole! whare the crick
    so still and deep
Looked like a baby-river that was laying half
    asleep,
And the gurgle of the worter round the drift
    jest below
Sounded like the laugh of something we onc't
    ust to know
Before we could remember anything but the
    eyes
Of the angels lookin' out as we left Paradise;
But the merry days of youth is beyond our
    controle,
And it's hard to part ferever with the old
    swimmin'-hole.

Oh! the old swimmin'-hole! In the happy
    days of yore,
When I ust to lean above it on the old sicka-
    more,
Oh! it showed me a face in its warm sunny
    tide
That gazed back at me so gay and glorified,
It made me love myself, as I leaped to caress
My shadder smilin' up at me with sich ten-
    derness.
But them days is past and gone, and old
    Time's tuck his toll
From the old man come back to the old swim-
    min'-hole.

Oh! the old swimmin'-hole! In the long, lazy
    days

When the humdrum of school made so many
    run-a-ways,
How plesant was the jurney down the old
    dusty lane,
Whare the tracks of our bare feet was all
    printed so plane
You could tell by the dent of the heel and
    the sole
They was lots o' fun on hand at the old swim-
    min'-hole.
But the lost joys is past! Let your tears in
    sorrow roll
Like the rain that ust to dapple up the old
    swimmin'-hole.

Thare the bulrushes growed, and the cat-
    tails so tall,

And the sunshine and shadder fell over it
    all;
And it mottled the worter with amber and
    gold
Tel the glad lilies rocked in the ripples that
    rolled;
And the snake-feeder's four gauzy wings flut-
    tered by
Like the ghost of a daisy dropped out of the
    sky,
Or a wownded apple-blossom in the breeze's
    controle
As it cut acrost some orchurd to'rds the old
    swimmin'-hole.

Oh! the old swimmin'-hole! When I last saw
    the place,

The scenes was all changed, like the change
    in my face;
The bridge of the railroad now crosses the
    spot
Whare the old divin'-log lays sunk and fer-
    got.
And I stray down the banks whare the trees
    ust to be—
But never again will theyr shade shelter
    me!
And I wish in my sorrow I could strip to the
    soul,
And dive off in my grave like the old swim-
    min'-hole.

When summer was over, children drifted back to school—often a one-room building —with the traditional reluctance children have always felt toward being cooped up after a season of outdoor freedom. Under the stern eye of their rod-wielding master, who stood for no nonsense, they learned the three R's (reading, writing and 'rithmetic) which, it was hoped, would help turn them from woodsy little savages into successful citizens.

Along about the middle of December, schoolmasters and parents noticed an astonishing change in children. They became obedient, well-mannered, even helpful—as if they had "Seen the Light" and realized the error of their ways. This sudden change was due to anticipation of a visit from Santa Claus.

In the first half of the nineteenth century, children didn't get model airplanes or electric trains for Christmas—mainly because they hadn't been invented yet. But they were quite happy to receive the following treasure . . .

UNDER THE NINETEENTH CENTURY CHRISTMAS TREE

from "Santa Claus" by Ralph Hoyt

Horses, with riders upon their backs,
    Coaches, and carts and gigs,
Each trying its best to win the race,
    Like the Democrats and Whigs.
Tiny houses, in every style,
    Put up in a fancy chest,
To build in a minute a thriving town,
    If you choose to move out West.

Ripe wooden pears like real fruit,
    Somehow made to unscrew;
Kittens with mice sewed to their mouths,
    And tabby cats crying mew.
Gay humming-tops that spin about,
    And make a senseless sound,
Like windy representatives
    In Congress often found.

Ships of the line equipt for sea,
    With officers and crew,
Each with a red cap on his head,
    And a jacket painted blue.
Bold pewter men with pistols armed,
    Like duellists so smart,
Each most wickedly taking aim
    At his little comrade's heart!

Fine marbles, and rich China-men,
    That you can play from taw,
As lawyers play rich clients down
    The ring-pits of the law.
Bright caskets filled with jewelry,
    Chains, bracelets, pins, and pearls,
All glittering with tinsel, like
    Some fashionable girls.

If children didn't do well at Christmas, they could always show the typically American enterprise demonstrated by Tom Sawyer in the famous whitewashing incident . . .

TOM SAWYER TURNS A FENCE TO PROFIT

from "The Adventures of Tom Sawyer"
by Mark Twain

Saturday morning was come, and all the summer world was bright and fresh, and brimming with life. There was a song in every heart; and if the heart was young the music issued at the lips. There was cheer in every face and a spring in every step. The locust trees were in bloom and the fragrance of the blossoms filled the air. Cardiff Hill, beyond the village and above it, was green with vegetation, and it lay just far enough away to seem a Delectable Land, dreamy, reposeful, and inviting.

Tom appeared on the sidewalk with a bucket of whitewash and a long-handled brush. He surveyed the fence, and all gladness left him and a deep melancholy settled down upon his spirit. Thirty yards of board fence nine feet high. Life to him seemed hollow, and existence but a burden. Sighing he dipped his brush and passed it along the topmost plank; repeated the operation; did it again; compared the insignificant whitewashed streak with the far-reaching continent of unwhitewashed fence, and sat down on a tree-box discouraged. Jim came skipping out at the gate with a tin pail, and singing "Buffalo Gals." Bringing water from the town pump had always been hateful work in Tom's eyes, before, but now it did not strike him so. He remembered that there was company at the pump. White, mulatto, and Negro boys and girls were always there waiting their turns, resting, trading playthings, quarreling, fighting, skylarking. And he remembered that although the pump was only a hundred and fifty yards off, Jim never got back with a bucket of water under an hour—and even then somebody generally had to go after him. Tom said:

"Say, Jim, I'll fetch the water if you'll whitewash some."

Jim shook his head and said:

"Can't, Mars Tom. Ole missis, she tole me I got to go an' git dis water an' not stop foolin' roun' wid anybody. She say she spec' Mars Tom gwine to ax me to whitewash, an' so she tole me go 'long an' 'tend to my own business—she 'lowed *she'd* 'tend to de whitewashin'."

"Oh, never you mind what she said, Jim. That's the way she always talks. Gimme the bucket—I won't be gone only a minute. *She* won't ever know."

"Oh, I dasn't, Mars Tom. Ole missis she'd take an' tar de head off'n me. 'Deed she would."

"*She!* She never licks anybody—whacks 'em over the head with her thimble—and who cares for that, I'd like to know. She talks awful, but talk don't hurt—anyways it don't if she don't cry. Jim, I'll give you a marvel. I'll give you a white alley!"

Jim began to waver.

"White alley, Jim! And it's a bully taw."

"My! Dat's a mighty gay marvel, *I* tell you! But Mars Tom, I's powerful 'fraid old missis—"

"And besides, if you will, I'll show you my sore toe."

Jim was only human—this attraction was too much for him. He put down his pail, took the white alley, and bent over the toe with absorbing interest while the bandage was being unwound. In another moment he was flying down the street with his pail and a tingling rear, Tom was whitewashing with vigor, and Aunt Polly was retiring from the field with a slipper in her hand and triumph in her eye.

But Tom's energy did not last. He began to think of the fun he had planned for this day, and his sorrows multiplied. Soon the free boys would come tripping along on all sorts of delicious expeditions, and they would make a world of fun of him for having to work—the very thought of it burnt him like fire. He got out his worldly wealth and examined it—bits of toys, marbles, and trash; enough to buy an exchange of *work,* maybe, but not half enough to buy so much as half an hour of pure freedom. So he returned his straitened means to his pocket, and gave up the idea of trying to buy the boys. At this dark and hopeless moment an inspiration burst upon him! Nothing less than a great, magnificent inspiration.

He took up his brush and went tranquilly to work. Ben Rogers hove in sight presently —the very boy, of all boys, whose ridicule he had been dreading. Ben's gait was the hop-skip-and-jump—proof enough that his heart was light and his anticipations high. He was eating an apple, and giving a long, melodious whoop, at intervals, followed by a deep-toned ding-dong-dong, ding-dong-dong, for he was personating a steamboat. As he drew near, he slackened speed, took the middle of the street, leaned far over to starboard and rounded to ponderously and with laborious pomp and circumstance—for he was personating the *Big Missouri,* and considered himself to be drawing nine feet of water. He was boat and captain and engine-bells combined, so he had to imagine himself standing on his own hurricane-deck giving the orders and executing them:

"Stop her, sir! Ting-a-ling-ling!" The headway ran almost out and he drew up slowly toward the sidewalk.

"Ship up to back! Ting-a-ling-ling!" His arms straightened and stiffened down his sides.

"Set her back on the stabboard! Ting-a-ling-ling! Chow! ch-chow-wow! Chow!" The left hand began to describe circles.

"Stop the stabboard! Ting-a-ling-ling! Stop the labboard! Come ahead on the stabboard! Stop her! Let your outside turn over slow! Ting-a-ling-ling! Chow-ow-ow! Get out that headline! *Lively* now! Come—out with your spring-line—what're you about there! Take a turn round that stump with the bight of it! Stand by that stage, now— let her go! Done with the engines, sir! Ting-a-ling-ling! *Sh't! sh't! sh't*" (trying the gauge-cocks).

Tom went on whitewashing—paid no attention to the steamboat. Ben stared a moment and then said:

"Hi-*yi! You're* up a stump, ain't you!"

No answer. Tom surveyed his last touch with the eye of an artist, then he gave his brush another gentle sweep and surveyed the result, as before. Ben ranged up alongside of him. Tom's mouth watered for the apple,

but he stuck to his work. Ben said:

"Hello, old chap, you got to work, hey?"

Tom wheeled suddenly and said:

"Why, it's you, Ben! I warn't noticing."

"Say—*I'm* going in a-swimming, *I* am. Don't you wish you could? But of course you'd druther *work*—wouldn't you? Course you would!" Tom contemplated the boy a bit, and said:

"What do you call work?"

"Why, aint *that* work?"

Tom resumed his whitewashing, and answered carelessly:

"Well, maybe it is, and maybe it ain't. All I know, is, it suits Tom Sawyer."

"Oh come, now, you don't mean to let on that you *like* it?"

The brush continued to move.

"Like it? Well, I don't see why I oughtn't

to like it. Does a boy get a chance to whitewash a fence every day?"

That put the thing in a new light. Ben stopped nibbling his apple. Tom swept his brush daintily back and forth—stepped back to note the effect—added a touch here and there—criticized the effect again—Ben watching every move and getting more interested, more and more absorbed. Presently he said:

"Say, Tom, let *me* whitewash a little."

Tom considered, was about to consent; but he altered his mind:

"No—no—I reckon it wouldn't hardly do, Ben. You see, Aunt Polly's awful particular about this fence—right here on the street, you know—but if it was the back fence I wouldn't mind and *she* wouldn't. Yes, she's awful particular about this fence; it's got to be done very careful; I reckon there ain't one boy in a thousand, maybe two thousand, that can do it the way it's got to be done."

"No—is that so? Oh come, now—lemme just try. Only just a little—I'd let *you,* if you was me, Tom."

"Ben, I'd like to, honest injun; but Aunt Polly—well, Jim wanted to do it, but she wouldn't let him; Sid wanted to do it, and she wouldn't let Sid. Now don't you see how I'm fixed? If you was to tackle this fence and anything was to happen to it—"

"Oh, shucks, I'll be just as careful. Now lemme try. Say—I'll give you the core of my apple."

"Well, here—No, Ben, now don't. I'm afeard—"

"I'll give you *all* of it!"

Tom gave up the brush with reluctance in his face, but alacrity in his heart. And while the late steamer *Big Missouri* worked and sweated in the sun, the retired artist sat on a barrel in the shade close by, dangled his legs, munched on his apple, and planned the slaughter of more innocents. There was no lack of material; boys happened along every little while; they came to jeer, but remained to whitewash. By the time Ben was fagged out, Tom had traded the next chance to Billy Fisher for a kite, in good repair; and when *he* played out, Johnny Miller bought in for a dead rat and a string to swing it with—and so on, and so on, hour after hour. And when the middle of the afternoon came, from being a poor poverty-stricken boy in the morning, Tom was literally rolling in wealth. He had besides the things before mentioned, twelve marbles, part of a jews'-harp, a piece of blue bottle-glass to look through, a spool cannon, a key that wouldn't unlock anything, a fragment of chalk, a glass stopper of a decanter, a tin soldier, a couple of tadpoles, six firecrackers, a kitten with only one eye, a brass door-knob, a dog-collar—but no dog—the handle of a knife, four pieces of orange-peel, and a dilapidated old window-sash.

He had had a nice, good, idle time all the while—plenty of company—and the fence had three coats of whitewash on it! If he hadn't run out of whitewash, he would have bankrupted every boy in the village.

Tom said to himself that it was not such a hollow world, after all. He had discovered a great law of human action, without knowing it—namely, that in order to make a man or boy covet a thing, it is only necessary to make the thing difficult to attain. If he had been a great and wise philosopher, like the writer of this book, he would now have comprehended that Work consists of whatever a body is *obliged* to do, and that Play consists of whatever a body is not obliged to do. And this would help him to understand why constructing artificial flowers or performing on a treadmill is work, while rolling tenpins or climbing Mont Blanc is only amusement. There are wealthy gentlemen in England who drive four-horse passenger-coaches twenty or thirty miles on a daily line, in the summer, because the privilege costs them considerable money; but if they were offered wages for the service, that would turn it into work and then they would resign.

The boy mused awhile over the substantial change which had taken place in his worldly circumstances, and then wended toward headquarters to report.

Americans on the whole believed, like Tom's friends, that work was the exhilarating "stuff of life"—provided they were able to choose their own fields of labor. American initiative was perfecting the reaper (1834), the telegraph (1844), the sewing machine (1846) . . . Partially, this dynamic progress resulted from the Puritan tradition, which taught that conquering nature, and bending its dark forces to man's will, was doing the work of God. And so—the wilderness began to melt away, its place taken by booming towns, cities, enterprises . . .

THE SHAPES ARISE!

from "Song of the Broad-Axe" by Walt Whitman

The shapes arise!
Shapes of factories, arsenals, foundries, markets,

93

Shapes of the two-threaded tracks of railroads,
Shapes of the sleepers of bridges, vast frame-
  works, girders, arches,
Shapes of the fleets of barges, tows, lake and
  canal craft, river craft,
Ship-yards and dry-docks along the Eastern
  and Western seas, and in many a bay
  and by-place,
The live-oak kelsons, the pine planks, the
  spars, the hackmatack-roots for knees,
The ships themselves on their ways, the tiers
  of scaffolds, the workmen busy outside
  and inside,
The tools lying around, the great auger and
  little auger, the adze, bolt, line, square,
  gouge and bead-plane.

* * *

The main shapes arise!
Shapes of Democracy total, result 'of cen-
  turies,
Shapes ever projecting other shapes,
Shapes of turbulent manly cities,
Shapes of the friends and home-givers of the
  whole earth,
Shapes bracing the earth and braced with the
  whole earth.

In 1830, the first American steam locomotive, the *Tom Thumb,* puffed and snorted its
way down the recently laid tracks of the Baltimore & Ohio Railroad at the outrageous
speed of eleven miles an hour! The age of
the railroad—destined to vastly accelerate
the settlement and commercial expansion of
the country—had begun. The following
poem of the 1840s captures the rhythm of
one of these pioneer trains and includes a
lively description of typical passengers.

RHYME OF THE RAIL

by John G. Saxe

Singing through the forests,
  Rattling over ridges,
Shooting under arches,
  Rumbling over bridges,
Whizzing through the mountains,
  Buzzing o'er the vale,—
Bless me! this is pleasant,
  Riding on the rail!

Men of different "stations"
  In the eye of Fame,
Here are very quickly
  Coming to the same.
High and lowly people,
  Birds of every feather,
On a common level
  Travelling together!

Gentleman in shorts,
  Looming very tall;
Gentleman at large;
  Talking very small;
Gentleman in tights,
  With a loose-ish mien;
Gentleman in gray,
  Looking rather green.

Gentleman quite old,
  Asking for the news;
Gentleman in black,
  In a fit of blues;
Gentleman in claret,
  Sober as a vicar;
Gentleman in Tweed,
  Dreadfully in liquor!

Stranger on the right,
  Looking very sunny,
Obviously reading
  Something rather funny.
Now the smiles are thicker,
  Wonder what they mean?
Faith, he's got the KNICKER-
  BOCKER Magazine!

Stranger on the left,
  Closing up his peepers,
Now he snores again,
  Like the Seven Sleepers;
At his feet a volume
  Gives the explanation,
How the man grew stupid
  From "Association!"

Ancient maiden lady
  Anxiously remarks,
That there must be peril
  'Mong so many sparks;
Roguish-looking fellow,
  Turning to the stranger,
Says it's his opinion
  She is out of danger!

Woman with her baby,
  Sitting vis-a-vis;
Baby keeps a-squalling,
  Woman looks at me;
Asks about the distance,
  Says it's tiresome talking,
Noises of the cars
  Are so very shocking!

Market woman careful
  Of the precious casket,
Knowing eggs are eggs,
  Tightly holds her basket;
Feeling that a smash,
  If it came, would surely
Send her eggs to pot
  Rather prematurely!

Singing through the forests,
  Rattling over ridges,
Shooting under arches,
  Rumbling over bridges,
Whizzing through the mountains,
  Buzzing o'er the vale;
Bless me! this is pleasant,
  Riding on the rail!

Many Americans, as always, preferred the unspoiled, quiet beauty of the country to the noisy march of progress. Back-to-nature philosopher Henry Thoreau wrote the following passage while living in a self-built cabin on the shores of Walden Pond (1845–1847).

WHAT'S THE RAILROAD TO ME?

from "Walden" by Henry David Thoreau

What's the railroad to me? I never go to see
Where it ends.
It fills a few hollows, and makes banks for
    the swallows,
It sets the sand a-blowing and the blackberries a-growing,
But I cross it like a cart-path in the woods . . .

Americans were curious mixtures of the shrewd, the practical—and the gullible. They were used to succeeding against amazing odds, reading about marvelous new inventions, stumbling across natural wonders like the Grand Canyon and the majestic redwood and sequoia trees of the Pacific coast. Constantly exposed to the improbable, they tended to believe that *anything* was possible, especially if it sounded "scientific," a label which enabled the practical Yankee side of their natures to swallow the most outrageous hokum and humbug. In the days before the Pure Food and Drug Act, "snake oil" salesmen thrived in America. Their patent medicines generally contained a variety of useless but exotic-sounding ingredients, generously laced with alcohol to provide sufferers with a temporary "glow" of health. Two of the more colorful cures of the day were advertised as follows.

Dr. Wheeler's Universally Celebrated
BALSAM OF MOSCATELLO
The most valuable vegetable preparation ever discovered for the cure of cholera morbus and the dangerous effects of drinking cold water when overheated.

Scorning the coy limitations of Dr. Wheeler's claim, one manufacturer advertised:

PHOENIX BITTERS
The most effectual remedy for the cure of all and every disease to which man is subject.

The diseases listed in patent medicine ads were often as exotic as the cures. They included King's Evil, Barber's Itch and Habitual Costiveness. In the 1830s, the "science" of phrenology, which claimed to be able to determine the mental powers of people through the shape of their skulls, swept the land. Here are the comments of one who lived through—and was caught up in—some of the wildest and woolliest fads of the times.

FADS AND FANCIES OF THE 1830'S

from "Forty Years of American Life, 1821–1861" by Thomas Low Nichols

When Doctor Spurzheim, the associate of Gall in the elaboration of the system of phrenology, came to America about 1834, he was received with enthusiasm. Phrenology became the rage. Plaster casts of heads, and lithographs marked with the organs [of the brain], were sold by thousands. There was a universal feeling of heads. Lecturers went from town to town, explaining the new science and giving public and private examinations. Periodicals were published to promulgate the new philosophy, and a library of phrenological books was rapidly published. I have no doubt that in five years after the event of Doctor Spurzheim there were more believers of phrenology in the United States than in all the world beside.

Mesmerism [hypnotism] trod closely on the heels of phrenology. Monsieur Poyen, a French Creole, from one of the West Indian islands, came to Boston and introduced the new science to the American public. His lectures were succeeded by experiments. At one of the hospitals a patient selected for the experiment was so thoroughly mesmerized that she remained asleep forty-eight hours, though suffering from an acute disease of the heart that usually deprived her of rest. During the trance she appeared placid and free from pain, but it was impossible to awaken her. At the end of the forty-eight hours she awoke of herself, much refreshed, and said she felt better than she had for months. The publication of this and a few similar cases, of course, set a great many people to mesmerizing each other. There were medical mesmerists and clairvoyants everywhere. Distinguished surgeons performed operations on patients who were insensible to pain during the magnetic sleep. Clairvoyants professed to inspect the internal organs of patients, describe their diseases, and prescribe remedies, which were not more varied or dangerous than those given by the regular and irregular faculty.

There were psychometrists, who could tell the lives, characters, fortunes, and diseases of people they had never seen, by holding a sealed letter, scrap of writing, lock of hair, or other connecting relic in their hands. There was one who, when a fossil of some remote geological era was placed in contact with her forehead, would give an animated description of the appearance of the planet at that period.

[The author goes on to talk about the fight for women's rights. (Among other things, they couldn't vote.) As a symbol of their struggle to receive equal treatment with men, Amelia Bloomer designed a trousered costume for women—a daring thing to do in the nineteenth century.]

The attempt on the part of certain American women to assume masculine or semi-masculine habiliments—a movement which received the name of Bloomerism from one of its prominent American advocates—was a bold and energetic one, but not successful. Some thousands of American women adopted what they thought a convenient and healthful costume and were brave to heroism and persevering to fanaticism, but the attempted reform was a failure. America could rebel against a foreign government; she may revolutionize her own; but America is not strong enough to war upon the fashions of civilization. A woman in New York may make a political speech to three or four thousand people, but to wear a Bloomer dress down Broadway is another affair, and a far greater difficulty would be to get others to follow her example. . . .

The one who took advantage of the American public's capacity for wonder in the most spectacular fashion was P. T. Barnum. He started his career exhibiting an aged Negro woman who claimed to be George Washington's nurse. When business flagged, he "confessed" publicly that she was a hoax. She wasn't even human, he announced contritely in print, but an ingenious mechanical robot . . . Naturally, business picked up at once. His American Museum in New York City during the 1840s featured such exhibits as the famous dwarf "General Tom Thumb" and a very dead and very doubtful "mermaid," consisting of the wrinkled body of a monkey ingeniously stitched to the tail of a fish. Barnum's actual hoaxes were few, and his true genius consisted of building up, through publicity, a legitimate (but not all that uncommon) exhibit to the dimensions of the Stupendous, the Fantastic, the Once-In-A-Lifetime. (Remind you of any television commercials you've seen lately?) Here are some examples of the old master at work.

BARNUM MUSEUM
ADVERTISEMENTS

* * *

RAYTHER PARTICULAR TALL

Two persons sixteen feet high weighing 845 pounds.

THE QUAKER GIANT AND GIANTESS
The tallest and decidedly the LARGEST PAIR OF HUMAN BEINGS the world has ever produced! Miss Elizabeth Simpson, a delicate young Quakeress of 21 years IS NEARLY EIGHT FEET HIGH and weighs 337 pounds! Mr. Barnum pledges himself to pay

★   ★   ★

ONE THOUSAND DOLLARS

★   ★   ★

to any person who can produce a female of her height and size within one year from this time.

AN ENORMOUS BOA CONSTRICTOR

The largest serpent ever captured alive being THIRTY FEET LONG and measuring twenty inches in circumference. Just previous to its arrival, it deposited SIXTY EGGS WEIGHING ONE POUND EACH during one night, one of which, on being broken, was found to contain a

JUVENILE SARPINT

about three feet long, which ran about the cage with great rapidity. The remainder of the eggs were saved and WILL BE EXHIBITED WITH THE SNAKE!

These were choice tidbits. Here's a complete menu:

Industrious fleas, educated dogs, jugglers, automatons, ventriloquists, living statuary, tableaux, gypsies, albinoes, fat boys, giants, dwarfs, rope dancers, caricature of phrenology, "live Yankees," pantomimes, music, singing and dancing, dioramas, panoramas, models of Dublin, Paris, Niagara, Jerusalem, mechanical figures, fancy glass blowing, knitting machines and other triumphs of the mechanical art, dissolving views and American Indians!

* * *

You'll notice that Barnum advertised "singing and dancing." Parents today who mutter about their youngsters' latest dance craze, and wish that it bore a closer resemblance to such respectable dances as the waltz and the polka, might well read the following editorial comment. It appeared in a New York newspaper during the 1840s.

A DISGRACEFUL DANCE OF THE 1840'S

The polka as now danced in our most highly respectable and fashionable circles is one of the most indecent, immodest and scandalous exhibitions ever exhibited out of the common gardens of Paris . . . the lowest and most vulgar movement danced in the villages of Hungary, and in the encampments of the soldiery who, in consequence of the spurs attached to their boots, are obliged to move their feet in a certain uneasy and strange position so as not to endanger their legs. Such is the origin of the polka, and yet our fine young men and our beautiful young ladies can be seen vieing with each other who shall dance with the greatest vigor and accuracy this low camp dance . . .

The public's taste for sensation of various kinds was also being supplied by authors and publishers of "penny dreadfuls" and other

popular novels. They bore such titles as *The Fatal Feud, or Passion and Piety . . . Nellie, the Ragpicker's Daughter . . . Guilford, or Tried by His Peers . . . The Drooping Lily . . . Diving Nell, or The Doom of the Friendless*. The dialogue in most of them could have been taken out of one novel and dropped into another, without anybody noticing the difference. Here are some samples:

POPULAR NOVEL DIALOGUE OF THE 1840'S

"Hide me, Mother, I am pursued . . . The police hounds are after me! I must be secreted."

"Unspotted from the world? My sweet blossom, how wilt thou keep so?"

"Demon—quit your hold or I will put my knife in your heart!"

"Whence have you taken this trembling dove?"

Popular poetry also tended to get a bit wild, as follows:

LIKE THE SWEET GOLDEN GOBLET

Like the sweet golden goblet found growing
On the wild emerald cucumber tree,
Rich, brilliant, like chrysoprase glowing,
Was my beautiful Rosalie Lee.

* * *

At the same time, much worthwhile literature was being read, including the works of such authors as Washington Irving, Nathaniel Hawthorne and Edgar Allan Poe. And pseudoscientific medical hoaxes were merely the lunatic fringe reflection of brilliant American accomplishments such as the discovery of anaesthetics in the 1840s.

While Americans in the centers of culture and industry were fermenting new ideas, inventions and fancies, the small farmer continued to provide a steady counterbalance, living his life in accord with the ancient rhythms of earth, weather and change of season. He took what nature sent his way, accepted it as God's will, and made the best of it. This included even a bleak New England snowstorm . . .

THE SUN THAT BRIEF DECEMBER DAY

from "Snow-Bound" by John Greenleaf Whittier

The sun that brief December day
Rose cheerless over hills of gray,
And, darkly circled, gave at noon
A sadder light than waning moon.
Slow tracing down the thickening sky
Its mute and ominous prophecy,
A portent seeming less than threat,
It sank from sight before it set.
A chill no coat, however stout,
Of homespun stuff could quite shut out,
A hard, dull bitterness of cold,
That checked, mid-vein, the circling race
Of life-blood in the sharpened face,
The coming of the snow-storm told.
The wind blew east; we heard the roar
Of Ocean on his wintry shore,
And felt the strong pulse throbbing there
Beat with low rhythm our inland air.

Meanwhile we did our nightly chores,—
Brought in the wood from out of doors,
Littered the stalls, and from the mows
Raked down the herd's-grass for the cows;
Heard the horse whinnying for his corn;
And, sharply clashing horn on horn,
Impatient down the stanchion rows
The cattle shake their walnut bows;
While, peering from his early perch
Upon the scaffold's pole of birch,
The cock his crested helmet bent
And down his querulous challenge sent.

Unwarmed by any sunset light
The gray day darkened into night,
A night made hoary with the swarm
And whirl-dance of the blinding storm,
As zigzag, wavering to and fro,
Crossed and recrossed the wingèd snow:
And ere the early bedtime came
The white drift piled the window-frame,
And through the glass the clothes-line posts
Looked in like tall and sheeted ghosts.

* * *

Even worse than a storm on land was one
at sea, especially near the sunken reefs off
the rocky Atlantic coast. Shipwrecks were
all too common.

PATROLING BARNEGAT

from "Sea-Drift" by Walt Whitman

Wild, wild the storm, and the sea high running,
Steady the roar of the gale, with incessant
undertone muttering,

Shouts of demoniac laughter fitfully piercing
and pealing,
Waves, air, midnight, their savagest trinity
lashing,
Out in the shadows there milk-white combs
careering,
On beachy slush and sand spirts of snow
fierce slanting,
Where through the murk the easterly death-
wind breasting,
Through cutting swirl and spray watchful
and firm advancing,
(That in the distance! is that a wreck? is the
red signal flaring?)
Slush and sand of the beach tireless till daylight wending,
Steadily, slowly, through hoarse roar never
remitting,
Along the midnight edge by those milk-white
combs careering,
A group of dim, weird forms, struggling, the
night confronting,
That savage trinity warily watching.

Inured to the dangers of the sea, New
Englanders were hardy seamen. They sailed
out of Boston, Salem and other ports, ranging as far as China on trading voyages.
Undisputed queens of the ocean (before the
steamship took over after the middle of the
century) were the slender, sharp-prowed
clipper ships. Carrying enormous masses of
white, billowing sail, bearing such names as
Nightingale, Java Head, Cutty Sark and
Witch of the Waves, they clipped through
the briny at speeds up to eighteen knots, in-
spiring poets and artists with their grace and
beauty . . .

THE YANKEE CLIPPER

from "Song of Myself" by Walt Whitman

The Yankee clipper is under her sky sails,
    she cuts the sparkle and scud,
My eyes settle the land, I bend at her prow
    or shout joyously from the deck . . .

AFTER THE SEA-SHIP

from "Sea-Drift" by Walt Whitman

After the sea-ship, after the whistling winds,
After the white-gray sails taut to their spars
    and ropes,
Below, a myriad myriad waves hastening,
    lifting up their necks,
Tending in ceaseless flow toward the track
    of the ship,
Waves of the ocean bubbling and gurgling,
    blithely prying,
Waves, undulating waves, liquid, uneven,
    emulous waves,
Toward that whirling current, laughing and
    buoyant, with curves,
Where the great vessel sailing and tacking
    displaced the surface,
Larger and smaller waves in the spread of
    the ocean yearnfully flowing,
The wake of the sea-ship after she passes,
    flashing and frolicsome under the sun,
A motley procession with many a fleck of
    foam and many fragments,
Following the stately and rapid ship, in the
    wake following.

New England salts even developed their
own folk hero—a sort of supersailorman . . .

OLD STORMALONG, THE DEEP-WATER SAILORMAN

from "Here's Audacity! American Legendary Heroes" by Frank Shay

"Certainly, I 'member Old Stormalong," said the oldest skipper on Cape Cod. "I was a 'prentice fust on his ship and later on I was Second when he was bosun on the *Courser,* out o' Boston. *That* was a ship, a wooden ship with iron men on her decks, a ship that ain't been eekaled by these hoity-toity steamboats. No, sir, an' never will. Donald Mc-Kay built that ship just because he found one sailorman who could handle her as she should be handled. But, you're aimin' to hear about a sailorman an' not about ships.

"Only t'other day a young whippersnapper was a-tellin' me about Stormie, sayin' as how he was fourteen fathoms tall. I've heard other tales about his height. I know! He was jes' four fathoms from the deck to the bridge of his nose.

"He was the first sailorman to have the letters 'A. B.' after his name. Those were jes' his 'nitials, put after his name on the ship's log just the same as always. Alfred Bulltop Stormalong was the name he gave his first skipper. The old man looked him over and says:

" 'A. B. S. Able-Bodied Sailor. By your size and strength they should measure the talents of all other seamen.'

"It makes me pretee mad when I see some of the hornswogglers of today with these letters after their names. They are only feeble imitators o' the greatest o' all deep-water sailormen.

"You landsmen know very little about real

sailormen, that is, bluewater sailors. This chap Stormalong was not only a sailorman for all waters, he was a whaler too. I mind the time he was anchored in the middle of the North 'Lantic finishin' off a right whale. The lookout sights a school off to the east'ard and Stormie, the bosun, gives the order to h'ist the mudhook. All hands for'ard but not a h'ist. The hook 'ud give a bit and then it 'ud sink right back into the mud. Seemed to be hands clutchin' it and draggin' it out o' our hands. Once we got it clear o' the bottom and almost shipped it when we seed what was wrong. Nothin' short of an octopus was wropped all 'round that mudhook. He was holdin' the anchor with half of his tentacles and with the other half hangin' on to the seaweed on the bottom.

"The mate yelled 'vast heavin'' and went back to tell the skipper. When the old man came for'ard to see for himself he was just in time to see Stormie go overboard with his sheath knife in his teeth. He went below the su'face and there began a terrific struggle. The water was churned and splashed about so that old hooker jes' rolled about like she was beam to the wind. All of us was sure our bosun had been tore 'part by the octopus. The struggle went on for about a quarter of an hour when Stormie's head came to the su'face. Some one called out to throw him a line but before one could be brought he had grabbed the anchor chain and came hand over hand to the deck. The strugglin' in the water kept on for a while but moved away from the ship.

" 'All right,' yelled Stormie, 'all hands lean on it and bring it home.'

"After the anchor was shipped I asked him

what he had done to the octopus.

" 'Jes' tied his arms in knots. Double Carrick bends. It'll take him a month o' Sundays to untie them.' "

The nineteenth century sailors who most capture our imagination are those who manned the whaling ships. Their bravery and skill are legendary. From 1840 to 1860, New Bedford, Massachusetts was the whaling capital of the world. Over five hundred ships a year put out to sea on long-term whaling voyages. Sperm oil and whale oil were used as lubricants, to make soap, and —before petroleum—to light the lamps of the world. Herman Melville sailed on the whaling ship *Acushnet* in 1841, and out of his experiences came the great American novel *Moby Dick*. In it, Ahab is captain of the *Pequod,* Stubb is second mate, and Queequeg (a South Sea islander), Tashtego (an Indian from Gay Head), and Daggoo (a giant Negro) are harpooners. Let's listen to the narrator, who calls himself Ishmael, as he describes the taking of a whale.

STUBB KILLS A WHALE

from "Moby Dick" by Herman Melville

The next day was exceedingly still and sultry, and with nothing special to engage them, the *Pequod's* crew could hardly resist the spell of sleep induced by such a vacant sea. For this part of the Indian Ocean through which we then were voyaging is not what whalemen call a lively ground; that is, it affords fewer glimpses of porpoises, dolphins, flying fish, and other vivacious denizens of more stirring waters, than those off the Rio de la Plata or the inshore ground off Peru.

It was my turn to stand at the foremast head, and with my shoulders leaning against the slackened royal shrouds, to and fro I idly swayed in what seemed an enchanted air. No resolution could withstand it; in that dreamy mood losing all consciousness, at last my soul went out of my body, though my body still continued to sway as a pendulum will, long after the power which first moved it is withdrawn.

Ere forgetfulness altogether came over me, I had noticed that the seamen at the main and mizzenmastheads were already drowsy. So that at last all three of us lifelessly swung from the spars, and for every swing that we made there was a nod from below from the slumbering helmsman. The waves, too, nodded their indolent crests; and across the wide trance of the sea, east nodded to west, and the sun over all.

Suddenly bubbles seemed bursting beneath my closed eyes; like vises my hands grasped the shrouds; some invisible, gracious agency preserved me; with a shock I came back to life. And lo! close under our lee, not forty fathoms off, a gigantic sperm whale lay rolling in the water like the capsized hull of a frigate, his broad, glossy back of an Ethiopian hue, glistening in the sun's rays like a mirror. But lazily undulating in the trough of the sea, and ever and anon tranquilly spouting his vapory jet, the whale looked like a portly burgher smoking his pipe of a warm afternoon. But that pipe, poor whale, was thy last. As if struck by some enchanter's wand, the sleepy ship and every sleeper in it all at once started into wakeful-

ness; and more than a score of voices from all parts of the vessel, simultaneously with the three notes from aloft, shouted forth the accustomed cry, as the great fish slowly and regularly spouted the sparkling brine into the air.

"Clear away the boats! Luff!" cried Ahab. And obeying his own order, he dashed the helm down before the helmsman could handle the spokes.

The sudden exclamations of the crew must have alarmed the whale, and ere the boats were down, majestically turning, he swam away to the leeward, but with such a steady tranquility, and making so few ripples as he swam, that thinking after all he might not as yet be alarmed, Ahab gave orders that not an oar should be used, and no man must speak but in whispers. So, seated like Ontario Indians on the gunwales of the boats, we swiftly but silently paddled along, the calm not admitting of the noiseless sails being set. Presently, as we thus glided in chase, the monster perpendicularly flitted his tail forty feet into the air, and then sank out of sight like a tower swallowed up.

"There go flukes!" was the cry, an announcement immediately followed by Stubb's producing his match and igniting his pipe, for now a respite was granted. After the full interval of his sounding had elapsed, the whale rose again, and being now in advance of the smoker's boat, and much nearer to it than to any of the others, Stubb counted upon the honor of the capture. It was obvious now that the whale had at length become aware of his pursuers. All silence or cautiousness was therefore no longer of use. Paddles were dropped, and oars came loudly into play. And still puffing at his pipe, Stubb cheered on his crew to the assault.

Yes, a mighty change had come over the fish. All alive to his jeopardy, he was going "head out," that part obliquely projecting from the mad yeast which he brewed.

"Start her, start her, my men! Don't hurry yourselves; take plenty of time—but start her; start her like thunderclaps, that's all," cried Stubb, spluttering out the smoke as he spoke. "Start her, now; give 'em the long and strong stroke, Tashtego. Start her, Tash, my boy—start her, all; but keep cool, keep cool—cucumbers is the word—easy, easy— only start her like grim death and grinning devils, and raise the buried dead perpendicular out of their graves, boys—that's all. Start her!"

"Woo-hoo! Wa-hee!" screamed the Gay-Header in reply, raising some old war whoop to the skies, as every oarsman in the strained boat involuntarily bounced forward with the one tremendous leading stroke which the eager Indian gave.

But his wild screams were answered by others quite as wild. "Kee-hee! Kee-hee!" yelled Daggoo, straining forwards and back-

wards on his seat like a pacing tiger in his cage.

"Ka-la! Koo-loo!" howled Queequeg, as if smacking his lips over a mouthful of grenadier's steak. And thus with oars and yells the keels cut the sea. Meanwhile Stubb, retaining his place in the van, still encouraged his men to the onset, all the while puffing the smoke from his mouth. Like desperadoes they tugged and they strained till the welcome cry was heard: "Stand up, Tashtego! —give it to him!" The harpoon was hurled. "Stern all!" The oarsmen backed water; the same moment something went hot and hissing along every one of their wrists. It was the magical line. An instant before, Stubb had swiftly caught two additional turns with it round the loggerhead, whence, by reason of its increased rapid circlings, a hempen blue smoke now jetted up and mingled with the steady fumes from his pipe. As the line passed round and round the loggerhead, so also, just before reaching that point, it blisteringly passed through and through both of Stubb's hands, from which the handcloths, or squares of quilted canvas sometimes worn at these times, had accidentally dropped. It was like holding an enemy's sharp two-edged sword by the blade, and that enemy all the time striving to wrest it out of your clutch.

"Wet the line! wet the line!" cried Stubb to the tub oarsman (him seated by the tub), who, snatching off his hat, dashed the sea water into it. More turns were taken, so that the line began holding its place. The boat now flew through the boiling water like a shark all fins. Stubb and Tashtego here changed places—stem for stern—a staggering business truly in that rocking commotion.

From the vibrating line extending the entire length of the upper part of the boat, and from its now being more tight than a harpstring, you would have thought the craft had two keels—one cleaving the water, the other the air—as the boat churned on through both opposing elements at once. A continual cascade played at the bows, a ceaseless whirling eddy in her wake, and at the slightest motion from within, even but of a little finger, the vibrating, cracking craft canted over her spasmodic gunwale into the sea. Thus they rushed, each man with might and main clinging to his seat to prevent being tossed to the foam, and the tall form of Tashtego at the steering oar crouching almost double in order to bring down his center of gravity. Whole Atlantics and Pacifics seemed passed as they shot on their way, till at length the whale somewhat slackened his flight.

"Haul in—haul in!" cried Stubb to the bowsman, and facing round towards the whale, all hands began pulling the boat up to him, while yet the boat was being towed on. Soon ranging up by his flank, Stubb, firmly planting his knee in the clumsy cleat, darted dart after dart into the flying fish, at the word of command the boat alternately sterning out of the way of the whale's horrible wallow, then ranging up for another fling.

The red tide now poured from all sides of the monster like brooks down a hill. His tormented body rolled not in brine but in blood, which bubbled and seethed for furlongs behind in their wake. The slanting sun, playing upon this crimson pond in the sea, sent back its reflection into every face, so that they all glowed to each other like red men. And all the while, jet after jet of white smoke was agonizingly shot from the spiracle of the whale, and vehement puff after puff from the mouth of the excited headsman, as at every dart, hauling in upon his crooked lance (by the line attached to it), Stubb straightened it again and again by a few rapid blows against the gunwale, then again and again sent it into the whale.

"Pull up—pull up!" he now cried to the bowsman, as the waning whale relaxed in his wrath. "Pull up!—close to!" and the boat ranged along the fish's flank. When reaching far over the bow, Stubb slowly churned his long, sharp lance into the fish and kept it there, carefully churning and churning, as if cautiously seeking to feel after some gold watch that the whale might have swallowed and which he was fearful of breaking ere he could hook it out. But that gold watch he sought was the innermost life of the fish. And now it is struck, for, starting from his trance into that unspeakable thing called his flurry, the monster horribly wallowed in his blood, overwrapped himself in impenetrable, mad, boiling spray, so that the imperiled craft, instantly dropping astern, had much ado blindly to struggle out from that frenzied twilight into the clear air of the day.

And now abating in his flurry, the whale once more rolled out into view, surging from side to side, spasmodically dilating and contracting his spout hole, with sharp, cracking, agonized respirations. At last, gush after gush of clotted red gore, as if it had been the purple lees of red wine, shot into the frighted air, and falling back again, ran dripping down his motionless flanks into the sea. His heart had burst!

"He's dead, Mr. Stubb," said Daggoo.

"Yes; both pipes smoked out!" And withdrawing his own from his mouth, Stubb scattered the dead ashes over the water and for a moment stood thoughtfully eying the vast corpse he had made.

Voyages for whales, fish or trade lasted for months—sometimes years—at a time. Left behind were the wives, keeping their coastal houses neat as a pin, sewing, cooking, raising families. How often they must have stood on their little balconies, known as "widows' walks," gazing out to sea, and thinking thoughts like these.

THE PURITAN'S BALLAD

by Elinor Wylie

My love came up from Barnegat,
  The sea was in his eyes;
He trod as softly as a cat
  And told me terrible lies.

His hair was yellow as new-cut pine
  In shavings curled and feathered;
I thought how silver it would shine
  By cruel winters weathered.

But he was in his twentieth year,
  This time I'm speaking of;
We were head over heels in love with fear
  And half a-feared of love.

His feet were used to treading a gale
  And balancing thereon;
His face was brown as a foreign sail
  Threadbare against the sun.

His arms were thick as hickory logs
   Whittled to little wrists;
Strong as the teeth of terrier dogs
   Were the fingers of his fists.

Within his arms I feared to sink
   Where lions shook their manes,
And dragons drawn in azure ink
   Leapt quickened by his veins.

Dreadful his strength and length of limb
   As the sea to foundering ships;
I dipped my hands in love for him
   No deeper than their tips.

But our palms were welded by a flame
   The moment we came to part,
And on his knuckles I read my name
   Enscrolled within a heart.

And something made our wills to bend
   As wild as trees blown over;
We were no longer friend and friend,
   But only lover and lover.

"In seven weeks or seventy years—
   God grant it may be sooner!—
I'll make a handkerchief for your tears
   From the sails of my captain's schooner.

"We'll wear our loves like wedding rings
   Long polished to our touch;
We shall be busy with other things
   And they cannot bother us much.

"When you are skimming the wrinkled
      cream
   And your ring clinks on the pan,
You'll say to yourself in a pensive dream,
   'How wonderful a man!'

"When I am slitting a fish's head
   And my ring clanks on the knife,
I'll say with thanks, as a prayer is said,
   'How beautiful a wife!'

"And I shall fold my decorous paws
   In velvet smooth and deep,
Like a kitten that covers up its claws
   To sleep and sleep and sleep.

"Like a little blue pigeon you shall bow
   Your bright alarming crest;
In the crook of my arm you'll lay your
      brow
   To rest and rest and rest."

Will he never come back from Barnegat
   With thunder in his eyes,
Treading as soft as a tiger cat,
   To tell me terrible lies?

Clipper ships to China, whaling vessels to the South Seas, settlers rolling westward— the young giant, America, was swelling its chest and spreading its arms wide. A spirit of aggressive optimism took over, and some people felt that America had a "manifest destiny" to expand, no matter who got in her way. While responsible men (Abraham Lincoln among them) challenged the doubtful ethics of this attitude, it did give politicians the chance to get their teeth into some ring-tailed roaring, spread-eagle, jingoistic speeches, guaranteed to win them votes from the land-hungry and those who substituted unthinking flag-waving for a true understanding of the ideals and goals set forth by the Founding Fathers of their country. A typical "manifest destiny" speech is the following, supposedly delivered by a General Buncombe in Congress, during the 1840s.

NOTHING BUT THE CONTINENT

Quoted in "Knickerbocker Magazine," August, 1855

"Mr. Speaker: When I take my eyes and throw them over the vast expanse of this expansive country: when I see how the yeast of freedom has caused it to rise in the scale of civilization and extension on every side; when I see it growing, swelling, roaring, like a spring-freshet—when I see all *this,* I cannot resist the idea, Sir, that the day will come when this great nation, like a young school-boy, will burst its straps, and become entirely too big for its boots!

"Sir, we want *elbow-room*—the continent, the *whole* continent, and nothing *but* the continent! And we will *have* it! Then shall Uncle Sam, placing his hat upon the Canadas, rest his right arm on the Oregon and California coast, his left on the eastern seaboard, and whittle away the British power, while reposing his leg, like a freeman, upon Cape Horn! Sir, the day *will*—the day *must* come!"

Uncle Sam got Oregon peacefully in a settlement with England, and California and the Southwest were acquired as the result of a successful war with Mexico. Meanwhile, Indians continued to get nothing but the short end of the stick. Whenever they got tired of being pushed out of their lands, they would put on some war paint and throw a bloody temper tantrum that generally ended in their being slaughtered by superior numbers. This reinforced white opinion that they were nothing but a race of "murdering savages," which naturally justified taking their land away in the name of civilization and the inevitable march of progress. Although beaten in the often ruthless struggle for the continent, the Indian has left behind a tradition of stoic bravery and such rich contributions to American culture as the following poem.

LAMENT OF A MAN FOR HIS SON
(Paiute)

Unknown Indian Author
Translated by Mary Austin

Son, my son!
I will go up to the mountain
And there I will light a fire
To the feet of my son's spirit,
And there will I lament him;
Saying,
O my son,
What is my life to me, now you are departed?

Son, my son,
In the deep earth
We softly laid thee
In a Chief's robe,
In a warrior's gear.
Surely there,
In the spirit land,
Thy deeds attend thee!
Surely,
The corn comes to the ear again!
But I, here,
I am the stalk that the seed-gatherers
Descrying empty, afar, left standing.
Son, my son!
What is my life to me, now you are departed?

This lament is a poignant symbol of a lost cause, for the Indian's warrior son might well have died in a futile attempt to recapture the glory of the past. Now, however, we come to the tale of 188 Americans who died in a cause that proved to be the wave of the future.

When Mexico broke away from Spain in 1821, it inherited most of the American Southwest, including Texas and California. At first, Americans were encouraged to come and help populate sparsely settled Texas. But when they obliged to the tune of some twenty thousand by the 1830s, the government in Mexico City realized its authority over the distant region was slipping away. In 1835, the Mexican dictator Santa Anna led an army across the Rio Grande to assert his rule over Texas. The American Texans decided to fight for independence. A group under the command of Colonel William Travis assembled at San Antonio. They determined to make a stand against the approaching columns—over two thousand strong—of Santa Anna, even though outnumbered by better than ten to one. Their spirits were bolstered by the arrival of our old friend from Tennessee, Davy Crockett, spoiling for a fight. The following account of the siege of the Alamo is from a diary he supposedly kept during the action. It may not actually have been written by him, but it is a vivid and accurate description of one of the most colorful chapters in American history.

REMEMBER THE ALAMO

from "Colonel Crockett's Exploits and Adventures in Texas"

I write this on the nineteenth of February, 1836, at San Antonio. We are all in high spirits, though we are rather short of provi-sions for men who have appetites that could digest anything but oppression; but no matter, we have a prospect of soon getting our bellies full of fighting, and that is victuals and drink to a true patriot any day. We had a little sort of convivial party last evening: just about a dozen of us set to work most patriotically to see whether we could not get rid of that curse of the land, whisky, and we made considerable progress. . . .

February 23.—Early this morning the enemy came in sight, marching in regular order to strike us with terror. But that was no go; they'll find that they have to do with men who will never lay down their arms as long as they can stand on their legs. We held a short council of war, and, finding that we should be completely surrounded and over-whelmed by numbers if we remained in the town, we concluded to withdraw to the for-tress of Alamo and defend it to the last ex-tremity. We accordingly filed off in good order, having some days before placed all the surplus provisions, arms, and ammuni-tion in the fortress. We have had a large na-tional flag made; it is composed of thirteen stripes, red and white alternately, on a blue ground with a large white star of five points in the center, and between the points the let-ters TEXAS. As soon as all our little band, about one hundred and fifty in number, had entered and secured the fortress in the best possible manner, we set about raising our flag on the battlements. The enemy marched into Bexar and took possession of the town, a blood-red flag flying at their head, to indi-cate that we need not expect quarter if we should fall into their clutches. In the after-noon a messenger was sent from the enemy to Colonel Travis, demanding an unconditional and absolute surrender of the garrison, threatening to put every man to the sword in case of refusal. The only answer he received was a cannon shot; so the messenger left us with a flea in his ear, and the Mexicans commenced firing grenades at us, but without doing any mischief. At night Colonel Travis sent an express to Colonel Fanning at Goliad, about three or four days' march from this place, to let him know that we are besieged. . . .

February 24.—Very early this morning the enemy commenced a new battery on the banks of the river about three hundred and fifty yards from the fort, and by afternoon they amused themselves by firing at us from that quarter. Our Indian scout came in this evening, and with him a reinforcement of thirty men from Gonzales, who are just in the nick of time to reap a harvest of glory; but there is some prospect of sweating blood before we gather it in. . . .

February 27.—The cannonading began early this morning, and ten bombs were thrown into the fort, but fortunately exploded without doing any mischief. So far it has been a sort of tempest in a teapot, not unlike a pitched battle in the Hall of Congress, where the parties array their forces, make fearful demonstrations on both sides, then fire away with loud-sounding speeches, which contain about as much meaning as the report of a howitzer charged with a blank cartridge. Provisions are becoming scarce, and the enemy are endeavoring to cut off our water. If they attempt to stop our grog in that manner, let them look out, for we shall become too wrathy for our shirts to hold us. We are not prepared to submit to an excise of that nature, and they'll find it out. This

discovery has created considerable excitement in the fort.

February 28.—Last night our hunters brought in some corn and hogs and had a brush with a scout from the enemy beyond gunshot of the fort. They put the scout to flight and got in without injury. They bring accounts that the settlers are flying in all quarters, in dismay, leaving their possessions to the mercy of the ruthless invader, who is literally engaged in a war of extermination more brutal than the untutored savage of the desert could be guilty of. Slaughter is indiscriminate, sparing neither sex, age, nor condition. Buildings have been burnt down, farms laid waste, and Santa Anna appears determined to verify his threat and convert the blooming paradise into a howling wilderness. For just one fair crack at that rascal even at a hundred yards distance I would bargain to break my Betsey and never pull trigger again. . . .

February 29.—Before daybreak we saw General Sesma leave his camp with a large body of cavalry and infantry and move off in the direction of Goliad. We think that he must have received news of Colonel Fanning's coming to our relief. . . .

I had a little sport this morning before breakfast. The enemy had planted a piece of ordnance within gunshot of the fort during the night, and the first thing in the morning they commenced a brisk cannonade point-blank against the spot where I was snoring. I turned out pretty smart and mounted the rampart. The gun was charged again, a fellow stepped forth to touch her off, but before he could apply the match I let him have it, and he keeled over. A second stepped up, snatched the match from the hand of the dying man, but Thimblerig, who had followed me, handed me his rifle, and the next instant the Mexican was stretched on the earth beside the first. A third came up to the cannon, my companion handed me another gun, and I fixed him off in like manner. A fourth, then a fifth, seized the match, who both met with the same fate, and then the whole party gave it up as a bad job and hurried off to the camp, leaving the cannon ready charged where they had planted it. I came down, took my bitters, and went to breakfast. Thimblerig told me that the place from which I had been firing was one of the snuggest stands in the whole fort, for he never failed picking off two or three stragglers before breakfast when perched up there. And I recollect now having seen him there, ever since he was wounded, the first thing in the morning and the last at night—and at times thoughtlessly playing at his eternal game.

March 1.—The enemy's forces have been increasing in numbers daily, notwithstanding they have already lost about three hundred men in the several assaults they have made upon us. I neglected to mention in the proper place that when the enemy came in sight we had but three bushels of corn in the garrison but have since found eighty bushels in a deserted house. Colonel Bowie's illness still continues, but he manages to crawl from his bed every day, that his comrades may see him. His presence alone is a tower of strength. —The enemy becomes more daring as his numbers increase. . . .

March 3.—We have given over all hopes of receiving assistance from Goliad or Refugio. Colonel Travis harangued the garrison and concluded by exhorting them, in case the enemy should carry the fort, to fight to the last gasp and render their victory even more serious to them than to us. This was followed by three cheers. . . .

March 5.—Pop, pop, pop! Bom, bom, bom! throughout the day. No time for memorandums now. Go ahead! Liberty and independence forever!

[Here ends Colonel Crockett's manuscript.]

Crockett and the other defenders of the Alamo died to a man, but "Remember the Alamo!" became the victory cry of General Sam Houston and his men as they whipped Santa Anna's army in April, 1836, captured the dictator, and forced him to accept the independence of Texas. It became the Lone Star Republic and, nine years later, a state in the Union. The Mexican War followed. When it was over, Mexico had agreed (with a bayonet at her throat—America had captured her capital) to sell California and most of New Mexico to the United States for a little over $18,000,000. The same year the war ended (1848), gold was discovered in California, and America went insane.

Bank clerks in Boston and butchers' assistants in New York dreamed of becoming millionaires. Responsible citizens all over the country abandoned homes and jobs, and joined gamblers, thieves and adventurers of every description in the mad race to the California hills.

They created their own kind of devil-may-care marching songs. One was to the tune of Stephen Foster's popular *Oh Susanna* (I come from Alabama with my banjo on my knee; I'm going to Louisiana, my true love for to see).

GOLD RUSH VERSION OF "OH SUSANNA"

Anonymous

I come from Salem City,
With my washboard on my knee;
I'm going to California,
The gold dust for to see . . .

The pilot bread is in my mouth,
The gold dust in my eye,
And though I'm going far away,
Dear brothers, don't you cry.

I soon shall be in Francisco,
And then I'll look around,
And when I see the gold lumps there,
I'll pick them off the ground.

I'll scrape the mountains clean, my boys,
I'll drain the rivers dry,
A pocket full of rocks bring home,
So brothers, don't you cry!

Oh, California!
That's the land for me,
I'm going to Sacramento,
With my washboard on my knee.

Another song was sung to the tune of "Yankee Doodle, keep it up, Yankee Doodle, dandy . . ."

GOLD RUSH VERSION OF "YANKEE DOODLE"

Anonymous

Gold is got in pan and pot,
Soup tureen and ladle,
Basket, bird cage and what not—
Even in a cradle!

Choose your able-bodied men,
All whose arms are brawny,
Give them picks and shades, and then,
Off for Californy!

Thousands of gold rushers traveled by land across the plains. Thousands of others took ship at Salem, New York and other ports for the long trip around South America (the Panama Canal hadn't been dug yet), or they traveled to the narrow Isthmus of Panama, which they crossed by horse and on foot. Those leaving from New York were regaled with such enterprising newspaper advertisements as the following.

CALIFORNIANS
HO! HIST!
ATTENTION

Our rubber boats and tents are unsurpassed. You cannot face the gold rivers without a rubber suit!

HO! HO! HO!
★ ---- ★ For California HO! ★ ---- ★

Last not least! Persons going out to the gold regions are seriously advised to take, among other necessaries, a good lot of monuments and tombstones. A great saving can be effected by having their inscriptions cut in New York beforehand.

The gold-fever epidemic had to be seen to be believed. One who saw and recorded it was Walter Colton, alcalde—or chief judge —of Monterey. The gold rush reached his area at the end of May, 1848. Here's his description of the bedlam that followed.

GOLD-FEVER DAYS IN CALIFORNIA

from "Three Years in California" by Walter Colton

Tuesday, June 20.—My messenger, sent to the mines, has returned with specimens of the gold; he dismounted in a sea of upturned faces. As he drew forth the yellow lumps from his pockets and passed them around among the eager crowd, the doubts, which had lingered till now, fled. All admitted they were gold except one old man who still persisted they were some Yankee invention, got up to reconcile the people to the change of flag. The excitement produced was intense, and many were soon busy in their hasty preparations for a departure to the mines. The family who had kept house for me caught the moving infection. Husband and wife were both packing up; the blacksmith dropped his hammer, the carpenter his plane, the mason his trowel, the farmer his sickle, the baker his loaf, and the tapster his bottle. All were off for the mines, some on horses, some on carts, and some on crutches; and one went in a litter. An American woman who had recently established a boarding-house here pulled up stakes and was off before her lodgers had even time to pay their bills. Debtors ran, of course. I have only a community of women left and a gang of prisoners, with here and there a soldier who will give his captain the slip at the first chance. I don't blame the fellow a whit; seven dollars a month, while others are making two or three hundred a day! That is too much for human nature to stand. . . .

Tuesday, July 18.—Another bag of gold from the mines and another spasm in the community. It was brought down by a sailor from Yuba River and contains a hundred and thirty-six ounces. It is the most beautiful gold that has appeared in the market; it looks like the yellow scales of the dolphin passing through his rainbow hues at death. My carpenters, at work on the schoolhouse, on seeing it, threw down their saws and planes, shouldered their picks, and are off for the Yuba. Three seamen ran from the *Warren*, forfeiting their four years' pay; and a whole platoon of soldiers from the fort left only their colors behind. One old woman declared she would never again break an egg or kill a chicken without examining yolk and gizzard. . . .

As the gold rush extended into the following year, thousands of would-be millionaires —now called "forty-niners"—crowded into the diggings. Roaring towns and mining camps blossomed overnight, bearing such names as Hell's Delight, Red Dog, Dry Diggings, Poker Flat, Hangtown . . . Eggs cost $10 a dozen, and landlords charged—and got— $1,000 a month for a single room. Gambling halls and saloons thrived, and many a prospector lost his hard-earned "poke" of gold in a single night's celebration. Life was cheap and humor rough in the mining camps. Men ruled by a greed for gold didn't tend to be very sentimental, as proved by the following "touching" ballad.

OH, MY DARLING CLEMENTINE

Anonymous

In a cavern, in a canyon,
Excavating for a mine,
Dwelt a miner, 'Forty-Niner,
And his daughter Clementine.

Chorus:
Oh, my darling, Oh, my darling,
Oh, my darling Clementine,
You are lost and gone forever,
Dreadful sorry, Clementine.

Light she was and like a fairy,
And her shoes were number nine;
Herring boxes, without topses
Sandals were for Clementine.

Drove she ducklings to the water,
Every morning just at nine;
Hit her foot against a splinter,
Fell into the foaming brine.

Ruby lips above the water,
Blowing bubbles soft and fine;
Alas for me! I was no swimmer,
So I lost my Clementine.

In a churchyard, near the canyon,
Where the myrtle doth entwine,
There grow roses and other posies,
Fertilized by Clementine.

115

Then the miner, 'Forty-Niner,
Soon began to peak and pine,
Thought he oughter jine his daughter,
Now he's with his Clementine.

In my dreams she still doth haunt me,
Robed in garments soaked in brine,
Though in life I used to hug her,
Now she's dead, I'll draw the line.

The few who made and kept a fortune in gold erected mansions in the growing town of San Francisco, installed solid-gold plumbing, and settled back to a life of ease, complete with diamond-studded shirts, fancy women, and dinner at Delmonico's. Of the many unlucky ones, some begged, borrowed or stole passage money, and slunk back to their home towns or hearths, sadder and wiser men. But many of them, once the gold fever had run its course and sense returned, resumed their careers as bank clerks, butchers' assistants or what-have-you, right there in California. The territory grew populous and prosperous, and in 1850, California became a state. It was a senator from California, William M. Gwin, who planned the fast mail route across the plains between St. Joseph, Missouri, and Sacramento, California, that became known as the Pony Express. It only lasted eighteen months, being supplanted by a telegraph line; but during its brief existence, the fleet, fearless Pony Express riders won undying fame. Mark Twain saw and described one in action.

THE PONY EXPRESS

from "Roughing It" by Mark Twain

In a little while all interest was taken up in stretching our necks and watching for the "pony rider"—the fleet messenger who sped across the continent from St. Joe to Sacramento, carrying letters nineteen hundred miles in eight days [1860]! Think of that for perishable horse and human flesh and blood to do! The pony rider was usually a little bit of a man, brimful of spirit and endurance. No matter what time of the day or night his watch came on and no matter whether it was winter or summer, raining, snowing, hailing, or sleeting, or whether his beat was a level straight road or a crazy trail over mountain crags and precipices, or whether it led through peaceful regions or regions that swarmed with hostile Indians, he must be always ready to leap into the saddle and be off like the wind! There was no idling time for a pony rider on duty. He rode fifty miles without stopping, by daylight, moonlight, starlight, or through the blackness of darkness—just as it happened. He rode a splendid horse that was born for a racer and fed and lodged like a gentleman; kept him at his utmost speed for ten miles, and then, as he came crashing up to the station where stood two men holding fast a fresh, impatient steed, the transfer of rider and mailbag was made in the twinkling of an eye, and away flew the eager pair and were out of sight before the spectator could get hardly the ghost of a look. Both rider and horse went "flying light." The rider's dress was thin and fitted close; he wore a roundabout and a skullcap and tucked his pantaloons into his boot tops like a race rider. He carried no arms—he carried nothing that was not absolutely necessary, for even the postage on his literary freight was worth *five dollars a letter*. He got but little frivolous correspondence to carry—his bag had busi-

an important business chapter and newspaper letter, but these were written on paper as airy and thin as gold leaf, nearly, and thus bulk and weight were economized. The stagecoach traveled about a hundred to a hundred and twenty-five miles a day (twenty-four hours), the pony rider about two hundred and fifty. There were about eighty pony riders in the saddle all the time, night and day, stretching in a long, scattering procession from Missouri to California, forty flying eastward and forty toward the west, and among them making four hundred gallant horses earn a stirring livelihood and see a deal of scenery every single day in the year.

We had had a consuming desire, from the beginning, to see a pony rider, but somehow or other all that passed us and all that met us managed to streak by in the night, and so we heard only a whiz and a hail, and the swift phantom of the desert was gone before we could get our heads out of the windows. But now we were expecting one along every moment and would see him in broad daylight. Presently the driver exclaims:

"Here he comes!"

ness letters in it mostly. His horse was stripped of all unnecessary weight too. He wore light shoes or none at all. The little flat mail pockets strapped under the rider's thighs would each hold about the bulk of a child's primer. They held many and many

Every neck is stretched farther and every eye strained wider. Away across the endless dead level of the prairie a black speck appears against the sky, and it is plain that it moves. Well, I should think so! In a second or two it becomes a horse and rider, rising and falling, rising and falling—sweeping toward us nearer and nearer—growing more and more distinct, more and more sharply defined—nearer and still nearer, and the flutter of the hoofs comes faintly to the ear —another instant a whoop and a hurrah from our upper deck, a wave of the rider's hand, but no reply, and man and horse burst past our excited faces and go swinging away like a belated fragment of a storm!

So sudden is it all and so like a flash of unreal fancy that, but for the flake of white foam left quivering and perishing on a mail sack after the vision had flashed by and disappeared, we might have doubted whether we had seen any actual horse and man at all, maybe.

While California and Texas were being settled by land hunger and gold fever, Utah was settled by religion. One of the most fascinating of the many different religious communities (or theocracies) that developed in America was the Mormon Church. It was founded in 1830 by Joseph Smith as the Church of Jesus Christ of Latter-Day Saints. In return for converting Indians (whom their faith taught were really the Lost Tribes of Israel) and for being industrious on earth, Mormons were promised great rewards in Heaven. Industrious they were—so much so that they aroused the envy of non-Mormons (or "Gentiles"), who were also opposed to the Mormon custom of one man taking several wives. After Smith was murdered by a Gentile mob, and the Mormons were driven from their thriving settlement in Illinois, a towering, Moseslike figure appeared to take command. His name was Brigham Young, and in 1847, he led twelve thousand "children of Israel" in a great westward trek across plains, mountains and desert to Utah. The new Promised Land was anything but a land of milk and honey; but Brigham Young and his energetic followers soon turned parched earth into prosperous, irrigated farms, founded Salt Lake City, and began building their Tabernacle. In 1855, a Frenchman named Jules Rémy visited the Mormon capital with a companion and recorded the following impressions.

INTERVIEW WITH A MORMON PROPHET

from "A Journey to Great-Salt-Lake City"
by Jules Rémy

Brigham Young is the supreme president of the Church of Latter-Day Saints throughout the world. He is the Mormon pope; he is at the same time, by election of the people, a prophet, "revelator," and seer; and still more, he was, at the time of our journey, Governor of the Territory of Utah, and recognized in that capacity by the President of the United States. He is a man fifty-four years of age, fair, of moderate height, stout almost to obesity. . . .

We found him in his official cabinet, dictating instructions to his secretaries, and at the same time preparing a quid of Virginia tobacco. . . . He continued dictating for half an hour, without appearing to take the least notice of our presence. Then, as soon as he had finished, he exchanged a few words with an Indian who had kissed his hand when he entered. Mr. Haws now presented us to his Excellency. Brigham Young shook hands with us, and then retired into an adjoining apartment, from which he returned in about two minutes with a plug of tobacco which he gave to the Indian. He then asked us to take a seat and sat down himself without taking off his hat. . . .

We learned afterward that we were looked upon as persons of bad character, sent by the Gentiles to assassinate the leader of the Mormons. . . .

Brigham Young, who much regretted his mistake, excused himself by saying that he distrusted strangers presented to him by persons who scarcely knew them . . . He begged us to return to his house . . . and to convince us that he was really sorry, sent us a present of nearly all the works which had been written and published by the Mormons, handsomely bound.

From this moment we were at ease. We were made much of everywhere; we were called Brother Brenchley, Brother Rémy. . . . Some talked of making us apostles on the first vacancy, or at least bishops; others gave out that we were going to finish the temple with our own good money. Everyone spoke of giving us parties; we were invited to dinner and to tea without end. . . . A ball, too, was given us, at which every gentleman danced with two ladies at once, an ingenious innovation, and not the only one with which Mormonism aspires to endow society with a view to its reformation. . . .

It is, moreover, one of the peculiarities of the Mormon Church to discourage the prac-

tice of medicine and to compel all medical men who embrace the faith to select another career . . . An invalid who has recourse to medicine would be suspected of verging on infidelity, and a new baptism alone could efface the pollution. Brother Brigham menaces with celestial wrath those weak enough to employ, in the treatment of diseases, other remedies than olive oil and the herbs of the fields. . . . We were told of numerous remarkable cures having been effected by the use of oil and prayer . . . Under the mysterious influence of an energetic faith, imagination may work miracles, even among pagans. Brigham Young told us one day, speaking of medicine, that doctors often wrote to him from California and the Eastern states to know if there was any chance of establishing a practice in Utah, announcing that in case there might be, they would have no objection to becoming converts to Mormonism. The Mormon pope, who now despises such impertinence too much to notice it, used at first to reply that his religion did not seek to purchase adherents.

While the West developed its farms, mines, ranches and Mormon communities, and the North boomed as the center of manufacturing towns, the great plantation became the dominant symbol of Southern life. Those who lived in stately-pillared "big houses," overlooking wide, rolling fields of cotton, tobacco, sugar cane or rice, developed an understandably strong, sentimental attachment to their gracious homes and luxurious way of life. The sentiment lingers on in Southern memory today, and was embodied in such romantic songs as the following.

MY OLD KENTUCKY HOME

by Stephen Foster

The sun shines bright in the old Kentucky
  home;
  'Tis summer, the darkeys are gay;
The corn-top's ripe, and the meadow's in the
  bloom,
  While the birds make music all the day.
The young folks roll on the little cabin floor,
  All merry, all happy and bright;
By-'n'-by hard times comes a-knocking at the
  door:—
  Then my old Kentucky home, good-night!

Weep no more, my lady,
  O, weep no more to-day!
We will sing one song for the old Kentucky
  home,
  For the old Kentucky home, far away.

They hunt no more for the possum and the
  coon,
  On the meadow, the hill, and the shore;
They sing no more by the glimmer of the
  moon,
  On the bench by the old cabin door.
The day goes by like a shadow o'er the
  heart,
  With sorrow, where all was delight;
The time has come when the darkeys have
  to part:—
  Then my old Kentucky home, good night!

The head must bow, and the back will have
  to bend,
  Wherever the darkey may go;
A few more days and the trouble all will end,
  In the field where the sugar-canes grow.
A few more days for to tote the weary
  load,—
  No matter, 'twill never be light;
A few more days till we totter on the
  road:—
  Then my old Kentucky home, good-night!

Weep no more, my lady,
  O, weep no more to-day!
We will sing one song for the old Kentucky
  home,
  For the old Kentucky home, far away.

If, as the first verse of the song suggests, "darkeys" were "gay," it was because they were trying to squeeze as much enjoyment as possible out of a life they did not choose, and over which they had no control. When Thomas Jefferson was writing the Declaration of Independence, he realized that the ideal of human liberty and the practice of human bondage didn't exactly mix. An escaped Negro slave, Crispus Attucks, had been among those who defied the British and were slain in the Boston Massacre. Five thousand Negroes had fought bravely for their freedom, alongside white comrades, in the Revolutionary War. Jefferson tried to include an implied antislavery clause in the Declaration, but it was defeated by Southern interests.

Over the ensuing years, slavery lay more and more like a dark, uneasy shadow over the land. There were passionate arguments both for it and against it. Let us go back to the days of human auction blocks and overseers, and seek out the truth of this ancient institution destined to split a nation in two.

PART FIVE

Let My People Go!

DURING most of recorded history, slavery was part of the world's accepted way of life. If your tribe or nation was defeated in war, you became your conqueror's property. (If conditions were reversed, you'd promptly do the same to him.) There were more slaves than citizens in democratic Athens, and many Greeks, in turn, were enslaved by conquering Romans.

And then, as time-honored values were reexamined in the light of the Renaissance, Western man began endorsing ideas about essential human dignity and individual rights. To many, these ideas didn't seem to make much sense if the fortunes of war or superior might gave one man the right to own another. On the other hand, slaves were so convenient . . . *Let's see, now— heathen savages . . . they're not quite human, really. Perfectly all right to enslave them— doing them a favor, actually, taking them out of their benighted environment, teaching them to be Christians and of use . . . Don't expect the ungrateful beggars to thank us for it, haven't got the intelligence to know what's good for 'em . . .*

And so, the wheels of rationalization smoothed out the dilemma. By assuming a "God-given" superiority over less-developed peoples, Western man found the way to have his cake (belief in human dignity) and eat it, too (the convenience of owning slaves).

At first, the conquistadors who followed Columbus to the New World had tried enslaving native Indians, but they showed a discouraging tendency to die off under the lash and the broiling sun. Negroes brought by Portuguese slave traders from Africa proved much more satisfactory. By the middle of the eighteenth century, Negro slaves were raising tobacco, sugar, rice, and coffee on plantations from the West Indies to Virginia, from South Carolina to Brazil. African coastal towns thrived as centers of the traffic in human flesh. Arab slavers would bring long lines of chained captives to market places, where traders of many nationalities came to look the "merchandise" over and make their bids.

THE AFRICAN CHIEF

by William Cullen Bryant

Chained in the market-place he stood,
  A man of giant frame,
Amid the gathering multitude
  That shrunk to hear his name—
All stern of look and strong of limb,
  His dark eye on the ground;
And silently they gazed on him
  As on a lion bound.

Vainly, but well, that chief had fought;
  He was a captive now,
Yet pride, that fortune humbles not,
  Was written on his brow.
The scars his dark, broad bosom wore
  Showed warrior true and brave;
A prince among his tribe before,
  He could not be a slave.

Then to his conqueror he spake:
  "My brother is a king;
Undo this necklace from my neck,
  And take this bracelet ring,
And send me where my brother reigns,
  And I will fill thy hands
With store of ivory from the plains,
  And gold-dust from the sands."

"Not for thy ivory nor thy gold
  Will I unbind thy chain;
That bloody hand shall never hold
  The battle-spear again.
A price thy nation never gave
  Shall yet be paid for thee;
For thou shalt be the Christian's slave,
  In lands beyond the sea."

Then wept the warrior chief, and bade
  To shred his locks away;
And one by one, each heavy braid
  Before the victor lay.
Thick were the platted locks, and long,
  And closely hidden there
Shone many a wedge of gold among
  The dark and crispèd hair.

"Look, feast thy greedy eye with gold
  Long kept for sorest need:
Take it—thou askest sums untold—
  And say that I am freed.
Take it—my wife, the long, long day,
  Weeps by the cocoa-tree,
And my young children leave their play,
  And ask in vain for me."

"I take thy gold, but I have made
  Thy fetters fast and strong,
And ween that by the cocoa-shade

Thy wife will wait thee long."
Strong was the agony that shook
  The captive's frame to hear,
And the proud meaning of his look
  Was changed to mortal fear.

His heart was broken—crazed his brain;
  At once his eye grew wild;
He struggled fiercely with his chain,
  Whispered, and wept, and smiled;
Yet wore not long those fatal bands,
  And once, at shut of day,
They drew him forth upon the sands,
  The foul hyena's prey.

Often, it was the lucky ones who died before leaving Africa. Once aboard ship, they were packed for days on end in dark, filthy, cramped, practically airless holds. Many died of suffocation and disease; but that was

all right—the shipowners allowed for a certain amount of cargo "spoilage" as part of their operating expenses . . . What kind of men would enter such a trade? Prominent among them during much of the eighteenth and nineteenth centuries were Bible-thumping New Englanders, who attended church on Sundays, were good to their mothers, and contributed generously to local Widows and Orphans funds . . . *Well, looky here, Mister, it says right here in the Old Testament: the sons of Ham are supposed to be bond servants. Now then, doesn't that prove I'm doing the Lord's work?* Of course, the "Lord's work" took strong stomachs and paid enormous profits; but the Devil has always been able to quote Scripture for his own ends . . . Let's assume now that an African chief like the hero of our last poem has survived to pass from the hands of an Arab into the hold of a Yankee slaver . . .

PRELUDE—THE SLAVER

from "John Brown's Body"
by Stephen Vincent Benét

He closed the Bible carefully, putting it
  down
As if his fingers loved it.

                  Then he turned.
"Mr. Mate."
          "Yes, sir."
          The captain's eyes held a shadow.
"I think, while this weather lasts," he said,
  after a pause,
"We'd better get them on deck as much as
  we can.
They keep better that way. Besides," he
  added, unsmiling,

"She's begun to stink already. You've noticed it?"

The mate nodded, a boyish nod of half-
apology,
"And only a week out, too, sir."
                    "Yes," said the skipper.
His eyes looked into themselves. "Well. The
trade," he said,
"The trade's no damn perfume-shop." He
drummed with his fingers.
"Seem to be quiet tonight," he murmured,
at last.
"Oh yes sir, quiet enough." The mate
flushed. "Not
What you'd call quiet at home but—quiet
enough."

"Um," said the skipper. "What about the big
fellow?"

"Tarbarrel, sir? The man who says he's a
king?
He was praying to something—it made the
others restless.
Mr. Olsen stopped it."
                    "I don't like that," said the skipper.
"It was only an idol, sir."
                    "Oh."
                              "A stone or something."
"Oh."
    "But he's a bad one, sir—a regular sullen
    one—
He—eyes in the dark—like a cat's—enough
to give you—"
The mate was young. He shivered. "The
creeps," he said.

"We've had that kind," said the skipper. His

mouth was hard
Then it relaxed. "Damn cheating Arabs!"
he said,
"I told them I'd take no more of their penny-
weight kings,
Worth pounds to look at, and then when you
get them aboard
Go crazy so they have to be knocked on the
head
Or else just eat up their hearts and die in a
week
Taking up room for nothing."

The mate hardly heard him, thinking of
something else.
"I'm afraid we'll lose some more of the
women," he said.
"Well, they're a scratch lot," said the skipper. "Any sickness?"

"Just the usual, sir."
                    "But nothing like plague or—"
                                        "No sir."
"The Lord is merciful," said the skipper.
His voice was wholly sincere—an old ship's
bell
Hung in the steeple of a meeting-house
With all New England and the sea's noise
in it.
"Well, you'd better take another look-see,
Mr. Mate."
The mate felt his lips go dry. "Aye aye, sir,"
he said,
Wetting his lips with his tongue. As he left
the cabin
He heard the Bible being opened again.

Lantern in hand, he went down to the hold.
Each time he went he had a trick of trying

To shut the pores of his body against the
stench
By force of will, by thinking of salt and
flowers,
But it was always useless.

He kept thinking:
When I get home, when I get a bath and
clean food,
When I've gone swimming out beyond the
Point
In that cold green, so cold it must be pure
Beyond the purity of a dissolved star,
When I get my shore-clothes on, and one of
those shirts
Out of the linen-closet that smells of lav-
ender,
Will my skin smell black even then, will my
skin smell black?

The lantern shook in his hand.

This was black, here,
This was black to see and feel and smell and
taste,
The blackness of black, with one weak lamp
to light it
As ineffectually as a firefly in Hell,
And, being so, should be silent.

But the hold
Was never silent.

There was always that breathing.
Always that thick breathing, always those
shivering cries.

A few of the slaves
Knew English—at least the English for wa-
ter and Jesus.
"I'm dying." "Sick." "My name Caesar."

Those who knew
These things, said these things now when
they saw the lantern

Mechanically, as tamed beasts answer the
whipcrack.
Their voices beat at the light like heavy
moths.
But most made merely liquid or guttural
sounds
Meaningless to the mate, but horribly like
The sounds of palateless men or animals
trying
To talk through a human throat.

The mate was used
To the confusion of limbs and bodies by
now.
At first it had made him think of the per-
turbed
Blind coil of blacksnakes thawing on a rock
In the bleak sun of Spring, or Judgment Day
Just after the first sounding of the trump
When all earth seethes and crumbles with the
slow
Vast, mouldy resurrection of the dead.
But he had passed such fancies.

He must see
As much as he could. He couldn't see very
much.
They were too tightly packed but—no plague
yet,
And all the chains were fast. Then he saw
something.
The woman was asleep but her baby was
dead.
He wondered whether to take it from her
now.
No, it would only rouse the others. Tomor-
row.
He turned away with a shiver.

His glance fell
On the man who said he had been a king,
the man

127

Called Tarbarrel, the image of black stone
Whose eyes were savage gods.

                  The huge suave muscles
Rippled like stretching cats as he changed
    posture,
Magnificence in chains that yet was ease.
The smolder in those eyes. The steady hate.

The mate made himself stare till the eyes
    dropped.
Then he turned back to the companionway.
His forehead was hot and sweaty. He wiped
    it off,
But then the rough cloth of his sleeve smelt
    black.

The captain shut the Bible as he came in.
"Well, Mister Mate?"

          "All quiet, sir."

                    The captain
Looked at him sharply. "Sit down," he said
    in a bark.
The mate's knees gave as he sat. "It's—hot
    down there,"
He said, a little weakly, wanting to wipe
His face again, but knowing he'd smell that
    blackness
Again, if he did.

        "Takes you that way, sometimes,"
Said the captain, not unkindly, "I remember
Back in the twenties."

        Something hot and strong
Bit the mate's throat. He coughed.

            "There," said the captain.
Putting the cup down. "You'll feel better
    now.
You're young for this trade, Mister, and
    that's a fact."

The mate coughed and didn't answer, much
    too glad
To see the captain change back to himself
From something made of steam, to want to
    talk.
But, after a while, he heard the captain talk-
    ing,
Half to himself.

        "It's a fact, that," he was saying,
"They've even made a song of me—ever
    heard it?"
The mate shook his head, quickly. "Oh yes
    you have.
You know how it goes." He cleared his
    throat and hummed:

"Captain Ball was a Yankee slaver,
Blow, blow, blow the man down!
He traded in niggers and loved his Saviour,
Give me some time to blow the man down."

The droning chanty filled the narrow cabin
An instant with grey Massachusetts sea,
Wave of the North, wave of the melted ice,
The hard salt-sparkles on the harder rock.
The stony islands.

        Then it died away.

*   *   *

    Although England and America outlawed
the slave trade in the first decade of the nineteenth century, it continued to flourish il-
legally. Over two million slaves were smuggled into the United States to supply the
labor on mushrooming plantations. King
cotton became the most important crop, due
to the invention of the cotton gin; but tobacco, rice and other crops were also raised.
Negroes were trained as field hands, me-

chanics of various kinds, or "big house" servants, according to their abilities. Many great plantations were made practically self-sustaining by Negro help. One such, both before and after the Revolution, was Gunston Hall in Virginia. The daughter of its founder, George Mason, has left us the following description.

ONE MAN'S "FAMILY" OF SLAVES

from "The Life of George Mason"
by Kate M. Rowland

Thus my father had among his slaves carpenters, coopers, sawyers, blacksmiths, tanners, curriers, shoemakers, spinners, weavers and knitters, and even a distiller. . . . His carpenters and sawyers built and kept in repair all the dwelling houses, barns, stables, plows, harrows, gates, etc., on the plantations and the outhouses at the home house. His coopers made the hogsheads the tobacco was prized in and the tight casks to hold the cider and other liquors. . . . The blacksmith did all the iron work required by the establishment, as making and repairing plows, harrows, teeth chains, bolts, etc., etc. The spinners, weavers, and knitters made all the coarse cloths and stockings used by the Negroes, and some of finer texture worn by the white family, nearly all worn by the children of it. The distiller made every fall a good deal of apple, peach, and persimmon brandy. . . .

My father kept no steward or clerk about him. He kept his own books and superintended, with the assistance of a trusty slave

or two, and occasionally of some of his sons, all the operations at or about the home house above described, except that during the Revolutionary War, and when it was necessary to do a great deal in that way to clothe all his slaves, he had in his service a white man, a weaver of the finer stuffs, to weave himself and superintend the Negro spinning-women. To carry on these operations to the extent required, it will be seen that a considerable force was necessary, besides the house servants, who for such a household, a large family and entertaining a great deal of company, must be numerous—and such a force was constantly kept there . . . As I had during my youth constant intercourse with all these people, I remember them all and their several employments as if it was yesterday.

For a supposedly inferior people, Negroes one step away from the jungle showed a surprising knack for learning and becoming skilled in most of the uses of civilization. Plantation owners loved to explain, with tolerant smiles, how their slaves were irresponsible—"just like children." Yet they trusted them with the building of their homes, the preparation of the food they ate, and the care of their own children. Many planters became so dependent upon the services of bondsmen to supply their every need that, eventually, they themselves were enslaved by slavery: they could imagine no other way of life . . .

White children were often suckled and raised by Negro "mammies." At least once —as described in the following fragment of Southern recollection—the process was reversed.

UNCLE ISAAC'S BOAST

from "Memorials of a Southern Planter"
by Susan Dabney Smedes

Uncle Isaac's boast was that he was a child of the same year as the master and that the master's mother had given to him in her own arms some of the baby Thomas's milk, as there was more of it than he wanted. He would draw himself up as he added, "I called marster brother till I was a right big boy, an' I called his mother Ma till I was old enough to know better an' to stop it myself. She never tole me to stop . . ."

Uncle Isaac had the sense to realize his own slight change in status: he had become his "brother's" possession, to be dealt with kindly or roughly, kept or disposed of as the master wished. The Uncle Isaacs of the South were fed a brand of Christianity especially adapted to plantation needs. It stressed the virtues of hard work and obedience, above all others, and implied that rewards were to be collected in Heaven, not on earth. The intensity with which Negroes yearned for this promised day of jubilee, when all burdens would be laid down, was poured into their glorious spirituals, one of the few native American art forms and—along with later Negro blues and jazz—the South's main contribution to the field of music.

SWING LOW, SWEET CHARIOT

Anonymous

I looked over Jordan and what did I see,
   Comin' for to carry me home?
A band of angels comin' afteh me,
   Comin' for to carry me home.

Chorus:
Swing low, sweet chariot,
   Comin' for to carry me home;
Swing low, sweet chariot,
   Comin' for to carry me home.

If you git there befo' I do,
   Comin' for to carry me home,
Jus' tell 'em I'm a-comin' too,
   Comin' for to carry me home.

I ain't been to heb'n, but I been tol',
   Comin' for to carry me home,
De streets in heb'n am paved wid gol',
   Comin' for to carry me home.

I'm sometimes up and sometimes down,
   Comin' for to carry me home;
But still my soul am hebenly-boun',
   Comin' for to carry me home.

But Heaven was far away, and meanwhile, they were slaves. It's true that many planters dealt as justly with their slaves as the system permitted. They even developed strongly paternal attachments to loyal servants (provided they didn't get "uppity"). An admirer of slavery wrote in the 1830s:

"It is now popular to treat slaves with kindness, and those planters who are known to be inhumanly rigorous to their slaves are scarcely countenanced by the more intelligent and humane portion of the population . . ."

But the point is planters *could* be inhumanly rigorous if they wanted to, and there was no court of appeal for the mistreated slave.

Certain enterprising souls even ran slave-breeding farms, where men and women selected for their "good points" were forced to enter into loveless unions in order to produce "prime stock." It is a tribute to Negro vitality and spirit that they were so often able to rise above the humiliation of slavery and make rich contributions to American culture. Before the Revolution, a slave girl named Phillis Wheatley was amazing literary circles with her mastery of the classical poetry forms then in vogue. But it was as an innovator of *new* forms that the Negro really excelled. Negro songs, jokes and dances such as the cakewalk were imitated by Dan Emmett and other white showmen in the most popular variety entertainment before vaudeville—the minstrel show. The Negro talent for original poetic imagery revealed itself in folk sermons, the flavor and spirit of which have been captured in our next selection.

THE CREATION
A Negro Sermon

by *James Weldon Johnson*

And God stepped out on space,
And He looked around and said,
"I'm lonely—
I'll make me a world."
As far as the eye of God could see
Darkness covered everything,
Blacker than a hundred midnights
Down in a cypress swamp.

Then God smiled,
And the light broke,
And the darkness rolled up on one side,
And the light stood shining on the other,
And God said, *"That's good!"*

Then God reached out and took the light
    in His hands,
And God rolled the light around in His
    hands,
Until He made the sun;
And He set that sun a-blazing in the
    heavens.
And the light that was left from making
    the sun
God gathered up in a shining ball
And flung against the darkness,
Spangling the night with the moon and
    stars.
Then down between
The darkness and the light
He hurled the world;
And God said, *"That's good!"*

Then God Himself stepped down—
And the sun was on His right hand,
And the moon was on His left;

The stars were clustered about His head,
And the earth was under His feet.
And God walked, and where He trod
His footsteps hollowed the valleys out
And bulged the mountains up.

Then He stopped and looked and saw
That the earth was hot and barren.
So God stepped over to the edge of the
world
And He spat out the seven seas;
He batted His eyes and the lightnings
flashed;
He clapped His hands and the thunders
rolled;
And the waters above the earth came down,
The cooling waters came down.

Then the green grass sprouted,
And the little red flowers blossomed,
The pine tree pointed his finger to the
sky,
And the oak spread out his arms;
The lakes cuddled down in the hollows
of the ground,
And the rivers ran down to the sea;
And God smiled again,
And the rainbow appeared,
And curled itself around His shoulder.

Then God raised His arm and He waved
His hand
Over the sea and over the land,
And He said, *"Bring forth! Bring forth!"*
And quicker than God could drop His
hand,
Fishes and fowls
And beasts and birds
Swam the rivers and the seas,

Roamed the forests and the woods,
And split the air with their wings,
And God said, *"That's good!"*

Then God walked around
And God looked around
On all that He had made.
He looked at His sun,
He looked at His moon,
And He looked at His little stars;
He looked on His world
With all its living things,
And God said, *"I'm lonely still."*

Then God sat down
On the side of a hill where He could
think;
By a deep, wide river He sat down;
With His head in His hands,
God thought and thought,
Till He thought, *"I'll make me a man!"*

Up from the bed of the river
God scooped the clay;
And by the bank of the river
He kneeled Him down;
And there the great God Almighty,
Who lit the sun and fixed it in the sky,
Who flung the stars to the most far corner
of the night,
Who rounded the earth in the middle of
His hand—
This Great God,
Like a mammy bending over her baby,
Kneeled down in the dust
Toiling over a lump of clay
Till He shaped it in His own image;
Then into it He blew the breath of life,
And man became a living soul.
Amen. Amen.

Negroes had need of prayer and music to lift their spirits. Even on humanely run plantations, slaves had to live with the constant fear that hard times might come and their kind master, whose only free-and-clear assets were often his slaves, would be forced to sell some of them "down the river" to make ends meet. Their new home often made the one they were forced to leave seem like Heaven. If they felt too sick to work, they might receive the tender care described below by the famous nineteenth-century actress Fanny Kemble, in her recollections of the time she spent as the wife of a Georgia slaveowner on a supposedly model plantation.

A "HOSPITAL" TO STAY AWAY FROM

from "Journal of a Residence on a Georgian Plantation in 1838–1839" by Frances Anne Kemble

In the afternoon I made my first visit to the hospital of the estate, and found it, as indeed I find everything else here, in a far worse state even than the wretched establishments on the Rice Island dignified by that name; so miserable a place for the purpose to which it was dedicated I could not have imagined on a property belonging to Christian owners. The floor (which was not boarded, but merely the damp hard earth itself) was strewn with wretched women, who, but for their moans of pain and uneasy restless motions, might very well have each been taken for a mere heap of filthy rags. The chimney refusing passage to the smoke from the pine-wood fire, it puffed out in clouds through the room, where it circled and hung, only gradually oozing away through the windows which were so well adapted to the purpose that there was not a single whole pane of glass in them. My eyes, unaccustomed to the turbid atmosphere, smarted and watered and refused to distinguish at first the different dismal forms from which cries and wails assailed me in every corner of the place. By degrees I was able to endure for a few minutes what they were condemned to live their hours and days of suffering and sickness through; and, having given what comfort kind words and promises of help in more substantial forms could convey, I went on to what seemed a yet more wretched abode of wretchedness. This was a room where there was no fire because there was no chimney and where the holes made for windows had no panes or glasses in them. The shutters being closed, the place was so dark that, on first entering it, I was afraid to stir lest I should fall over some of the deplorable creatures extended upon the floor. As soon as they perceived me, one cry of "Oh, missis!" rang through the darkness, and it really seemed to me as if I was never to exhaust the pity and amazement and disgust which this receptacle of suffering humanity was to excite in me. . . .

I wandered home, stumbling with crying as I went, and feeling so utterly miserable that I really hardly saw where I was going.

Enduring conditions like these, it's little wonder that Negroes often expressed in their work songs and spirituals a veiled but deeply felt yearning for freedom on earth rather than jubilee in Heaven . . .

133

GO DOWN, MOSES

Anonymous

When Israel was in Egypt's land,
   Let my people go;
Oppressed so hard they could not stand,
   Let my people go.

Chorus:
Go down, Moses,
   Way down in Egypt land,
Tell old Pha-roh,
   Let my people go.

Thus spoke the Lord, bold Moses said,
   Let my people go;
If not I'll smite your first-born dead,
   Let my people go.

No more shall they in bondage toil,
   Let my people go;
Let them come out with Egypt's spoil,
   Let my people go.

In the early days, Southern Negroes were sometimes permitted to work overtime and buy their freedom. But as slavery became more repressive, this practice was discouraged, and the lot of a "free" Negro in the South was made intolerable. The only way a Negro could gain true liberty was through the grave—or by running away in an attempt to reach the free territory. To discourage runaways, slaveowners supported teams of trained men and bloodhounds, and were generally ready to form mounted posses themselves to help a neighbor get back his missing "property."

If a runaway slave were fortunate, he might elude bloodhounds and posses long enough to make contact with the Underground Railroad. This was an informal network of secret hiding places and transportation facilities (begun in the 1820s by Quakers and others who opposed slavery), by means of which a runaway was spirited northward to freedom. Many owners of small farms in the East and Midwest—"Minuteman" stock and strong believers in democratic freedom—permitted their homes to be used as "stations" on the Underground Railroad.

THE RUNAWAY SLAVE CAME TO MY HOUSE

from "Song of Myself" by Walt Whitman

The runaway slave came to my house and
   stopt outside,
I heard his motions crackling the twigs of
   the woodpile,
Through the swung half-door of the kitchen
   I saw him limpsy and weak,
And went where he sat on a log and led him
   in and assured him,
And brought water and fill'd a tub for his
   sweated body and bruis'd feet,
And gave him a room that enter'd from my
   own, and gave him some coarse clean
   clothes,
And remember perfectly well his revolving
   eyes and his awkwardness,
And remember putting plasters on the galls
   of his neck and ankles;
He staid with me a week before he was re-
   cuperated and pass'd north,
I had him sit next me at table, my fire-lock
   lean'd in the corner.

The North had originally compromised with slavery in the framing of the Constitution (back in 1787), hoping that it would be contained within a few Southern states and gradually—under the weight of moral opinion—wither away. Instead, it spread like a cancer into the new Western territories as Southern senators dominated the Senate from the 1820s on . . . Frustrated by the "fence-straddling" wheeling and dealing of the two major political parties (Whigs and Democrats) on the issue, militant antislavery groups formed their own splinter parties —the Liberty (1840) and later the Free Soil party (1848). "Stop the extension of this evil system!" was their rallying cry. The South retorted that it was a "necessary" evil protected by the Constitution; what was good for the South was good for the whole country and the North had better muzzle its Abolitionists or else! There were already dark mutterings about secession in the 1840s, and men feared for the future of the nation. In such an atmosphere, Longfellow wrote his long poem "The Building of the Ship," ending with this famous appeal for the preservation of the Union.

THOU, TOO, SAIL ON, O SHIP OF STATE!

by Henry Wadsworth Longfellow

Thou, too, sail on, O Ship of State!
Sail on, O *Union,* strong and great!
Humanity with all its fears,
With all the hopes of future years,
Is hanging breathless on thy fate!
We know what Master laid thy keel,
What Workmen wrought thy ribs of steel,

Who made each mast, and sail, and rope,
What anvils rang, what hammers beat,
In what a forge, and what a heat
Were shaped the anchors of thy hope!
Fear not each sudden sound and shock,
'Tis of the wave and not the rock;
'Tis but the flapping of the sail,
And not a rent made by the gale!
In spite of rock and tempest's roar,
In spite of false lights on the shore,
Sail on, nor fear to breast the sea!
Our hearts, our hopes, are all with thee,
Our hearts, our hopes, our prayers, our
    tears,
Our faith triumphant o'er our fears,
Are all with thee—are all with thee!

But the Union was in serious trouble. The territories acquired in the Mexican War brought the issue of slavery to a head. Texas was already in as a slave state, and Henry Clay proposed the following compromise for the other territories: California should be admitted as a free state, in return for a more stringent fugitive slave law. The question of slavery in New Mexico and Utah should be left up to the people living there (the "popular sovereignty" theory). "A shameful compromise!" shouted Northern liberals. They confidently waited for the New England champion, Daniel Webster, to stand up in the Senate and blast it for a Devil's bargain. He stood up all right—to use all his marvelous powers of oratory in urging its acceptance . . . As a result, the Compromise of 1850 became law.

The Fugitive Slave Law, which was part of the Compromise, said in effect that a slaveowner could walk into a free state, claim any escaped slave that caught his fancy as his runaway property, and haul him back down South with the approval of the Federal courts. This law caused great indignation among Northern abolitionists, who expressed how they felt in hymns such as this.

THE ABOLITIONIST HYMN

Anonymous

We ask not that the slave should lie
As lies his master: at his ease,
Beneath a silken canopy,
Or in the shade of blooming trees.

We ask not "Eye for Eye" that all
Who forge the chain and ply the whip
Should feel their torture, while the thrall
Should wield the scourge of mastership.

We mourn not that the man should toil:
'Tis Nature's need, 'tis God's decree;
But—let the hand that tills the soil,
Be, like the wind that fans it, free.

The law also helped inspire Harriet Beecher Stowe to write her famous antislavery novel, *Uncle Tom's Cabin*. Militant Negroes today understandably have little patience with Uncle Tom's meek acceptance of the injustices piled on his old gray head; but Eliza crossing the ice, Topsy who just "growed," the saintly Little Eva, the magnificently evil Simon Legree—these are characters who once discovered are never forgotten. While the author's main characters are undoubtedly overdrawn, the true power of the book stems from scenes such as the following, which, although fiction, Mrs. Stowe was careful to base on documented fact.

SLAVES FOR SALE

from "Uncle Tom's Cabin"
by Harriet Beecher Stowe

About eleven o'clock the next day, a mixed throng was gathered around the court-house steps—smoking, chewing, spitting, swearing, and conversing, according to their respective tastes and turns—waiting for the auction to commence. The men and women to be sold sat in a group apart, talking in a low tone to each other. The woman who had been advertised by the name of Hagar was a regular African in feature and figure. She might have been sixty, but was older than that by hard work and disease, was partially blind, and somewhat crippled with rheumatism. By her side stood her only remaining son, Albert, a bright-looking little fellow of fourteen years. The boy was the only survivor of a large family, who had been successively sold away from her to a southern market. The mother held on to him with both her shaking hands, and eyed with intense trepidation every one who walked up to examine him.

"Don't be 'feared, Aunt Hagar," said the oldest of the men. "I spoke to mas'r Thomas 'bout it, and he thought he might manage to sell you in a lot both together."

"Dey needn't call me worn out yet," said she, lifting her shaking hands. "I can cook yet, and scrub, and scour—I'm wuth a buying, if I do come cheap;—tell 'em dat ar—you *tell* 'em," she added, earnestly.

Haley [a slave trader] here forced his way into the group, walked up to the old man, pulled his mouth open and looked in, felt of his teeth, made him stand and straighten himself, bend his back, and perform various evolutions to show his muscles; and then passed on to the next, and put him through the same trial. Walking up last to the boy, he felt of his arms, straightened his hands and looked at his fingers, and made him jump, to show his agility.

"He ain't gwine to be sold widout me!" said the old woman, with passionate eagerness; "he and I goes in a lot togedder; I's rail strong yet, Mas'r, and can do heaps o' work—heaps on it, Mas'r."

"On plantation?" said Haley, with a contemptuous glance. "Likely story!" and, as if satisfied with his examination, he walked out and looked, and stood with his hands in his pockets, his cigar in his mouth, and his hat cocked on one side, ready for action.

"What think of 'em?" said a man who had been following Haley's examination, as if to make up his own mind from it.

"Wal," said Haley, spitting, "I shall put in, I think, for the youngerly ones and the boy."

"They want to sell the boy and the old woman together," said the man.

"Find it a tight pull;—why, she's an old rack o' bones—not worth her salt."

"You wouldn't, then?" said the man.

"Anybody'd be a fool 't would. She's half blind, crooked with rheumatism, and foolish to boot."

"Some buys up these yer old critturs, and ses there's a sight more wear in 'em than a body'd think," said the man, reflectively.

"No go, 't all," said Haley; "wouldn't take her for a present—fact—I've *seen,* now."

"Wal, 't is kinder pity, now, not to buy her with her son, her heart seems so sot on him—s'pose they fling her in cheap?"

"Them that's got money to spend that ar way, it's all well enough. I shall bid off on that ar boy for a plantation-hand;—wouldn't be bothered with her, no way—not if they'd give her to me," said Haley.

"She'll take on desp't," said the man.

"Nat'lly, she will," said the trader, coolly.

The conversation was here interrupted by a busy hum in the audience; and the auctioneer, a short, bustling, important fellow, elbowed his way into the crowd. The old woman drew in her breath, and caught instinctively at her son.

"Keep close to yer mammy, Albert, close

—dey'll put us up togedder," she said.

"Oh, mammy, I'm 'feared they won't," said the boy.

"Dey must, child; I can't live, no ways, if they don't!" said the old creature, vehemently.

The stentorian tones of the auctioneer, calling out to clear the way, now announced that the sale was about to commence. A place was cleared, and the bidding began. The different men on the list were soon knocked off at prices which showed a pretty brisk demand in the market: two of them fell to Haley.

"Come now, young un," said the auctioneer, giving the boy a touch with his hammer, "be up and show your springs, now."

"Put us two up togedder, togedder—do please, Mas'r," said the old woman, holding fast to her boy.

"Be off," said the man, gruffly, pushing her hands away; "you come last. Now darkey, spring;" and, with the word, he pushed the boy toward the block, while a deep, heavy groan rose behind him. The boy paused, and looked back; but there was no time to stay, and, dashing the tears from his large, bright eyes, he was up in a moment.

His fine figure, alert limbs, and bright face raised an instant competition, and half a dozen bids simultaneously met the ear of the auctioneer. Anxious, half frightened, he looked from side to side, as he heard the clatter of contending bids—now here, now there—till the hammer fell. Haley had got him. He was pushed from the block toward his new master, but stopped one moment, and looked back, when his poor old mother, trembling in every limb, held out her shaking hands toward him.

"Buy me too, Mas'r, for de dear Lord's sake!—buy me—I shall die if you don't!"

"You'll die if I do, that's the kink of it," said Haley, "no!" And he turned on his heel . . .

Uncle Tom's Cabin sold 300,000 copies in the first year of its publication. Its world-wide impact may be illustrated by this unusual letter sent many years later to Mrs. Stowe by Anna Leonowens, an English lady employed as governess in the family of the King of Siam. (You may remember her as Anna in *The King and I.*)

UNCLE TOM IN SIAM

Dear Madam—The following is the fact, the result of the translation of *Uncle Tom's Cabin* into the Siamese language, by my friend Sonn Klean, a lady of high rank at the court of Siam . . . She would read it over and over again, though she knew all the characters by heart and spoke of them as if she had known them all her life. On the 3rd of January, 1867, she voluntarily liberated all her slaves, men, women and children, one hundred and thirty in all, saying, "I am wishful to be good like Harriet Beecher Stowe . . ." and her sweet voice trembled with love and music whenever she spoke of the lovely American lady who had taught her as even Buddha had taught kings to respect the rights of her fellow-creatures.

I remain,

Yours very truly,

A. H. Leonowens

As well as touching the consciences of whites, the book influenced the actions of at least one Negro slave. The following remarkable account is included in the reminiscences of a leader in the Underground Railroad.

A SLAVE TURNS FICTION INTO FACT

from "The Reminiscences of Levi Coffin"

At another time when I was in the city accompanied by my wife and daughter, Hiram S. Gillmore, a noted abolitionist and one of my particular friends, asked me if I knew of any person in from the country with a wagon who would take a fugitive slave girl out to a place of safety. He then gave me the outlines of her story. She had come from Boone County, Kentucky, having run away because she learned that she was to be sold to the far South. Knowing that she would be pursued and probably retaken if she started northward immediately, she conceived a plan like that adopted by Cassie and Emmeline when they ran away from Legree in *Uncle Tom's Cabin*. She hid herself in the interior of a large straw pile near her master's barn, having previously arranged apertures for air and a winding passage with concealed entrance by which her fellow servants who brought her food could enter. Here she remained six weeks, while her master with a posse of men scoured the country in search of her. Like Cassie, who looked from her hiding place in the garret and heard the discomfited Legree swearing at his ill luck as he returned from the unsuccessful pursuit, this young woman could hear in her hiding place in the straw pile the noises of horses' feet and the sound of talking as her master and his men returned from their fruitless search for her. When the hunt was over, she stole out and made her way safely to the Ohio River, crossed in a skiff, and reached the house of a family of abolitionists in Cincinnati, where she was kindly received and furnished with comfortable clothing.

Before the middle of the century, England and other civilized countries had totally rejected slavery. However, mounting opposition merely made the South shriller in its defense of the "peculiar institution" and more grimly determined than ever to spread it beyond its present boundaries. Southern spokesmen—such as John C. Calhoun—not only misused the Bible to imply that God Himself was a staunch advocate of slavery; they dared to invoke Thomas Jefferson's States' Rights theory in support of it—Jefferson, who had freed his own slaves, fought to include an implied condemnation of slavery in the Declaration of Independence, and dedicated his life to battling all forms of tyranny over the bodies and souls of men! In 1854, Senator Stephen A. Douglas of Illinois engineered the Kansas-Nebraska Bill, which threw open these territories to slavery, provided the people who settled there voted for it ("Popular Sovereignty" again). Slavery and antislavery settlers poured in and fought each other for control. The result was "Bleeding Kansas," a miniature reflection of the Civil War to come. Feelings in both sections of the country were approaching the boiling point. Northerners passed state laws to nullify the Fugitive Slave

Law, while Southerners burned abolitionists in effigy. It took the army, the navy, the militia and the police to drag the runaway Anthony Burns back to slavery from a Boston mob that tried to rescue him. In 1855, Abraham Lincoln, now a lawyer with political ambitions, who had served one term in Congress, wrote the following letter to a Southern friend, Joshua Speed. It illustrates the widening gulf between the best minds in the North and South.

LINCOLN WRITES A REVEALING LETTER

from Abraham Lincoln's Letter to Joshua Speed, 24 August, 1855

You know I dislike slavery and you fully admit the abstract wrong of it. So far there is no cause of difference. But you say that sooner than yield your legal right to the slave, especially at the bidding of those who are not themselves interested, you would see the Union dissolved. . . .

You say that if Kansas fairly votes herself a free state, as a Christian you will rejoice at it. All decent slave holders talk that way, and I do not doubt their candour. But they never vote that way. Although in a private letter or conversation you will express your preference that Kansas shall be free, you will vote for no man for Congress who would say the same thing publicly. No such man could be elected from any district in a slave state. . . . The slave breeders and slave traders are a small, odious and detested class among you, and are as completely your masters as you are masters of your own Negroes. . . .

After "Bleeding Kansas," the fence-straddling Whig party died. Out of its ashes—and those of the Free Soilers—arose the new Republican party, dedicated to promoting the interests of the industrial North and preventing the further extension of slavery. Its first presidential candidate, the explorer John C. Frémont, scared the South by almost winning a close election in 1856. However, slavery interests were still powerful. A Southern-dominated Supreme Court handed down the famous Dred Scott decision in 1857, which not only stated that a former slave had no rights under the law, but offered the opinion (which had nothing to do with the case before it) that Congress had no right whatsoever to limit the spread of slavery in the territories. The decision was denounced in the Northern press and by such abolitionist papers as the white William Lloyd Garrison's *The Liberator* and the Negro Frederick Douglass' *North Star*. The Republican party girded itself for new battles. In 1858, Lincoln was the Republican nominee for senator from Illinois, running against the Democrat Stephen Douglas. At the party convention, he delivered his famous "house divided" speech, containing the following statements.

A HOUSE DIVIDED

from a Speech by Abraham Lincoln, 16 June, 1858

"A house divided against itself cannot stand." I believe this government cannot endure permanently half slave and half free. I do not expect the Union to be dissolved— I do not expect the house to fall—but I do expect it will cease to be divided. It will become all one thing, or all the other. Either the opponents of slavery will arrest the further spread of it, and place it where the public mind shall rest in the belief that it is in the course of ultimate extinction; or its advocates will push it forward till it shall become alike lawful in all the States, old as well as new, North as well as South.

During the campaign, the tall, gangling Lincoln engaged in a series of seven debates with Douglas, the fiery "Little Giant." Audiences would arrive prepared to laugh at Lincoln's awkwardness and high, nasal voice— but stayed to applaud his wit, his shrewdness, his warm humanity and incisive grasp of issues. Lincoln lost out as senator, but emerged as a figure of Presidential timbre. Meanwhile, events were moving swiftly toward a climax. In October, 1859, a fanatical abolitionist named John Brown invaded Virginia with twenty-one followers and captured the United States Armory, planning to use the arms to free slaves. He was captured by a force of Marines (under Colonel Robert E. Lee), tried for treason, and sentenced to death. Although an unbalanced, violent man, Brown showed an impressive dignity in court, where he spoke the following words.

JOHN BROWN'S SPEECH

Quoted by James Redpath in "The Public Life of Captain John Brown"

This court acknowledges, as I suppose, the validity of the law of God. I see a book kissed here which I suppose to be the Bible, or at least the New Testament. That teaches me that all things whatsoever I would that men should do to me, I should do even so to them. It teaches me, further, to "remember them that are in bonds, as bound with them." I endeavor to act up to that instruction. I say, I am yet too young to understand that God is any respecter of persons. I believe that to have interfered as I have done—as I have always freely admitted I have done—in behalf of His despised poor, was not wrong but right. Now if it is deemed necessary that I should forfeit my life for the furtherance of the ends of justice and mingle my blood further with the blood of my children and with the blood of millions in this slave country whose rights are disregarded by wicked, cruel, and unjust enactments—I submit; so let it be done!

John Brown's raid stirred the South's deepest fears of slave uprisings—something they had good reason to fear. Planters noted that the North hailed Brown as a martyr. Their hatred of abolitionist sentiment drove them to irrational political extremes. Even Douglas, with his doctrine of popular sovereignty, wasn't enough for them now. They no longer wanted people in territories to be able to choose whether or not they would have slavery; they wanted slavery established in *all* new territories, protected by Federal law and Federal force. When Douglas became the Presidential candidate of the Northern Democrats in 1860, the Southern wing split off with its own candidate, fatally weakening the party.

Meanwhile, the Republicans were having their own convention, in a huge wooden "wigwam" in Chicago. The main contenders for the nomination were William H. Seward of New York—and Abraham Lincoln. A journalist of the day has left us a colorful description of what occurred.

"OLD ABE" IS NOISILY NOMINATED

from "Caucuses of 1860" by Murat Halstead

Mr. Evarts of New York nominated Mr. Seward. Mr. Judd of Illinois nominated Mr. Lincoln.

Everybody felt that the fight was between them and yelled accordingly.

The applause when Mr. Evarts named Seward was enthusiastic. When Mr. Judd named Lincoln, the response was prodigious, rising and raging far beyond the Seward shriek. . . . It now became the Seward men to make another effort, and when Blair of Michigan seconded his nomination,

At once there rose so wild a yell,
Within that dark and narrow dell;
As all the fiends from heaven that fell
Had pealed the banner cry of hell.

The effect was startling. Hundreds of persons stopped their ears in pain. . . . No Comanches, no panthers, ever struck a higher note or gave screams with more infernal intensity. . . .

Now the Lincoln men had to try it again, and as Mr. Delano of Ohio on behalf "of a portion of the delegation of that state" seconded the nomination of Lincoln, the uproar was beyond description. Imagine all the hogs ever slaughtered in Cincinnati giving their death squeals together, a score of

big steam whistles going (steam at a hundred and sixty pounds per inch), and you conceive something of the same nature. I thought the Seward yell could not be surpassed, but the Lincoln boys were clearly ahead and, feeling their victory, as there was a lull in the storm, took deep breaths all round and gave a concentrated shriek that was positively awful, and accompanied it with stamping that made every plant and pillar in the building quiver. . . . [Lincoln was nominated after the third ballot.]

A man who had been on the roof and was engaged in communicating the results of the ballotings to the mighty mass of outsiders now demanded, by gestures at the skylight over the stage, to know what had happened. One of the secretaries, with a tally sheet in his hands, shouted: "Fire the salute! Abe Lincoln is nominated!"

The city was wild with delight. The "Old Abe" men formed processions and bore rails through the streets. Torrents of liquor were poured down the hoarse throats of the multitude. A hundred guns were fired from the top of the Tremont House.

I left the city on the night train on the Fort Wayne and Chicago road. The train consisted of eleven cars, every seat full and people standing in the aisles and corners. I never before saw a company of persons so prostrated by continued excitement. The Lincoln men were not able to respond to the cheers which went up along the road for "Old Abe." They had not only done their duty in that respect, but exhausted their capacity. At every station where there was a village, until after two o'clock, there were tar barrels burning, drums beating, boys carry-

ing rails, and guns, great and small, banging away. The weary passengers were allowed no rest, but plagued by the thundering jar of cannon, the clamor of drums, the glare of bonfires, and the whooping of the boys, who were delighted with the idea of a candidate for the Presidency who thirty years ago split rails on the Sangamon River—classic stream now and forevermore—and whose neighbors named him "honest."

Lincoln's nomination was followed by his election as sixteenth President of the not-very United States of America. South Carolina promptly seceded, other Southern states followed, and the Confederacy was born. Why did the Southern states secede? They had nothing to fear from Lincoln; he wasn't threatening at that point to take their "property" away. However, he was against the further *extension* of slavery, and the South had reached the emotional point where they

felt it was "all or nothing at all." Lincoln had said "This government cannot permanently endure half slave and half free." "We agree," the South replied in effect, "so we'll form our own country where we don't have to be on the defensive or contend with those depraved abolitionists all the time; where we are surrounded and governed by gentlemen who believe in the gracious Southern way of life" (including slavery). "Those Northern rascals are growing stronger every year. Now or never is the time to strike the blow for Southern independence and liberty." ("Liberty" here is our old friend slavery again, in a disguise that would confuse anybody but an ante-bellum Southern planter.)

Thus, as the first uneasy months of 1861 crept forward, a nation of thirty-one and a half million people slowly split in two, and nobody seemed able to stop it. Lincoln offered the South guarantees and appealed to it to return peacefully to the Union. Here are the closing paragraphs of his first Inaugural Address.

LINCOLN APPEALS TO THE SOUTH TO RETURN

from Abraham Lincoln's First Inaugural Address

In your hands, my dissatisfied fellow countrymen, and not in mine, is the momentous issue of civil war. The government will not assail you. You can have no conflict without being yourselves the aggressors. You have no oath registered in heaven to destroy the government, while I shall have the most solemn one to "preserve, protect, and defend" it.

I am loath to close. We are not enemies, but friends. We must not be enemies. Though passion may have strained, it must not break, our bonds of affection. The mystic chords of memory, stretching from every battlefield and patriot grave to every living heart and hearthstone all over this broad land, will yet swell the chorus of the Union when again touched, as surely they will be, by the better angels of our nature.

Only a few souls at this point shared Lincoln's hope of invoking the "mystic chords of memory"—the sense that all Americans, North and South, were united by a common heritage and destiny as the hope of mankind . . . The poet Walt Whitman was one of the few. Let's join him now as he sweeps us across the face of a great nation trembling on the brink of civil war, recording the varied rhythms of its people, still dreaming a dream of peace.

THE PURE CONTRALTO SINGS

from "Song of Myself" by Walt Whitman

The pure contralto sings in the organ loft,
The carpenter dresses his plank, the tongue
    of his foreplane whistles its wild ascending lisp,
The married and unmarried children ride
    home to the Thanksgiving dinner,
The pilot seizes the king-pin, he heaves down
    with a strong arm,
The mate stands braced in the whale-boat,
    lance and harpoon are ready,
The duck-shooter walks by silent and cautious stretches,
The deacons are ordain'd with cross'd hands
    at the altar,
The spinning-girl retreats and advances to
    the hum of the big wheel . . .

* * *

The quadroon girl is sold at the auction-stand, the drunkard nods by the barroom stove,
The machinist rolls up his sleeves, the policeman travels his beat, the gate-keeper
    marks who pass,
The young fellow drives the express-wagon
    (I love him, though I do not know
    him);
The half-breed straps on his light boots to
    compete in the race,
The western turkey-shooting draws old and
    young, some lean on their rifles, some
    sit on logs,
Out from the crowd steps the marksman,
    takes his position, levels his piece;
The groups of newly-come immigrants cover
    the wharf or levee,

As the woolly-pates hoe in the sugar-field,
the overseer views them from his saddle,
The bugle calls in the ball-room, the gentlemen run for their partners, the dancers
bow to each other,
The youth lies awake in the cedar-roof'd garret and harks to the musical rain . . .

* * *

Seasons pursuing each other, the plougher
ploughs, the mower mows, and the win-
ter-grain falls in the ground;
Off on the lakes the pike-fisher watches and
waits by the hole in the frozen surface,
The stumps stand thick round the clearing,
the squatter strikes deep with his axe,
Flatboatmen make fast towards dusk near
the cotton-wood or pecan-trees,
Coon-seekers go through the regions of the
Red river or through those drain'd by
the Tennessee, or through those of the
Arkansas,
Torches shine in the dark that hangs on the
Chattahooche or Altamahaw,
Patriarchs sit at supper with sons and grand-
sons and great-grandsons around them,
In walls of adobie, in canvas tents, rest hunt-
ers and trappers after their day's sport,
The city sleeps and the country sleeps,
The living sleep for their time, the dead sleep
for their time,
The old husband sleeps by his wife and the
young husband sleeps by his wife;
And these tend inward to me, and I tend
outward to them,
And such as it is to be of these more or less
I am,
And of these one and all I weave the song of
myself.

Whitman's and Lincoln's mystic vision of American brotherhood was soon obscured by gunsmoke. The South had committed it-self to the Confederacy. Already it was thinking of expanding further southward to annex Cuba and Mexico as gigantic slave-breeding farms. Federal forts in Southern territory were called upon to surrender. Fort Sumter, in Charleston Bay, South Carolina, refused. Confederate forces besieged it. Lincoln dispatched reinforcements and sup-plies by ship. On April 12, 1861, Confed-erate batteries commenced firing on the fort. Two days later, it surrendered. Here is the report of the action sent by its commander to President Lincoln.

THE AMERICAN FLAG DEPARTS FROM FORT SUMTER

Having defended Fort Sumter for thirty-four hours, until the quarters were entirely burned, the main gates destroyed by fire, the gorge walls seriously impaired, the magazine surrounded by flames and its door closed from the effects of the heat, four barrels and three cartridges of powder only being avail-able and no provisions remaining but pork, I accepted terms of evacuation offered by General Beauregard (being the same offered by him on the 11th instant, prior to the com-mencement of hostilities) and marched out of the fort on Sunday afternoon, the 14th in-stant, with colors flying and drums beating, bringing away company and private prop-erty, and saluting my flag with fifty guns.

Robert Anderson
Major First Artillery

BEAT! BEAT! DRUMS!

from "Drum-Taps" by Walt Whitman

Beat! beat! drums!—blow! bugles! blow!
Through the windows—through doors—
    burst like a ruthless force,
Into the solemn church, and scatter the con-
    gregation,
Into the school where the scholar is studying;
Leave not the bridegroom quiet—no happi-
    ness must he have now with his bride,
Nor the peaceful farmer any peace, plough-
    ing his field or gathering his grain,
So fierce you whirr and pound you drums—
    so shrill you bugles blow.

Beat! beat! drums!—blow! bugles! blow!
Over the traffic of cities—over the rumble of
    wheels in the streets;
Are beds prepared for sleepers at night in
    the houses? no sleepers must sleep in
    those beds,
No bargainers' bargains by day—no brokers
    or speculators—would they continue?
Would the talkers be talking? would the
    singer attempt to sing?
Would the lawyer rise in the court to state
    his case before the judge?
Then rattle quicker, heavier drums—you
    bugles wilder blow.

147

Beat! beat! drums!—blow! bugles! blow!
Make no parley—stop for no expostulation,
Mind not the timid—mind not the weeper
    or prayer,
Mind not the old man beseeching the young
    man,
Let not the child's voice be heard, nor the
    mother's entreaties,
Make even the trestles to shake the dead
    where they lie awaiting the hearses,
So strong you thump O terrible drums—so
    loud you bugles blow.

Lincoln called for volunteers. Jefferson Davis called for volunteers.

Young men in New England and New York kissed their wives and parents good-by, put on blue uniforms, and marched off, singing "John Brown's body lies a-mould'ring in the grave . . ."

Young men in South Carolina and Virginia kissed their wives and parents good-by, put on gray uniforms, and marched off, whistling *Dixie*.

The Civil War had begun.

The Bettmann Archive

PART SIX

The Blue
and
the Gray

ONCE the War between the States had actually started, the young men who streamed toward the recruiting stations of both sides didn't concern themselves much with the pros and cons of slavery, States' Rights, high and low tariffs . . . Their heads were filled with dreams of trumpet blasts, victorious charges against overwhelming odds, bemedalled honor . . . "Who'll fight for 'Old Glory'!" "Who'll defend the 'Stars and Bars'!" Many of them marched off to war as though it were some bright, new game.

To the wives and mothers left behind, however, war would come to seem anything but a game.

WAR IS KIND

by Stephen Crane

Do not weep, maiden, for war is kind.
Because your lover threw wild hands toward
   the sky
And the affrighted steed ran on alone,
Do not weep.
War is kind.

Hoarse, booming drums of the regiment,
Little souls who thirst for fight,
These men were born to drill and die.
The unexplained glory flies above them,
Great is the battle-god, great, and his
   kingdom—
A field where a thousand corpses lie.

Do not weep, babe, for war is kind.
Because your father tumbled in the yellow
    trenches,
Raged at his breast, gulped and died,
Do not weep.
War is kind.

    Swift blazing flag of the regiment,
    Eagle with crest of red and gold,
    These men were born to drill and die.
    Point for them the virtue of slaughter,
    Make plain to them the excellence of
      killing
    And a field where a thousand corpses lie.

Mother whose heart hung humble as a button
On the bright splendid shroud of your son,
Do not weep.
War is kind.

A young recruit would await his first battle with a confusion of thoughts and feelings, swinging constantly back and forth between self-doubt . . . heroic fantasy . . . fear of cowardice . . . The waiting was the worst part. If only the battle would come, then all these speculations could stop; then he would know the truth about himself. Nowhere have these feelings been set down more vividly than in Stephen Crane's magnificent Civil War novel, *The Red Badge of Courage*.

A YOUTH'S FIRST BATTLE

from "The Red Badge of Courage"
by Stephen Crane

There were moments of waiting. The youth thought of the village street at home before the arrival of the circus parade on a day in the spring. He remembered how he had stood, a small, thrillful boy, prepared to follow the dingy lady upon the white horse, or the band in its faded chariot. He saw the yellow road, the lines of expectant people, and the sober houses. He particularly remembered an old fellow who used to sit upon a cracker box in front of the store and feign to despise such exhibitions. A thousand details of color and form surged in his mind. The old fellow upon the cracker box appeared in middle prominence.

Some one cried, "Here they come!"

There was rustling and muttering among the men. They displayed a feverish desire to have every possible cartridge ready to their hands. The boxes were pulled around into various positions and adjusted with great care. It was as if seven hundred new bonnets were being tried on.

The tall soldier, having prepared his rifle, produced a red handkerchief of some kind. He was engaged in knitting it about his throat with exquisite attention to its position, when the cry was repeated up and down the line in a muffled roar of sound.

"Here they come! Here they come!" Gun locks clicked.

Across the smoke-infested fields came a brown swarm of running men who were giving shrill yells. They came on, stooping and swinging their rifles at all angles. A flag, tilted forward, sped near the front.

As he caught sight of them, the youth was momentarily startled by a thought that perhaps his gun was not loaded. He stood trying to rally his faltering intellect so that he might recollect the moment when he had loaded, but he could not.

A hatless general pulled his dripping horse to a stand near the colonel of the

304th. He shook his fist in the other's face. "You've got to hold 'em back!" he shouted, savagely; "you've got to hold 'em back!"

In his agitation the colonel began to stammer. "A-all r-right, General, all right, by Gawd! We-we'll do our—we-we'll d-d-do— do our best, General." The general made a passionate gesture and galloped away. The colonel, perchance to relieve his feelings, began to scold like a wet parrot. The youth, turning swiftly to make sure that the rear was unmolested, saw the commander regarding his men in a highly resentful manner, as if he regretted above everything his association with them.

The man at the youth's elbow was mumbling, as if to himself: "Oh, we're in for it now! Oh, we're in for it now!"

The captain of the company had been pacing excitedly to and fro in the rear. He coaxed in schoolmistress fashion, as to a congregation of boys with primers. His talk was an endless repetition. "Reserve your fire, boys—don't shoot till I tell you—save your fire—wait till they get close up—don't be damned fools—"

Perspiration streamed down the youth's face, which was soiled like that of a weeping urchin. He frequently, with a nervous movement, wiped his eyes with his coat sleeve. His mouth was still a little way open.

He got the one glance at the foe-swarming field in front of him and instantly ceased to debate the question of his piece being loaded. Before he was ready to begin—before he had announced to himself that he was about to fight—he threw the obedient, well-balanced rifle into position and fired a first wild shot. Directly he was working at his weapon like an automatic affair.

He suddenly lost concern for himself and forgot to look at a menacing fate. He became not a man but a member. He felt that something of which he was a part—a regiment, an army, a cause, or a country—was in a crisis. He was welded into a common personality which was dominated by a single desire. For some moments he could not flee, no more than a little finger can commit a revolution from a hand.

If he had thought the regiment was about to be annihilated perhaps he could have amputated himself from it. But its noise gave him assurance. The regiment was like a firework that, once ignited, proceeds superior to circumstances until its blazing vitality fades. It wheezed and banged with a mighty power. He pictured the ground before it as strewn with the discomfited.

There was a consciousness always of the presence of his comrades about him. He felt the subtle battle brotherhood more potent even than the cause for which they were fighting. It was a mysterious fraternity born of the smoke and danger of death.

He was at a task. He was like a carpenter who has made many boxes, making still another box, only there was furious haste in his movements. He, in his thought, was careering off in other places, even as the carpenter who as he works whistles and thinks of his friend or his enemy, his home or a saloon. And these jolted dreams were never perfect to him afterward, but remained a mass of blurred shapes.

Presently he began to feel the effects of the war atmosphere—a blistering sweat, a sensation that his eyeballs were about to crack like hot stones. A burning roar filled his ears.

Following this came a red rage. He developed the acute exasperation of a pestered animal, a well-meaning cow worried by dogs. He had a mad feeling against his rifle, which could only be used against one life at a time. He wished to rush forward and strangle with his fingers. He craved a power that would enable him to make a world-sweeping gesture and brush all back. His impotency appeared to him and made his rage into that of a driven beast.

Buried in the smoke of many rifles, his anger was directed not so much against the men whom he knew were rushing toward him as against the swirling battle phantoms which were choking him, stuffing their smoke robes down his parched throat. He fought frantically for respite for his senses, for air, as a babe being smothered attacks the deadly blankets.

There was a blare of heated rage mingled with a certain expression of intentness on all faces. Many of the men were making low-toned noises with their mouths, and these subdued cheers, snarls, imprecations, prayers, made a wild, barbaric song that went as an undercurrent of sound, strange and chant-like with the resounding chords of the war march. The man at the youth's elbow was babbling. In it there was something soft and tender like the monologue of a babe. The tall soldier was swearing in a loud voice. From his lips came a black procession of curious oaths. Of a sudden another broke out in a querulous way like a man who has mislaid his hat. "Well, why don't they support us? Why don't they send supports? Do they think—"

The youth in his battle sleep heard this as one who dozes hears.

There was a singular absence of heroic poses. The men bending and surging in their haste and rage were in every impossible attitude. The steel ramrods clanked and clanged with incessant din as the men pounded them furiously into the hot rifle barrels. The flaps of the cartridge boxes were all unfastened, and bobbed idiotically with each movement. The rifles, once loaded, were jerked to the shoulder and fired without apparent aim into the smoke or at one of the blurred and shifting forms which, upon the field before the regiment, had been growing larger and larger like puppets under a magician's hand.

The officers, at their intervals, rearward, neglected to stand in picturesque attitudes. They were bobbing to and fro, roaring directions and encouragements. The dimensions of their howls were extraordinary. They expended their lungs with prodigal wills. And often they nearly stood upon their heads in their anxiety to observe the enemy on the other side of the tumbling smoke.

The lieutenant of the youth's company had encountered a soldier who had fled screaming at the first volley of his comrades. Behind the lines these two were acting a little isolated scene. The man was blubbering and staring with sheeplike eyes at the lieutenant, who had seized him by the collar and was pommeling him. He drove him back into the ranks with many blows. The soldier went mechanically, dully, with his animal-like eyes upon the officer. Perhaps there was to him a divinity expressed in the voice of the other—stern, hard, with no reflection of fear in it. He tried to reload his gun, but his shaking hands prevented. The lieutenant was obliged to assist him.

The men dropped here and there like bundles. The captain of the youth's company had been killed in an early part of the action. His body lay stretched out in the position of a tired man resting, but upon his face there was an astonished and sorrowful look, as if he thought some friend had done him an ill turn. The babbling man was grazed by a shot that made the blood stream widely down his face. He clapped both hands to his head. "Oh!" he said, and ran. Another grunted suddenly as if he had been struck by a club in the stomach. He sat down and gazed ruefully. In his eyes there was mute, indefinite reproach. Farther up the line a man, standing behind a tree, had had his knee joint splintered by a ball. Immediately he had dropped his rifle and gripped the tree with both arms. And there he remained, clinging desperately and crying for assistance that he might withdraw his hold upon the tree.

At last an exultant yell went along the quivering line. The firing dwindled from an uproar to a last vindictive popping. As the smoke slowly eddied away, the youth saw that the charge had been repulsed. The enemy were scattered into reluctant groups. He saw a man climb to the top of the fence, straddle the rail, and fire a parting shot. The waves had receded, leaving bits of dark *débris* upon the ground.

Some in the regiment began to whoop frenziedly. Many were silent. Apparently they were trying to contemplate themselves.

After the fever had left his veins, the youth thought that at last he was going to suffocate. He became aware of the foul atmosphere in which he had been struggling. He was grimy and dripping like a laborer in a foundry. He grasped his canteen and took a long swallow of the warmed water.

A sentence with variations went up and down the line. "Well, we've helt 'em back.

We've helt 'em back; derned if we haven't." The men said it blissfully, leering at each other with dirty smiles.

The youth turned to look behind him and off to the right and off to the left. He experienced the joy of a man who at last finds leisure in which to look about him.

Underfoot there were a few ghastly forms motionless. They lay twisted in fantastic contortions. Arms were bent and heads were turned in incredible ways. It seemed that the dead men must have fallen from some great height to get into such positions. They looked to be dumped out upon the ground from the sky.

From a position in the rear of the grove a battery was throwing shells over it. The flash of the guns startled the youth at first. He thought they were aimed directly at him. Through the trees he watched the black figures of the gunners as they worked swiftly and intently. Their labor seemed a complicated thing. He wondered how they could remember its formula in the midst of confusion.

The guns squatted in a row like savage chiefs. They argued with abrupt violence. It was a grim pow-wow. Their busy servants ran hither and thither.

A small procession of wounded men were going drearily toward the rear. It was a flow of blood from the torn body of the brigade.

To the right and to the left were the dark lines of other troops. Far in front he thought he could see lighter masses protruding in points from the forest. They were suggestive of unnumbered thousands.

Once he saw a tiny battery go dashing along the line of the horizon. The tiny riders were beating the tiny horses.

From a sloping hill came the sound of cheerings and clashes. Smoke welled slowly through the leaves.

Batteries were speaking with thunderous oratorical effort. Here and there were flags, the red in the stripes dominating. They splashed bits of warm color upon the dark lines of troops.

The youth felt the old thrill at the sight of the emblem. They were like beautiful birds strangely undaunted in a storm.

As he listened to the din from the hillside, to a deep pulsating thunder that came from afar to the left, and to the lesser clamors which came from many directions, it occurred to him that they were fighting, too, over there, and over there, and over there. Heretofore he had supposed that all the battle was directly under his nose.

As he gazed around him, the youth felt a flash of astonishment at the blue, pure sky and the sun gleaming on the trees and fields. It was surprising that Nature had gone tranquilly on with her golden process in the midst of so much devilment.

Many young recruits died in the First Battle of Bull Run (July 21, 1861) when an invading Northern army was thrown back from Virginia. Many more would die before the war was over . . .

The Civil War was actually a unique combination of the old and the new. It was the last major war in which infantrymen fought with muzzle-loading rifles. It was also the last great war in which calvary played an important part.

CAVALRY CROSSING A FORD

from "Drum-Taps" by Walt Whitman

A line in long array where they wind be-
    twixt green islands,
They take a serpentine course, their arms
    flash in the sun—hark to the musical
    clank,
Behold the silvery river, in it the splashing
    horses loitering stop to drink,
Behold the brown-faced men, each group,
    each person a picture, the negligent
    rest on the saddles,
Some emerge on the opposite bank, others
    are just entering the ford—while,
Scarlet and blue and snowy white,
The guidon flags flutter gayly in the wind.

The Civil War was also the first really modern war, employing large-scale trench warfare, observation balloons, extensive use of railroad and telegraph lines—and iron-clad ships. Early in the war, the federal navy blockaded Southern ports, thus cutting off the South's exporting of cotton and other crops—so vital to its economy—and the importing of necessary supplies. A few small, fast "blockade runners" managed to sneak in and out, but the cargoes they carried supplied but a fraction of the South's needs. And then, enterprising Southern engineers fitted what amounted to a suit of armor over the hull of a captured federal steam frigate —the *Merrimac,* renamed the *Virginia*— equipped it with an iron ram, and sent it forth from Norfolk, Virginia, to tear up the blockading fleet.

It quickly disposed of two old-style wooden ships, and retired. When it steamed forth again to destroy the federal *Minnesota,* which had run aground, it found its victim guarded by a small, strange vessel resembling a cheesebox on a raft. This was the iron-clad *Monitor,* a new Union ship, and the round "cheesebox" was a revolving gun turret of revolutionary design. The duel between the *Monitor* and the *Merrimac* on March 9, 1862, started a new era in naval warfare. In the following account, you relive this history-making battle, as described by the officer who was second-in-command of the *Monitor.*

THE MONITOR AND THE MERRIMAC FIGHT A DUEL

from "Soldiers' Letters from Camp, Battle-field and Prison"

At 8 A.M. on Sunday the *Merrimac* got under way, accompanied by several steamers, and started direct for the *Minnesota.* When a mile distant she fired two guns at her. By this time our anchor was up, the men at quarters, the guns loaded, and everything ready for action. As the *Merrimac* came close, the captain passed the word to commence firing. I triced up the port, ran out the gun, and fired the *first* gun, and thus commenced the great battle between the *Monitor* and the *Merrimac.*

Now mark the condition our men and officers were in. Since Friday morning, forty-eight hours, they had had no rest and very little food, as we could not conveniently cook. They had been hard at work all night, and nothing to eat for breakfast except hard bread, and were thoroughly worn out. As for myself, I had not slept a wink for fifty-one hours and had been on my feet almost constantly. But after the first gun was fired we forgot all fatigues, hard work, and everything else and fought as hard as men ever fought. We loaded and fired as fast as we could. I pointed and fired the guns myself. Every shot I would ask the captain the effect, and the majority of them were encouraging. The captain was in the pilothouse, directing the movements of the vessel; Acting Master Stodder was stationed at the wheel which turns the tower but, as he could not manage it, was relieved by Steiners. The speaking trumpet from the tower to the pilothouse was broken; so we passed the word from the captain to myself on the berth deck by Paymaster Keeler and Captain's Clerk Toffey. Five times during the engagement we touched each other, and each time I fired a gun at her, and I will vouch the hundred and sixty-eight pounds penetrated her sides. Once she tried to run us down with her iron prow but did no damage whatever. After fighting for two hours we hauled off for half an hour to hoist shot in the tower. At it we went again as hard as we could, the shot, shell, grape, canister, musket, and rifle balls flying in every direction but doing no damage. Our tower was struck several times, and though the noise was pretty loud, it did not affect us any. Stodder and one of the men were carelessly leaning against the tower when a shot struck it exactly opposite them and disabled them for an hour or two. At about 11:30 A.M. the captain sent for me. I went forward, and there stood as noble a man as lives, at the foot of the ladder to the pilothouse, his face perfectly black with powder and iron, and apparently perfectly blind. I

asked him what was the matter. He said a shot had struck the pilothouse exactly opposite his eyes and blinded him, and he thought the pilothouse was damaged. He told me to take charge of the ship and use my own discretion. I led him to his room, laid him on the sofa, and then took his position. On examining the pilothouse I found the iron hatch on top, on the forward side, was completely cracked through. We still continued firing, the tower being under the direction of Steiners. We were between two fires, the *Minnesota* on one side and the *Merrimac* on the other. The latter was retreating to Sewall's Point, and the *Minnesota* had struck us twice on the tower. I knew if another shot should strike our pilothouse in the same place, our steering apparatus would be disabled, and we should be at the mercy of the batteries on Sewall's Point. We had *strict* orders to act on the defensive and protect the *Minnesota*. We had evidently finished the *Merrimac* as far as the *Minnesota* was concerned. Our pilothouse was damaged, and we had orders *not* to follow the *Merrimac* up; therefore, after the *Merrimac* had retreated, I went to the *Minnesota* and remained by her until she was afloat. General Wool and Secretary Fox both commended me for acting as I did and said it was the strict military plan to follow. This is the reason we did not sink the *Merrimac,* and everyone here capable of judging says we acted perfectly right.

Although not sunk, the severely damaged *Merrimac* was forced to retire to Norfolk for repairs. When that city was taken by General Wool in May, 1862, the Confederates blew up their armor-clad champion rather than let it fall into the hands of its enemies. A fittingly dramatic finish to a brief but sensational career . . .

Meanwhile, the Civil War was also breaking military precedent on land. For the first time, artillery was mounted on railroad flatcars—a step toward the mobile "big guns" of future wars. Most artillery duels, however, were fought from fixed positions, close to the tumult of the battle. Those who fed and fired the cannon would never forget the thunder, the smoke, the heated excitement . . .

THE ARTILLERYMAN'S VISION

from "Drum-Taps" by Walt Whitman

While my wife at my side lies slumbering,
 and the wars are over long,
And my head on the pillow rests at home,
 and the vacant midnight passes,
And through the stillness, through the dark,
 I hear, just hear, the breath of my
 infant,
There in the room as I wake from sleep this
 vision presses upon me;
The engagement opens there and then in
 fantasy unreal,
The skirmishers begin, they crawl cautiously
 ahead, I hear the irregular snap! snap!
I hear the sounds of the different missiles,
 the short *t-h-t! t-h-t!* of the rifle-balls,
I see the shells exploding leaving small white
 clouds, I hear the great shells shrieking
 as they pass,
The grape like the hum and whirr of wind
 through the trees (tumultuous now the
 contest rages),

All the scenes at the batteries rise in detail
 before me again,
The crashing and smoking, the pride of the
 men in their pieces,
The chief-gunner ranges and sights his piece
 and selects a fuse of the right time,
After firing I see him lean aside and look
 eagerly off to note the effect;
Elsewhere I hear the cry of a regiment charging (the young colonel leads himself
 this time with brandish'd sword),
I see the gaps cut by the enemy's volleys
 (quickly fill'd up, no delay),
I breathe the suffocating smoke, then the flat
 clouds hover low concealing all;
Now a strange lull for a few seconds, not a
 shot fired on either side,
Then resumed the chaos louder than ever,
 with eager calls and orders of officers,
While from some distant part of the field the
 wind wafts to my ears a shout of ap-

159

plause (some special success),

And ever the sound of the cannon far or
near (rousing even in dreams a devilish exultation and all the old mad joy
in the depths of my soul),

And ever the hastening of infantry shifting
positions, batteries, cavalry, moving
hither and thither

(The falling, dying, I heed not, the wounded
dripping and red I heed not, some to
the rear are hobbling),

Grime, heat, rush, aides-de-camp galloping
by or on a full run,

With the patter of small arms, the warning
s-s-t of the rifles (these in my vision I
hear or see),

And bombs bursting in air, and at night the
vari-color'd rockets.

In spite of artillery, ironclads and dashing
cavalry charges, this was still mainly a
muddy-footed infantryman's war. The land
campaign was divided into two fronts—Eastern and Western. On the Eastern front,
roughly comprising the areas of Virginia,
Pennsylvania and Maryland, Union armies
were hurled back again and again in their
attempts to take the Confederate capital of
Richmond, only one hundred miles from
Washington, D.C. Southern success against
superior numbers was mainly the result of
the leadership provided by Generals Robert
E. Lee and "Stonewall" Jackson, whose brilliant tactics are still being studied. Jackson
got his nickname at the First Battle of Bull
Run, when he stood "like a stone wall"
against invading Northerners. Union forces
had crossed the Potomac confident of victory. They returned to Washington on July

22, 1861, in a far different frame of mind.
The impact of the defeat on the Union army
and capital is here described by an English
journalist of the day, who viewed both the
battle and its aftermath.

THE RETURN FROM BULL RUN

from "My Diary North and South"
by William Howard Russell

July 22d.—I awoke from a deep sleep this
morning about six o'clock The rain was
falling in torrents and beat with a dull, thud-
ding sound on the leads outside my window;
but louder than all came a strange sound as
if of the tread of men, a confused tramp and
splashing and a murmuring of voices. I got
up and ran to the front room, the windows
of which looked on the street, and there, to
my intense surprise, I saw a steady stream
of men covered with mud, soaked through
with rain, who were pouring irregularly,
without any semblance of order, up Pennsylvania Avenue toward the Capitol. A dense
stream of vapor rose from the multitude, but
looking closely at the men, I perceived they
belonged to different regiments, New York-
ers, Michiganders, Rhode Islanders, Massa-
chusetters, Minnesotans, mingled pellmell together. Many of them were without knap-
sacks, crossbelts, and firelocks. Some had
neither greatcoats nor shoes; others were
covered with blankets. Hastily putting on
my clothes, I ran downstairs and asked an
officer who was passing by, a pale young
man who looked exhausted to death and
who had lost his sword, for the empty sheath
dangled at his side, where the men were all

coming from. "Where from? Well, sir, I guess we're all coming out of Virginny as far as we can, and pretty well whipped too." "What! The whole army, sir?" "That's more than I know. They may stay that like. I know I'm going home. I've had enough of fighting to last my lifetime."

The news seemed incredible. But there before my eyes were the jaded, dispirited, broken remnants of regiments passing onward, where and for what I knew not, and it was evident enough that the mass of the grand army of the Potomac was placing that river between it and the enemy as rapidly as possible. "Is there any pursuit?" I asked of several men. Some were too surly to reply; others said, "They're coming as fast as they can after us"; others, "I guess they've stopped it now—the rain is too much for them." A few said they did not know and looked as if they did not care. . . .

There is no provost guard, no patrol, no authority visible in the streets. . . . The Secretary of War knows not what to do; Mr. Lincoln is equally helpless, and Mr. Seward, who retains some calmness, is notwithstanding his military rank and militia experience, without resource or expedient. There are a good many troops hanging on about the camps and forts on the other side of the river, it is said; but they are thoroughly disorganized and will run away if the enemy comes in sight, without a shot, and then the capital must fall at once. Why Beauregard does not come I know not, nor can I well guess. I have been expecting every hour since noon to hear his cannon. Here is a golden opportunity. If the Confederates do not grasp that which will never come again on such terms, it stamps them with mediocrity.

However, the Confederates did fail to follow up their victory, and the North, with its vastly superior numbers, simply kept equipping new armies and hurling them toward Richmond. Lee's men, on the whole, kept winning, but the North seemed to have an inexhaustible supply of men and guns.

Meanwhile, in the West, Union General Ulysses S. Grant was pushing doggedly forward in an attempt to cut the Confederacy in two by way of the Mississippi River. His offensive drive through Tennessee met with a sudden surprise attack by Confederate Generals Johnston and Beauregard. This resulted in the savage battle of Shiloh, April, 1862. The outcome of the battle was indecisive and proved only a temporary check on Grant's drive. Losses on both sides were extremely heavy.

SHILOH

A Requiem

by Herman Melville

Skimming lightly, wheeling still,
  The swallows fly low
Over the field in clouded days,
  The forest-field of Shiloh—
Over the field where April rain
Solaced the parched one stretched in pain
Through the pause of night
That followed the Sunday fight
  Around the church of Shiloh—
The church so lone, the log-built one,
That echoed to many a parting groan
    And natural prayer
  Of dying foemen mingled there—
Foemen at morn, but friends at eve—
  Fame or country least their care:

(What like a bullet can undeceive!)
 But now they lie low,
While over them the swallows skim,
 And all is hushed at Shiloh.

A battle lost, a battle won . . . To the infantryman, it made little difference. He cleaned his rifle, patched up his wounds, found what was left of his squad, platoon or company, and slogged wearily on toward the next day's fighting . . .

A MARCH IN THE RANKS HARD-PREST

from "Drum-Taps" by Walt Whitman

A march in the ranks hard-prest, and the
 road unknown,
A route through a heavy wood with muffled
 steps in the darkness,
Our army foil'd with loss severe, and the
 sullen remnant retreating,
Till after midnight glimmer upon us the
 lights of a dim-lighted building,
We come to an open space in the woods, and
 halt by the dim-lighted building,
'Tis a large old church at the crossing roads,
 now an impromptu hospital,
Entering but for a minute I see a sight beyond all the pictures and poems ever
 made,
Shadows of deepest, deepest black, just lit
 by moving candles and lamps,
And by one great pitchy torch stationary
 with wild red flame and clouds of
 smoke,
By these, crowds, groups of forms vaguely I
 see on the floor, some in the pews laid
 down,

At my feet more distinctly a soldier, a mere
    lad, in danger of bleeding to death (he
    is shot in the abdomen),
I stanch the blood temporarily (the young-
    ster's face is white as a lily),
Then before I depart I sweep my eyes o'er
    the scene fain to absorb it all,
Faces, varieties, postures beyond descrip-
    tion, most in obscurity, some of them
    dead,
Surgeons operating, attendants holding
    lights, the smell of ether, the odor of
    blood,
The crowd, O the crowd of the bloody forms,
    the yard outside also fill'd,
Some on the bare ground, some on planks or
    stretchers, some in the death-spasm
    sweating,
An occasional scream or cry, the doctor's
    shouted orders or calls,
The glisten of the little steel instruments
    catching the glint of the torches,
These I resume as I chant, I see again the
    forms, I smell the odor,
Then hear outside the orders given, *Fall in,
    my men, fall in;*
But first I bend to the dying lad, his eyes
    open, a half-smile gives he me,
Then the eyes close, calmly close, and I
    speed forth to the darkness,
Resuming, marching, ever in darkness
    marching, on in the ranks,
The unknown road still marching.

Providing adequate care for the enormous
number of men wounded in battle proved a
never-ending—and almost impossible—task.
Various voluntary associations, such as the
Sanitary Commission, did heroic work in
this field. Here, an officer of the Sanitary
Commission describes one of the less pleasant aspects of war.

A TRAINLOAD OF WOUNDED ARRIVES

*from "A Memoir of the Embarkation of the Sick
and Wounded" by an Officer of the U.S. Sanitary
Commission*

At the time of which I am now writing
(Monday afternoon), wounded men were
arriving by every train, entirely unattended,
or with at most a detail of two soldiers, two
hundred or more of them in a train. They
were packed as closely as they could be
stowed in the common freight cars, without
beds, without straw, at most with a wisp of
hay under their heads. Many of the lighter
cases came on the roof of the cars. They arrived dead and living together, in the same
close box, many with awful wounds fester-
ing and swarming with maggots. Recollect
it was midsummer in Virginia, clear and
calm. The stench was such as to produce
vomiting with some of our strong men, ha-
bituated to the duty of attending the sick.
How close they were packed you may infer
from a fact reported by my messenger to
Doctor Tripler, who, on his return from
headquarters, was present at the loading of a
car. A surgeon was told that it was not possible to get another man upon the floor of
the car. "Then," said he, "these three men
must be laid in *across the others,* for they
have got to be cleared out from here by this
train!" This outrage was avoided, however.

Need I tell you that the women were always ready to press into these places of horror, going to them in torrents of rain, groping their way by dim lantern light, at all hours of night, carrying spirits and ice water; calling back to life those in despair from utter exhaustion, or again and again catching for mother or wife the last faint whispers of the dying?

Our old friend Walt Whitman worked as a male nurse during the Civil War, and among the women who gave of their time and skill were Dorothea Dix (who had already done much for the mentally ill) and Clara Barton (later the first President of the American Red Cross). The talent, energy and unsparing devotion to duty displayed by such women contrasted vividly with the prejudice which kept them from getting the right to vote . . . A woman even provided one of the most famous symbols of courage to come out of the war. The incident involving ninety-year-old Barbara Frietchie and "Stonewall" Jackson may or may not actually have happened, but it gave John Greenleaf Whittier the chance to create an ever-popular legend about the spirit of an old woman and the gallantry of a rebel commander.

BARBARA FRIETCHIE

by John Greenleaf Whittier

Up from the meadows rich with corn,
Clear in the cool September morn,
The clustered spires of Frederick stand
Green-walled by the hills of Maryland.
Round about them orchards sweep,

Apple and peach tree fruited deep,
Fair as the garden of the Lord
To the eyes of the famished rebel horde,
On that pleasant morn of the early fall
When Lee marched over the mountain-wall;
Over the mountains winding down,
Horse and foot, into Frederick town.

Forty flags with their silver stars,
Forty flags with their crimson bars,
Flapped in the morning wind: the sun
Of noon looked down, and saw not one.
Up rose old Barbara Frietchie then,
Bowed with her fourscore years and ten;
Bravest of all in Frederick town
She took up the flag the men hauled down;
In her attic window the staff she set,
To show that one heart was loyal yet.
Up the street came the rebel tread,
Stonewall Jackson riding ahead.
Under his slouched hat left and right
He glanced; the old flag met his sight.

"Halt!"—the dust-brown ranks stood fast.
"Fire!"—out blazed the rifle-blast.
It shivered the window, pane and sash;
It rent the banner with seam and gash.
Quick, as it fell, from the broken staff
Dame Barbara snatched the silken scarf.
She leaned far out on the window-sill,
And shook it forth with a royal will.
"Shoot, if you must, this old gray head,
But spare your country's flag," she said.

A shade of sadness, a blush of shame,
Over the face of the leader came;
The nobler nature within him stirred
To life at that woman's deed and word;
"Who touches a hair of yon gray head
Dies like a dog! March on!" he said.

All day long through Frederick street
Sounded the tread of marching feet:
All day long that free flag tost
Over the heads of the rebel host.
Ever its torn folds rose and fell
On the loyal winds that loved it well;
And through the hill-gaps sunset light
Shone over it with a warm goodnight.

Barbara Frietchie's work is o'er,
And the Rebel rides on his raids no more.
Honor to her! and let a tear
Fall, for her sake, on Stonewall's bier.
Over Barbara Frietchie's grave,
Flag of Freedom and Union, wave!
Peace and order and beauty draw
Round thy symbol of light and law;
And ever the stars above look down
On thy stars below in Frederick town!

Abraham Lincoln, too, has been raised to
the status of a legend—turned, like Washington before him, into a towering symbol
of democratic leadership. For a refreshing
glimpse of the man behind the legend, we
have the following report by the novelist Nathaniel Hawthorne of his White House interview with the President in 1862.

HAWTHORNE MEETS
UNCLE ABE

from "Tales, Sketches, and Other Papers"
by Nathaniel Hawthorne

Nine o'clock had been appointed as the
time for receiving the deputation, and we
were punctual to the moment; but not so the
President, who sent us word that he was eating his breakfast and would come as soon as
he could. . . .

By and by there was a little stir on the
staircase and in the passageway, and in
lounged a tall, loose-jointed figure, of an ex-
aggerated Yankee port and demeanor, whom
(as being about the homeliest man I ever
saw, yet by no means repulsive or disagree-
able) it was impossible not to recognize as
Uncle Abe.

Unquestionably, Western man though he
be and Kentuckian by birth, President Lincoln is the essential representative of all
Yankees and the veritable specimen, physi-
cally, of what the world seems determined to
regard as our characteristic qualities. It is
the strangest and yet the fittest thing in the
jumble of human vicissitudes that he, out of
so many millions, unlooked for, unselected
by any intelligible process that could be
based upon his genuine qualities, unknown
to those who chose him, and unsuspected of
what endowments may adapt him for his tremendous responsibility, should have found
the way open for him to fling his lank personality into the chair of state—where, I pre-
sume, it was his first impulse to throw his
legs on the council table and tell the cabinet
ministers a story. There is no describing his
lengthy awkwardness nor the uncouthness of
his movement, and yet it seemed as if I had
been in the habit of seeing him daily and had
shaken hands with him a thousand times in
some village street; so true was he to the as-
pect of the pattern American, though with a
certain extravagance which, possibly, I exag-
gerated still further by the delighted eagerness with which I took it in. If put to guess
his calling and livelihood, I should have

165

taken him for a country schoolmaster as soon as anything else. He was dressed in a rusty black frock coat and pantaloons, unbrushed, and worn so faithfully that the suit had adapted itself to the curves and angularities of his figure and had grown to be an outer skin of the man. He had shabby slippers on his feet. His hair was black, still unmixed with gray, stiff, somewhat bushy, and had apparently been acquainted with neither brush nor comb that morning, after the disarrangement of the pillow; and as to a nightcap, Uncle Abe probably knows nothing of such effeminacies. . . .

A great deal of native sense; no bookish cultivation, no refinement; honest at heart, and thoroughly so, and yet, in some sort, sly —at least, endowed with a sort of tact and wisdom that are akin to craft, and would impel him, I think, to take an antagonist in flank, rather than to make a bull run at him right in front. But, on the whole, I like this sallow, queer, sagacious visage, with the homely human sympathies that warmed it and, for my small share in the matter, would as lief have Uncle Abe for a ruler as any man whom it would have been practicable to put in his place.

Immediately on his entrance the President accosted our member of Congress, who had us in charge, and with a comical twist of his face made some jocular remark about the length of his breakfast. He then greeted us all round, not waiting for an introduction, but shaking and squeezing everybody's hand with the utmost cordiality, whether the individual's name was announced to him or not. His manner toward us was wholly without pretense, but yet had a kind of natural dignity, quite sufficient to keep the forwardest of us from clapping him on the shoulder and asking him for a story.

Lincoln's opposite number, President Jefferson Davis of the Confederacy, has been overshadowed in deed and legend by his foremost general. Robert E. Lee was admired by those who fought both with him and against him. (Lincoln had even offered him the command of the Union armies at the beginning of the war, when he held a commission in the United States Army.) Lee's personal qualities shone in both victory and defeat. We get a little ahead of our story to bring you a rare observation of Lee the moment after a crucial battle was lost. The moment is described by a British observer at the Battle of Gettysburg.

A BATTLEFIELD SCENE
WITH ROBERT E. LEE

from "The Battle of Gettysburg"
by Colonel Fremantle

Soon afterward I joined General Lee, who had in the meanwhile come to the front on becoming aware of the disaster. If Longstreet's conduct was admirable, that of Lee was perfectly sublime. He was engaged in rallying and in encouraging the broken troops and was riding about a little in front of the wood, quite alone, the whole of his staff being engaged in a similar manner farther to the rear. His face, which is always placid and cheerful, did not show signs of the slightest disappointment, care, or annoy-

166

ance; and he was addressing to every soldier he met a few words of encouragement, such as: "All this will come right in the end; we'll talk it over afterwards; but in the meantime, all good men must rally. We want all good and true men just now," etc. He spoke to all the wounded men that passed him, and the slightly wounded he exhorted to "bind up their hurts and take up a musket" in this emergency. Very few failed to answer his appeal, and I saw many badly wounded men take off their hats and cheer him.

He said to me, "This has been a sad day for us, Colonel—a sad day; but we can't expect always to gain victories." I saw General Willcox come up to him and explain, almost crying, the state of his brigade. General Lee immediately shook hands with him and said cheerfully: "Never mind, General, all this has been *my* fault—it is I that have lost this fight, and you must help me out of it in the best way you can."

In this way I saw General Lee encourage and reanimate his somewhat dispirited troops and magnanimously take upon his own shoulders the whole weight of the repulse. It was impossible to look at him or to listen to him without feeling the strongest admiration.

The men in gray fought with remarkable courage, daring and endurance against an enemy that had an overwhelming superiority in men, arms and supplies. They believed they were fighting for their homes, their freedom, their right to the "Southern way of life." Although we have seen that this right was based on the wrong of slavery, although we must condemn their cause as unjust, we cannot but respect them as outstanding sol-

diers. They had—as all armies have—their favorite marching songs. *Maryland, My Maryland* was one; but the most famous one —ironically—was a Negro-dialect minstrel song, probably composed by Dan Emmett in 1859.

DIXIE

by Daniel Decatur Emmett

I wish I was in de land ob cotton,
Old times dar am not forgotten;
   Look away, look away, look away, Dixie land!
In Dixie land whar I was born in,
Early on one frosty mornin',
   Look away, look away, look away, Dixie land!

Chorus:
   Den I wish I was in Dixie! Hooray! Hooray!
   In Dixie land we'll take our stand, to lib an' die in Dixie,
   Away, away, away down south in Dixie!
   Away, away, away down south in Dixie!

Old missus marry Will de weaber,
William was a gay deceaber,
When he put his arm around 'er,
He looked as fierce as a forty-pounder.

His face was as sharp as a butcher cleaber,
But dat did not seem to greab 'er;
Will run away, missus took a decline, O,
Her face was the color of bacon rhine, O.

While missus libbed, she libbed in clover,
When she died, she died all over;

167

How could she act de foolish part,
An' marry a man to break her heart?

Buck wheat cakes an' stony batter
Makes you fat or a little fatter;
Here's a health to de next old missus,
An' all de gals dat want to kiss us.

Now if you want to drive 'way sorrow,
Come an' hear dis song to-morrow;
Den hoe it down an' scratch your grabble,
To Dixie's land I'm bound to trabble.

In 1862, a New England poet named Julia Ward Howe was near the Eastern battle front, singing with some friends the popular Northern army song "John Brown's body lies a-mould'ring in the ground; His soul is marching on . . ." A friend suggested that she write some words for the stirring tune which would convey something less grisly than the image of a decaying body. That night, as she lay in bed, the words came to her, and she wrote them down. Thus was born the anthem of the Union cause, and one of the most spirited poems in American history.

THE BATTLE-HYMN OF THE REPUBLIC

by Julia Ward Howe

Mine eyes have seen the glory of the coming
of the Lord;
He is trampling out the vintage where the
grapes of wrath are stored;

He hath loosed the fateful lightning of His
terrible swift sword;
His truth is marching on.

I have seen Him in the watch-fires of a hundred circling camps;
They have builded Him an altar in the evening dews and damps;
I can read His righteous sentence by the dim
and flaring lamps;
His day is marching on.

I have read a fiery gospel, writ in burnished
rows of steel:
"As ye deal with my contemners, so with you
my grace shall deal;
Let the Hero, born of woman, crush the
serpent with his heel,
Since God is marching on."

He has sounded forth the trumpet that shall
never call retreat;
He is sifting out the hearts of men before His
judgment-seat:
Oh, be swift, my soul, to answer Him! be
jubilant, my feet!
Our God is marching on.

In the beauty of the lilies Christ was born
across the sea,
With a glory in His bosom that transfigures
you and me:
As He died to make men holy, let us die to
make men free,
While God is marching on.

"Let us die to make men free . . ." The war was over a year old before Lincoln issued the Emancipation Proclamation. He held back because the Union forces had suffered so many defeats in their attempts to take Richmond. In the Spring of 1862, General McClellan was hurled back by Lee and Jackson in the disastrous Seven Days Battle. His successor, Pope, did no better in the summer, losing the Second Battle of Bull Run. Lee's forces were taking the offensive, preparing to cross the Potomac and invade Maryland . . . Lincoln's Cabinet was afraid that an Emancipation Proclamation would be interpreted as a desperate measure to recruit ex-slaves for defeated Union armies. As Secretary of State Seward put it, "It may be viewed as . . . the government stretching forth its hand to Ethiopia instead of Ethiopia stretching forth her hands to the government."

Then, in September, 1862, McClellan (who had resumed command) defeated Lee's invading army at Antietam, Maryland, and the Southern forces returned again across the Potomac. Lincoln decided to wait no longer. On September 22, he issued a Proclamation which stated that, beginning on January 1st, all slaves in rebellious states "shall be then, thenceforward, and forever free . . ." Later, he amended the Proclamation to make ex-slaves acceptable as recruits to be "received into the armed service of the United States to garrison forts, positions, stations and other places, and to man vessels of all sorts in said service." Almost 200,000 Negroes would eventually serve in Union ranks, 93,000 from Confederate states. Now Southern slaves had an official promise that marching men in blue brought with them this strange and wonderful thing called freedom . . .

ETHIOPIA SALUTING THE COLORS

from "Drum-Taps" by Walt Whitman

Who are you dusky woman, so ancient
    hardly human,
With your woolly-white and turban'd head,
    and bare bony feet?
Why rising by the roadside here, do you the
    colors greet?

('Tis while our army lines Carolina's sands
    and pines,
Forth from thy hovel door thou Ethiopia
    com'st to me,
As under doughty Sherman I march toward
    the sea.)

Me master years a hundred since from my
    parents sunder'd,
A little child, they caught me as the savage
    beast is caught,
Then hither me across the sea the cruel
    slaver brought.

No further does she say, but lingering all the
    day,
Her high-borne turban'd head she wags, and
    rolls her darkling eye,
And courtesies to the regiments, the guidons
    moving by.

What is it fateful woman, so blear, hardly
    human?
Why wag your head with turban bound, yellow, red and green?
Are the things so strange and marvelous you
    see or have seen?

The moral commitment implied in the Emancipation Proclamation did a good deal to firm liberal overseas support for the Union cause. Even England, whose textile mills had depended on Southern cotton, voted not to help the Confederacy but to look elsewhere for its cotton, mainly to India. This was a severe blow to Southern hopes, as was the capture of New Orleans and Mobile by David Farragut's Union fleet. After Lee won the Battle of Chancellorsville (losing, however, his "right arm"—Jackson), he decided to gamble everything on a bold thrust into the North. He knew that Grant would soon capture Vicksburg in the West, but by seizing and holding the heartland of the Union, he hoped to force a quick end to the war. He nearly succeeded. His forces crossed the Potomac in June, 1863, and were soon in Pennsylvania. The following letter was written by one of his officers.

A SOUTHERN INVADER WRITES A LETTER HOME

from "The Rebellion Record"
edited by Frank Moore

Camp near Greenwood, Pa., June 28, 1863.—My own darling wife: You can see by the date of this that we are now in Pennsylvania. We crossed the line day before yesterday and are resting today near a little one-

horse town on the road to Gettysburg, which we will reach tomorrow. We are paying back these people for some of the damage they have done us, though we are not doing them half as bad as they done us. . . .

I felt when I first came here that I would like to revenge myself upon these people for the desolation they have brought upon our own beautiful home, that home where we could have lived so happy, and that we loved so much, from which their vandalism has driven you and my helpless little ones. But though I had such severe wrongs and grievances to redress and such great cause for revenge, yet when I got among these people I could not find it in my heart to molest them. They looked so dreadfully scared and talked so humble that I have invariably endeavored to protect their property and have prevented soldiers from taking chickens, even in the main road; yet there is a good deal of plundering going on, confined principally to the taking of provisions. No houses were searched and robbed, like our houses were done by the Yankees. Pigs, chickens, geese, etc., are finding their way into our camp; it can't be prevented, and I can't think it ought to be. We must show them something of war. I have sent out today to get a good horse; I have no scruples about that, as they have taken mine. We took a lot of Negroes yesterday. I was offered my choice, but as I could not get them back home I would not take them. In fact my humanity revolted at taking the poor devils away from their homes. They were so scared that I turned them all loose. . . .

You never saw such a land of plenty. We could live here mighty well for the next twelve months, but I suppose old Hooker will try to put a stop to us pretty soon. Of course we will have to fight here, and when it comes it will be the biggest on record. Our men feel that there is to be no back-out. A defeat here would be ruinous. This army has never done such fighting as it will do now, and if we can whip the armies that are now gathering to oppose us, we will have everything in our own hands. We must conquer a peace. If we can come out of this country triumphant and victorious, having established a peace, we will bring back to our own land the greatest joy that ever crowned a people. We will show the Yankees this time how we can fight.

They did show the Yankees how they could fight, and vice versa. The occasion was the three-day Battle of Gettysburg, the battle which has come to be called the turning point of the war. Lee's advancing army was stopped by General Meade's Army of the Potomac. Meade had the superior numbers, and his men were entrenched in a superior position—the commanding height of Cemetery Ridge, from which a devastating artillery fire poured on the Confederate ranks. Lee's men were repulsed again and again. On the final day of the battle—July 3, 1863—Confederate General Pickett led his men in a last desperate attempt to take Cemetery Ridge, preceded by a three-hour cannonade by 115 Confederate guns. The charge itself is magnificently re-created in the following selection.

PICKETT'S CHARGE

from "John Brown's Body"
by Stephen Vincent Benét

The cannonade fell still. All along the fish-
hook line,
The tired men stared at the smoke and
waited for it to clear;
The men in the centre waited, their rifles
gripped in their hands,
By the trees of the riding fate, and the low
stone wall, and the guns.

These were Hancock's men, the men of the
Second Corps,
Eleven States were mixed there, where Min-
nesota stood
In battle-order with Maine, and Rhode Is-
land beside New York,
The metals of all the North, cooled into an
axe of war.

The strong sticks of the North, bound into a
fasces-shape,
The hard winters of snow, the wind with the
cutting edge,
And against them came that summer that
does not die with the year,
Magnolia and honeysuckle and the blue Virginia flag.

Tall Pickett went up to Longstreet—his
handsome face was drawn.
George Pickett, old friend of Lincoln's in
days gone by with the blast,
When he was a courteous youth and Lincoln
the strange shawled man
Who would talk in a Springfield street with
a boy who dreamt of a sword.

Dreamt of a martial sword, as swords are
martial in dreams,
And the courtesy to use it, in the old bright
way of the tales.
Those days are gone with the blast. He has
his sword in his hand.
And he will use it today, and remember that
using long.

He came to Longstreet for orders, but Longstreet would not speak.
He saw Old Peter's mouth and the thought
in Old Peter's mind.
He knew the task that was set and the men
that he had to lead,
And a pride came into his face while Longstreet stood there dumb.

"I shall go forward, sir," he said and turned
to his men.
The commands went down the line. The
grey ranks started to move.
Slowly at first, then faster, in order, stepping
like deer,
The Virginians, the fifteen thousand, the
seventh wave of the tide.

There was a death-torn mile of broken
ground to cross,
And a low stone wall at the end, and behind
it the Second Corps,
And behind that force another, fresh men
who had not yet fought.
They started to cross that ground. The
guns began to tear them.

From the hill they say that it seemed more
like a sea than a wave,
A sea continually torn by stones flung out
of the sky,

And yet, as it came, still closing, closing and
rolling on,
As the moving sea closes over the flaws and
rips of the tide.

You could mark the path that they took by
the dead that they left behind,
Spilled from that deadly march as a cart
spills meal on a road,
And yet they came on unceasing, the fifteen
thousand no more,
And the blue Virginia flag did not fall, did
not fall, did not fall.

They halted but once to fire as they came.
Then the smoke closed down
And you could not see them, and then, as it
cleared again for a breath,
They were coming still but divided, gnawed
at by blue attacks,
One flank half-severed and halted, but the
centre still like a tide.

Cushing ran down the last of his guns to the
battle-line.
The rest had been smashed to scrap by Lee's
artillery fire.
He held his guts in his hand as the charge
came up the wall
And his gun spoke out for him once before
he fell to the ground.

Armistead leapt the wall and laid his hand
on the gun,
The last of the three brigadiers who ordered
Pickett's brigades,
He waved his hat on his sword and "Give
'em the steel!" he cried,
A few men followed him over. The rest were
beaten or dead.

A few men followed him over. There had
been fifteen thousand
When that sea began its march toward the
fish-hook ridge and the wall.
So they came on in strength, light-footed,
stepping like deer,
So they died or were taken. So the iron entered their flesh.

Lee, a mile away, in the shade of a little
wood,
Stared, with his mouth shut down, and saw
them go and be slain,
And then saw for a single moment, the blue
Virginia flag.
Planted beyond the wall, by that other flag
that he knew.

The two flags planted together, one instant,
like hostile flowers.
Then the smoke wrapped both in a mantle—
and when it had blown away,
Armistead lay in his blood, and the rest
were dead or down,
And the valley grey with the fallen and the
wreck of the broken wave.

Pickett gazed around him, the boy who had
dreamt of a sword
And talked with a man named Lincoln. The
sword was still in his hand.
He had gone out with fifteen thousand. He
came back to his lines with five.
He fought well till the war was over, but a
thing was cracked in his heart.

With the failure of Pickett's gallant
charge, the battle was lost. Lee gathered together his broken army and recrossed the

173

Potomac. He would never lead his men north again . . . Forty-three thousand men were among the killed, wounded and missing at Gettysburg. In November, 1863, the site of the battle was made a national cemetery. At the dedication ceremony, President Lincoln was asked to deliver a few "appropriate remarks" after the principal address by Edward Everett. Coming after Mr. Everett's two-hour oration, Lincoln's three paragraphs seemed skimpy and unimportant at the time. History has judged otherwise.

THE GETTYSBURG ADDRESS

by Abraham Lincoln

Fourscore and seven years ago our fathers brought forth on this continent a new nation, conceived in liberty, and dedicated to the proposition that all men are created equal.

Now we are engaged in a great civil war, testing whether that nation or any nation so conceived and so dedicated can long endure. We are met on a great battlefield of that war. We have come to dedicate a portion of that field as a final resting place for those who here gave their lives that that nation might live. It is altogether fitting and proper that we should do this.

But, in a larger sense, we cannot dedicate, we cannot consecrate, we cannot hallow this ground. The brave men, living and dead, who struggled here, have consecrated it far above our poor power to add or detract. The world will little note nor long remember what we say here, but it can never forget what they did here. It is for us the living, rather, to be dedicated here to the unfinished work which they who fought here have thus far so nobly advanced. It is rather for us to be here dedicated to the great task remain-

ing before us—that from these honored dead we take increased devotion to that cause for which they gave the last full measure of devotion; that we here highly resolve that these dead shall not have died in vain; that this nation, under God, shall have a new birth of freedom; and that government of the people, by the people, and for the people, shall not perish from the earth.

The Civil War didn't bring out the best in all people, as it did in Lincoln and Lee. There were war profiteering, military desertion, and various shades of corruption and avoidance of duty on both sides. There was fierce resentment of the Negro among poor immigrant laborers of the North, who feared that emancipated slaves would flood the cities, working for cheap wages, taking their jobs away. There were horrible conditions at military prisons, terrible food riots down South and draft riots in New York. Yet most people, justifying the faith of the Founding Fathers in American democracy, did their best and carried on. Listen to a scene observed by a British traveler during the Civil War.

AN UNPRETENTIOUS BIT OF HEROISM

from "Six Months in the Federal States"
by Edward Dicey

In traveling up one night from Baltimore, the cars were crowded with sick and wounded soldiers on their way home from the peninsula. On the bench behind me there was a woman in deep black, carrying a sick child in her arms, and beside her there was a discharged soldier whose health had broken down in the swamps. The woman was a widow just returned from the deathbed of her brother, who, like her husband, had been killed in the campaign. The man looked dreadfully worn and ill; he complained, and I fear, truly, that he should never be fit for a day's work again; he had a grievance, too, of his own against the government, which he considered had behaved shabbily about the amount of bounty paid him on his discharge. Being seated near them, I could hear the soldier and the soldier's widow telling each other of their hardships and their sorrows; and at last the man consoled the woman by saying to her, "Well, after all, it's for our country, and we're bound to do it." The woman answered him, "Yes, that's so"; and though the words might be commonplace, it seemed to me that there was about them something of true heroism.

After Gettysburg, the Confederates fought on furiously in what became for them a completely defensive war. Grant and other Union generals, operating in the West, took Vicksburg and cut the Confederacy in two. The South won the bloody Battle of Chickamauga, but it was merely postponing the inevitable. Grant was made commander-in-chief of all Union forces, and Sherman took Atlanta and began his devastating march to the sea. In 1864, Lincoln was re-elected by a war-weary country. His second Inaugural Address reaffirmed the basic issue of the conflict, closing with this passage.

175

WITH MALICE TOWARD NONE . . .

from Abraham Lincoln's Second Inaugural Address

Fondly do we hope, fervently do we pray, that this mighty scourge of war may speedily pass away. Yet, if God wills that it continue until all the wealth piled by the bondsman's two hundred and fifty years of unrequited toil shall be sunk, and until every drop of blood drawn with the lash shall be paid by another drawn with the sword, as was said three thousand years ago, so still it must be said, "The judgments of the Lord are true and righteous altogether."

With malice toward none, with charity for all, with firmness in the right as God gives us to see the right, let us strive on to finish the work we are in, to bind up the nation's wounds, to care for him who shall have borne the battle and for his widow and his orphan, to do all which may achieve and cherish a just and lasting peace among ourselves and with all nations.

The South was burned out—devastated and bankrupt. In March, 1865, Lee's army of fifty thousand men was forced to abandon its defense of Richmond because of the attacks of Grant's army, more than double its size. Retreating toward the mountains of West Virginia, Lee was cut off by a force under command of Phil Sheridan. His escape route gone, his gallant army exhausted and starving, Lee sent a messenger to Grant to request discussion of surrender terms. Grant met him at the house of a Mr. McLean at Appomattox Courthouse on April 9, 1865. The historic interview that followed has been described by Grant in his memoirs. Here are some excerpts.

THE SURRENDER AT APPOMATTOX

from the "Personal Memoirs of U. S. Grant"

When I had left camp that morning I had not expected so soon the result that was then taking place and consequently was in rough garb. I was without a sword, as I usually was when on horseback on the field, and wore a soldier's blouse for a coat, with the shoulder straps of my rank to indicate to the army who I was. When I went into the house I found General Lee. We greeted each other and, after shaking hands, took our seats. . . .

What General Lee's feelings were I do not know. As he was a man of much dignity, with an impassible face, it was impossible to say whether he felt inwardly glad that the end had finally come or felt sad over the result and was too manly to show it. Whatever his feelings, they were entirely concealed from my observation; but my own feelings, which had been quite jubilant on the receipt of his letter, were sad and depressed. I felt like anything rather than rejoicing at the downfall of a foe who had fought so long and valiantly and had suffered so much for a cause, though that cause was, I believe, one of the worst for which a people ever fought and one for which there was the least excuse. I do not question, however, the sincerity of the great mass of those who were opposed to us.

General Lee was dressed in a full uniform

which was entirely new and was wearing a sword of considerable value, very likely the sword which had been presented by the State of Virginia; at all events, it was an entirely different sword from the one that would ordinarily be worn in the field. In my rough traveling suit, the uniform of a private with the straps of a lieutenant general, I must have contrasted very strangely with a man so handsomely dressed, six feet high, and of faultless form. But this was not a matter that I thought of until afterward.

We soon fell into a conversation about old army times. He remarked that he remembered me very well in the old army, and I told him that as a matter of course I remembered him perfectly, but from the difference in our rank and years (there being about sixteen years' difference in our ages), I had thought it very likely that I had not attracted his attention sufficiently to be remembered by him after such a long interval. Our conversation grew so pleasant that I almost forgot the object of our meeting. After the conversation had run on in this style for some time, General Lee called my attention to the object of our meeting and said that he had asked for this interview for the purpose of getting from me the terms I proposed to give his army. I said that I

meant merely that his army should lay down their arms, not to take them up again during the continuance of the war, unless duly and properly exchanged. . . .

In an atmosphere of mutual respect, the surrender was completed. Thus, after four years, the Civil War was over, the Union was preserved, and half a million men lay buried beneath the ground.

THE BLUE AND THE GRAY

by Francis Miles Finch

By the flow of the inland river,
  Whence the fleets of iron have fled,
Where the blades of the grave grass quiver,
  Asleep are the ranks of the dead;—
    Under the sod and the dew,
      Waiting the judgment day;—
    Under the one, the Blue;
      Under the other, the Gray.

These in the robings of glory,
  Those in the gloom of defeat,
All with the battle blood gory,
  In the dusk of eternity meet;—
    Under the sod and the dew,
      Waiting the judgment day;—
    Under the laurel, the Blue;
      Under the willow, the Gray.

From the silence of sorrowful hours
  The desolate mourners go,
Lovingly laden with flowers
  Alike for the friend and the foe;—
    Under the sod and the dew,
      Waiting the judgment day;—
    Under the roses, the Blue;
      Under the lilies, the Gray.

So with an equal splendor
  The morning sun rays fall,
With a touch, impartially tender,
  On the blossoms blooming for all;—
    Under the sod and the dew,
      Waiting the judgment day;—
    'Broidered with gold, the Blue;
      Mellowed with gold, the Gray.

So, when the summer calleth,
  On forest and field of grain
With an equal murmur falleth
  The cooling drip of the rain;—
    Under the sod and the dew,
      Waiting the judgment day;—
    Wet with the rain, the Blue;
      Wet with the rain, the Gray.

Sadly, but not with upbraiding,
  The generous deed was done;
In the storm of the years that are fading,
  No braver battle was won;—
    Under the sod and the dew,
      Waiting the judgment day;—
    Under the blossoms, the Blue;
      Under the garlands, the Gray.

No more shall the war cry sever,
  Or the winding rivers be red;
They banish our anger forever
  When they laurel the graves of our dead!
    Under the sod and the dew,
      Waiting the judgment day;—
    Love and tears for the Blue,
      Tears and love for the Gray.

PART SEVEN

Growing Pains

"THE war being at an end, the Southern states having laid down their arms, and the questions at issue between them and the Northern states having been decided, I believe it to be the duty of everyone to unite in the restoration of the country and the reestablishment of peace and harmony."

This was the counsel given by Robert E. Lee right after the Civil War. Had Lincoln lived to carry out his policy of "malice toward none . . . charity for all," Lee's constructive wish might have come true. A generous peace might have gone a long way toward removing the bitterness between defeated South and victorious North. A sense that all Americans are brothers might have slowly reasserted itself in the shared goal of binding up "the wounds of the nation."

However, Lincoln never lived to carry out his plan. Five days after the surrender at Appomattox, he was struck down by the bullet of the deranged actor John Wilkes Booth. His Secretary of the Navy wrote of the hours after his death: "On the avenue in front of the White House were several hundred colored people, mostly women and children, weeping and wailing their loss. This crowd did not appear to diminish through the whole of that cold, wet day; they seemed not to know what was to be their fate since their great benefactor was dead, and their hopeless grief affected me more than almost anything else, though strong and brave men wept when I met them . . ."

181

O CAPTAIN! MY CAPTAIN!

by Walt Whitman

O Captain! my Captain! our fearful trip is
    done,
The ship has weathered every rack, the prize
    we sought is won,
The port is near, the bells I hear, the people
    all exulting,
While follow eyes the steady keel, the vessel
    grim and daring;
  But O heart; heart! heart!
    O the bleeding drops of red.
      Where on the deck my Captain lies,
      Fallen cold and dead.

O Captain! my Captain! rise up and hear
    the bells;
Rise up—for you the flag is flung—for you
    the bugle trills,
For you bouquets and ribboned wreaths—
    for you the shores a-crowding,
For you they call, the swaying mass, their
    eager faces turning;
  Here Captain! dear father!
    This arm beneath your head!
      It is some dream that on the deck,
      You've fallen cold and dead.

My Captain does not answer, his lips are
    pale and still,
My father does not feel my arm, he has no
    pulse nor will,
The ship is anchored safe and sound, its voy-
    age closed and done,
From fearful trip the victor ship comes in
    with object won;
  Exult, O shores, and ring, O bells!
    But I with mournful tread,
      Walk the deck my Captain lies,
      Fallen cold and dead.

The tragic assassination of Lincoln pro-
voked a revenge-seeking mood of indignation in the North, enabling the Radical Republicans to gain control of Congress.
Ruled by extreme political partisanship (they
wanted to sweep Congress clean of Democrats), it suited their purposes to hold the
entire South accountable for the act of one
madman. Formerly rebellious states were
arbitrarily divided into military districts,
ruled by martial law. Whites who had taken
part in the rebellion were disenfranchised.
"Malice toward all, charity for none" became the order of the day. Lincoln's successor, Johnson, proved too weak to stop
these vengeful Congressmen, and was almost impeached for his pains. The effect
these shortsighted Reconstruction policies
had was to increase Southern bitterness and
resentment, drive the sections farther apart
instead of, as Lincoln had hoped, bringing
them closer together . . . And yet, there were
men in both North and South who tried to
put past hatreds behind them, and concentrated on rebuilding for the future. A Northern visitor to Charleston in 1865 gives us a
shrewd glimpse of the different emotions and
attitudes underlying a typical Southern city
in early Reconstruction days.

CHARLESTON UNDER MILITARY RULE

from "The South Since the War" by Sidney Andrews

On the surface Charleston is quiet and
well behaved, and I do not doubt that the
more intelligent citizens are wholly sincere
in their expressions of a desire for peace and
reunion. The city has been humbled as no
other city has been, and I can't see how any

man, after spending a few days here, can desire that it be further humiliated merely for revenge. Whether it has been humiliated enough for health is another thing. Said one of the Charlestonians on the boat: "You won't see the real sentiment of our people, for we are under military rule; we are whipped, and we are going to make the best of things; but we hate Massachusetts as much as we ever did." This idea of making the best of things is one I have heard from scores of persons. . . . "We made the best fight we could, but you were too strong for us, and now we are only anxious to get back into the old Union and live as happily as we can," said a large cotton factor. I find very few who make any special profession of Unionism, but they are almost unanimous in declaring that they have no desire but to live as good and quiet citizens under the laws.

For the first two months of our occupancy of the city scarcely a white woman but those of the poorer classes was seen on the street, and very few were even seen at the windows and doors of the residences. That order of things is now happily changed. There doesn't yet appear to be as much freedom of appearance as would be natural, but very many of what are called the first ladies are to be seen shopping in the morning and promenading in the evening. They, much more than the men, have contemptuous motions for the Negro soldiers; and scorn for Northern men is frequently apparent in the swing of their skirts when passing on the sidewalk.

One doesn't observe so much pleasantness and cheerfulness as would be agreeable, but the general demeanor is quite consonant with the general mourning costume. A stroller at sunset sees not a few pale and pensive-faced young women of exquisite beauty, and a rambler during the evening not infrequently hears a strain of touching melody from the darkened parlor of some roomy old mansion, with now and then one of the ringing, passionate airs with which the Southern heart has been fired during the war.

It was little wonder that many Southerners, simmering with frustration and resentment at Reconstruction policies right after the war, began to escape to romanticized dreams of past glory. The Radical rulers of Congress presented them with a bleak present and a none-too-promising future. Cut off from political power themselves, they were forced to watch while their legislatures were filled with former field hands and cotton pickers, dominated by corrupt Northern "carpetbag" politicians and Southern "scalawag" collaborators. These wheelers and dealers deliberately sought out not the best examples of Negro leadership—such as the Harriet V. Tubmans and the Frederick Douglasses—but the worst, the least educated and most gullible, those who would provide the most pliable tools for helping them line their own pockets with graft. Certainly they provided travesties of government, but no more so than if the South, before the Civil War, had elected to its legislatures the worst elements—the shiftless, ignorant "white trash"—in its own population. The untutored ex-slave, thrust unprepared into a position of towering responsibility and complexity, did the best he could. He actually enacted some valuable legislation, especially in the field of public education. An observer of a Negro legislature pointed out the following.

183

THE DAY OF JUBILEE

from "The Prostrate State" by James Shepherd Pike

Seven years ago these men were raising corn and cotton under the whip of the overseer. Today they are raising points of order and questions of privilege. They find they can raise one as well as the other. They prefer the latter. It is easier and better paid. Then, it is the result of an accomplished result. It means escape and defense from old oppressors. It means liberty. It means the destruction of prison walls only too real to them. It is the sunshine of their lives. It is their day of jubilee. It is their long-promised vision of the Lord God Almighty.

But they didn't enjoy their day of jubilee for long. An extreme emotional allegiance to white supremacy began to dominate Southern thinking, as a counterreaction to the corrupt carpetbag governments and the sudden power attained by ex-slaves. Secret organizations were formed to intimidate the Negro through fear and violence, to bring him back down to the status of a slave, and to reassert white control. The most powerful of these was the Ku Klux Klan.

Many Negroes were intimidated by the gangsterism of the Klan. They stayed away from the polls and accepted the status of second-class citizenship rather than risk a lynching in the night. But other Negroes refused to accept the principle that "ignorance is bliss." They knew that they and their children needed education in order to fight for their rights and to build a better life; they needed knowledge to be really emancipated from slavery. While white supremacists didn't want to help them, and carpetbaggers wanted to keep them as ignorant tools, there were decent people North and South who did want to help. The Freedman's Bureau was set up. Colleges and institutes for Negroes were founded.

However, Negroes didn't depend alone on white "do-good" charity. They soon showed an impressive determination to struggle upward by their own efforts. An outstanding early example was the great Negro educator Booker T. Washington. He determined to found a college-level school that would develop practical agricultural and industrial skills as well as reading, writing and other subjects. In 1881, he opened the doors of a little shanty and abandoned church (donated by the Negroes of Tuskegee, Alabama) and announced that Tuskegee Institute was in session. He was twenty-five years old at the time. Soon, there were so many students that new quarters were a must. Here is a description of what happened.

A PLANTATION IS TURNED INTO A NEGRO SCHOOL

from "Up From Slavery" by Booker T. Washington

About three months after the opening of the school and at the time when we were in the greatest anxiety about our work, there came into the market for sale an old and abandoned plantation which was situated about a mile from the town of Tuskegee. The mansion house or "big house," as it would have been called, which had been occupied by the owners during slavery, had been burned. After making a careful examination of this place, it seemed to be just the location that we wanted in order to make our work effective and permanent. . . .

I lost no time in getting ready to move the school on to the new farm. At the time we occupied the place there were standing upon it a cabin, formerly used as the dining room, an old kitchen, a stable, and an old hen-house. Within a few weeks we had all of these structures in use. The stable was repaired and used as a recitation room, and very presently the henhouse was utilized for the same purpose.

I recall one morning, when I told an old colored man who lived near and who sometimes helped me that our school had grown so large that it would be necessary for us to use the henhouse for school purposes and that I wanted him to help me give it a thorough cleaning out the next day, he replied in the most earnest manner: "What you mean, boss? You sholy ain't gwine clean out de henhouse in de *daytime?*"

A canvass was also made among the people of both races for direct gifts of money, and most of those applied to gave small sums. It was often pathetic to note the gifts of the older colored people, most of whom had spent their best days in slavery. Sometimes they would give five cents, sometimes twenty-five cents. Sometimes the contribution was a quilt or a quantity of sugar cane. I recall one old colored woman, who was about seventy years of age, who came to see me when we were raising money to pay for the farm. She hobbled into the room where I was, leaning on a cane. She was clad in rags, but they were clean. She said: "Mr. Washin'ton, God knows I spent de bes' days

of my life in slavery. God knows I's ignorant an' poor, but," she added, "I knows what you an' Miss Davidson is tryin' to do. I knows you is tryin' to make better men an' better women for de colored race. I ain't got no money, but I wants you to take dese six eggs what I's been savin' up, an' I wants you to put dese six eggs into de eddication of dese boys an' gals."

Since the work at Tuskegee started, it has been my privilege to receive many gifts for the benefit of the institution, but never any, I think, that touched me so deeply as this one.

Booker T. Washington has been accused by some Negro intellectuals of being a bit of an "Uncle Tom" because he seemed to accept the segregationist *status quo*. But he knew that until Negroes had developed a well-educated, well-organized, well-financed middle class, they were helpless to fight the white supremacists who had gained control of the South due to the bitter taste left by the Reconstruction. Washington was planning for the future. The white Kentucky editor Henry Watterson said of him: "No man, since the war of sections, has . . . done such real good for the country—especially to the South." It was at Tuskegee that the great Negro scientist George Washington Carver performed many of his experiments with the peanut, soybean and sweet potato—experiments that created hundreds of new products and boosted the South's economy . . . The Negro would have a difficult time asserting his rights; but each succeeding generation saw him produce leaders in new fields, and grow in his determination to achieve first-class citizenship.

Meanwhile, New York *Tribune* editor Horace Greeley had been urging the discontented laborer and land-hungry immigrant in the East to "Go West, Young Man!" As a result, Americans rolled westward in ever-increasing numbers, spurred onward by the promise of the Homestead Act of 1862, which guaranteed 160 acres of "God's country" to anybody willing to go out there and stake a claim. Much of the rolling was done in covered wagons or "prairie schooners" of various kinds, traveling in groups for mutual protection. Life in a wagon train beyond the Mississippi is picturesquely described in our next selection, written in the 1860s by a literary "squatter."

WAGONS ROLL WESTWARD

from "Beyond the Mississippi"
by Albert D. Richardson

Toward evening we passed several parties of immigrants, chiefly from Missouri. Come to this encampment and see how kindly frontier families take to a roving life. The long, heavy wagon, its roof covered with white cotton cloth, stands a few yards from the road. It is packed with provisions and household utensils, and two or three pots and kettles are suspended from the hind axle. The tired oxen graze upon the neighboring prairie. The white-haired children are playing hard by—five or six in number, for these new countries are marvelously prolific. The husband is milking the patient cows; the wife is preparing a supper of griddlecakes, bacon,

and coffee, in the open air, at the camp stove; the hens are cackling socially from their coop, while the old family dog wags his tail approvingly, but watches with solicitous care the baby creeping about the wagon.

When crossing the great deserts to Utah or California, they toil wearily along from twelve to twenty miles per day. The long-bearded, shaggy drivers, tanned to the hue of Arapahoes, look like animated pillars of earth, and seem under the perpetual sentence: Dust thou art and unto dust shalt thou return. Each keeps his trusty rifle or shotgun within grasp, and at night the wagons are parked in a circle and the cattle driven into the extemporized yard which they inclose, as a protection against Indian surprises. Eternal vigilance is the price of travel. The children of the immigrants revel in dirt and novelty, but their mothers cast eager, longing eyes toward their new homes. There is profound truth in the remark that plains travel and frontier life are peculiarly severe upon women and oxen.

After the Civil War, a crop of colorful desperadoes thrived on the wide-open frontier, where law and order were hard to find and differences were often settled neatly by the one who could draw the quickest and shoot the straightest. Men turned outlaw for a variety of reasons. Some were "drifters," whose roots had been torn away by the violence of the war, and who roamed around as traveling gunmen, hiring out to the highest bidder in range wars and local feuds. Others nursed a grudge against society or simply preferred getting "easy money" at the point of a gun to sweating for it. Men such as Billy

the Kid and Sam Bass were legends in their own day; but the most famous badman of all was Jesse James, who, with his brother Frank, led a gang of bank and train robbers on a series of daring, successful raids during the 1870s. Jesse's mortal career ended when he was treacherously shot in the back by Robert Ford, a member of his own gang. However, he has since been raised in the popular imagination to the level of an all-American folk hero—taking from the rich and giving to the poor, in the best Robin Hood tradition.

JESSE JAMES

by William Rose Benét

Jesse James was a two-gun man,
  (*Roll on, Missouri!*)
Strong-arm chief of an outlaw clan,
  (*From Kansas to Illinois!*)
He twirled an old Colt forty-five;
  (*Roll on, Missouri!*)
They never took Jesse James alive.
  (*Roll, Missouri, roll!*)

Jesse James was King of the Wes';
  (*Cataracts in the Missouri!*)
He'd a di'mon' heart in his lef' breas';
  (*Brown Missouri rolls!*)
He'd a fire in his heart no hurt could stifle;
  (*Thunder, Missouri!*)
Lion eyes an' a Winchester rifle.
  (*Missouri, roll down!*)

Jesse James rode a pinto hawse;
Come at night to a water-cawse;
Tetched with the rowel that pinto's flank;
She sprung the torrent from bank to bank.

Jesse rode through a sleepin' town;
Looked the moonlit street both up an' down;
Crack-crack-crack, the street ran flames
An' a great voice cried, "I'm Jesse James!"

Hawse an' afoot they're after Jess!
  (*Roll on, Missouri!*)
Spurrin' an' spurrin'—but he's gone Wes'.
  (*Brown Missouri rolls!*)
He was ten foot tall when he stood in his boots;
  (*Lightnin' like the Missouri!*)

187

More'n a match fer sich galoots.
  (*Roll, Missouri, roll!*)

Jesse James rode outa the sage;
Roun' the rocks come the swayin' stage;
Straddlin' the road a giant stan's
An' a great voice bellers, "Throw up yer
    han's!"

Jesse raked in the di'mon' rings,
The big gold watches an' the yuther things;
Jesse divvied 'em then an' thar
With a cryin' child had lost her mar.

* * *

They're creepin'; they're crawlin'; they're
    stalkin' Jess;
  (*Roll on, Missouri!*)
They's a rumor he's gone much further Wes';
  (*Roll, Missouri, roll!*)
They's word of a cayuse hitched to the bars
  (*Ruddy clouds on Missouri!*)
Of a golden sunset that busts into stars.
  (*Missouri, roll down!*)

Jesse James rode hell fer leather;
He was a hawse an' a man together;
In a cave in a mountain high up in air
He lived with a rattlesnake, a wolf, an' a
    bear.

Jesse's heart was as sof' as a woman;
Fer guts an' stren'th he was sooper-human;
He could put six shots through a woodpeck-
    er's eye
And take in one swaller a gallon o' rye.

They sought him here an' they sought him
    there,
  (*Roll on, Missouri!*)

But he strides by night through the ways of
    the air;
  (*Brown Missouri rolls!*)
They say he was took an' they say he is dead,
  (*Thunder, Missouri!*)
But he ain't—he's a sunset overhead!
  (*Missouri down to the sea!*)

Jesse James was a Hercules.
When he went through the woods he tore up
    the trees.
When he went on the plains he smoked the
    groun'
An' the hull lan' shuddered fer miles aroun'.

Jesse James wore a red bandanner
That waved on the breeze like the Star-Span-
    gled Banner;
In seven states he cut up dadoes.
He's gone with the buffler an' the despera-
    does.

Yes, Jesse James was a two-gun man
  (*Roll on, Missouri!*)
The same as when this song began;
  (*From Kansas to Illinois!*)
An' when you see a sunset bust into flames
  (*Lightnin' light the Missouri!*)
Or a thunderstorm blaze—that's Jesse
    James!
  (*Hear that Missouri roll!*)

Another kind of outlaw flourished during this period. Instead of spurs, he sported a solid-gold watch and a shiny top hat. Instead of a gun he carried a Havana cigar. Instead of robbing banks, he robbed people blind by means of phony stock deals or bond issues . . . or drove them out of business through underhanded cut-throat competition. Nobody thought of turning such financial robber barons as Jim Fiske and Jay Gould into folk heroes. They and their associates—the crooked politicians, carpetbaggers and scalawags of the '60s and '70s—had the rapacious instincts of the early conquistadors: Grab the gold, and the devil take the hindmost! The Gilded Age in which they bloomed, especially during the two administrations of honest but naïve President Grant, was the seamiest in American history. Even that great believer in America, Walt Whitman, was moved to write the following:

WALT WHITMAN VERSUS THE GILDED AGE

from "Democratic Vistas" by Walt Whitman

I say we had best look our times and lands searchingly in the face, like a physician diagnosing some deep disease. . . . Genuine belief seems to have left us. . . . We live in an atmosphere of hypocrisy throughout. . . . The depravity of the business classes of our country is not less than has been supposed but infinitely greater. The official services of America, national, state, and municipal, in all their branches and departments except the judiciary, are saturated in corruption, bribery, falsehood, maladministration; and the judiciary is tainted. The great cities reek with respectable as much as nonrespectable robbery and scoundrelism. In business (this all-devouring modern word, business) the one sole object is, by any means, pecuniary gain. The magician's serpent in the fable ate up all the other serpents, and moneymaking is our magician's serpent, remaining today sole master of the field. The best class we show is but a mob of fashionably dressed speculators and vulgarians. . . . It is as if we were somehow being endowed with a vast and more and more thoroughly appointed body and then left with little or no soul.

The American dream had always encouraged the material improvement of people's lives; but now uncontrolled, ruthlessly acquisitive materialism threatened to run the whole show. Giant monopolies gained control of developing railroad and oil industries, among others. "The public be damned!" was the attitude of many ruthless financiers. A new crop of multimillionaires turned its en-

ergies to competing with older, well-established families for control of Society. The "First Family" Brahmins still ruled in Boston, but elsewhere, other values than birth and breeding began to dominate the American version of caste.

CASTE

"Tell me, I pray, what is this *caste?*"

by George F. Jones

* * *

Some say, 'tis birth; this can't be true,
    We *all* descend from Adam;
When this I answer, surely you
    Are bound to own, I had 'em.
Besides, Miss B., who rules it now
    As a social queen of belles,
Descended from a soap-fat man
    And not from F. F. [First Family] swells.
'Tis surely to the present, not the past
Belongs this "Open Sesame," called *Caste.*

Others again unblushingly
    Affirm, that caste means brains,
When dancing men don't know enough
    To go in when it rains;
While authors, artists, poets, men
    Happ'ning to be needy,
Can't enter good society,
    Because they're pronounced *seedy.*
Brains are not caste, so cast your eyes
        around,
If, parhazard, you find some better ground.

What then can this thing be,
    This word of mystic might,
Whose power like a spell
    Unlocks the social right?
It is not birth or brains,

It surely can't be fame,
For that comes after death;
    And besides is but a name.
No, caste is money, and money is caste;
Behold the true solution found at last.

However, money in the bank wasn't enough. The point was to accumulate status symbols on a larger scale than the next millionaire. There weren't any big black Cadillacs or Rolls Royces to be chauffered around in, but you could always take the air in your "coach and four," fill up your New York town house with liveried servants, and build a hundred-room mansion in Newport. To show your "culture," you could buy up some handsomely covered first editions for display purposes (mustn't read them; might wear them out that way). An assemblage of Greek or Roman statues scattered around your lawn—or used as hat and coat racks, if you were of a practical turn of mind—would be bound to impress your callers . . . For Americans of "simple" tastes, Oliver Wendell Holmes had the following suggestions.

CONTENTMENT

"Man wants but little here below"

by Oliver Wendell Holmes

* * *

I care not much for gold or land;—
    Give me a mortgage here and there,—
Some good bankstock, some note of hand,
    Or trifling railroad share,—
I only ask that Fortune send
    A *little* more than I shall spend.

* * *

Jewels are baubles; 'tis a sin
    To care for such unfruitful things;—
One good-sized diamond in a pin,—
    Some, *not so large,* in rings,—
A ruby, and a pearl, or so,
Will do for me;—I laugh at show.

* * *

Of pictures, I should like to own
    Titians and Raphaels three or four,—
I love so much their style and tone,
    One Turner, and no more,
(A landscape,—foreground golden dirt,—
The sunshine painted with a squirt.)

* * *

Busts, cameos, gems,—such things as these,
    Which others often show for pride,
I value for their power to please,
    And selfish churls deride;—
One Stradivarius, I confess,
Two Meerschaums, I would fain possess.

* * *

Thus humble let me live and die,
    Nor long for Midas' golden touch;
If Heaven more generous gifts deny,
    I shall not miss them *much,*—
Too grateful for the blessing lent
Of simple tastes and mind content!

The list of society's cream—New York's "Four Hundred"—was created by social arbiter Ward McAllister in 1892, when Mrs. William Astor was giving a ball. Finding her ballroom would accommodate only four hundred people, she asked McAllister to cut her list down to the required number, and thus the famous term was born. Previous to this, McAllister wrote a book including, among other things, the following description of a private dinner he attended at a famous New York City restaurant . . .

DINNER AT DELMONICO'S, COMPLETE WITH SWANS

from "Society As I Have Found It"
by Ward McAllister

The banquet was given at Delmonico's in Fourteenth Street. There were seventy-two guests in the large ballroom looking on Fifth Avenue.

The table covered the whole length and breadth of the room, only leaving a passageway for the waiters to pass around it. It was a long extended oval table, and every inch of it was covered with flowers, excepting a space in the center, left for a lake, and a border around the table for the plates. This lake was indeed a work of art; it was an oval pond, thirty feet in length, by nearly the width of the table, inclosed by a delicate golden wire network reaching from table to ceiling, making the whole one grand cage; four superb swans, brought from Prospect Park, swam in it, surrounded by high banks of flowers of every species and variety, which prevented them from splashing the water on the table. There were hills and dales; the modest little violet carpeting the valleys, and other bolder sorts climbing up and covering the tops of those miniature mountains. Then, all around the enclosure and in fact above the entire table, hung little golden cages with fine songsters who filled the room with their melody, occasionally interrupted by the splashing of the waters of the lake by

191

the swans and the cooing of these noble birds
and at one time by a fierce combat between
these stately, graceful, gliding white creatures. The surface of the whole table, by
clever art, was one unbroken series of undulations, rising and falling like the billows of
the sea, but all clothed and carpeted with
every form of blossom. It seemed like the
abode of fairies, and when surrounding this
fairyland with lovely young American wom-
anhood, you had indeed an unequaled scene
of enchantment. But this was not to be alone
a feast for the eye; all that art could do, all
that the cleverest men could devise to spread
before the guests, such a feast as the gods
should enjoy, was done, and so well done that
all present felt, in the way of feasting, that
man could do no more! The wines were perfect. Blue seal Johannisberger flowed like
water. Incomparable '48 claret, superb Bur-

gundies, and amber-colored Madeira, all were there to add to the intoxicating delight of the scene. Then soft music stole over one's senses; lovely women's eyes sparkled with delight at the beauty of their surroundings, and I felt that the fair being who sat next to me would have graced Alexander's feast.

Social extravagance, business ruthlessness and political corruption—these were the marks of the age. Yet, there was another side to the picture. Steel magnate Andrew Carnegie ended up donating much of his fortune to the furtherance of world peace. Other industrialists, possibly pricked by uneasy consciences, endowed universities, built public libraries, and supported various philanthropies. The most notorious of the corrupt politicians—"Boss" Tweed of New York—was finally defeated by a reform movement, given impetus by the crusading editorials of *The New York Times* and the political cartoons of Thomas Nast. (A famous Nast caricature depicted Tweed as a pious-looking vulture saying "Let us prey" to his followers. Nast also created the symbolic Tammany tiger, Democratic donkey and Republican elephant.) In regard to politics as a whole, the canny old promoter P. T. Barnum had this to say:

BARNUM ON "HUMBUG" IN POLITICS

from "The Humbugs of the World"
by P. T. Barnum

But need I explain to my own beloved countrymen that there is humbug in politics? Does anybody go into a political campaign without it? Are no exaggerations of *our* candidate's merits to be allowed? No depreciations of the *other* candidate? Shall we no longer prove that the success of the party opposed to us will overwhelm the land with ruin? Let me see. Leaving out the two elections of General Washington, eighteen times that very fact has been proved by the party that was beaten, and immediately we have *not* been ruined, notwithstanding that the dreadful fatal fellows on the other side got their hands on the offices and their fingers into the treasury.

Barnum was paying tribute—in a rather cynical way—to the essential strength of America. Civil war, financial scandals, panics, depressions, corruption—these things might temporarily disrupt the country; but it showed a remarkable ability to survive them all and shake off their effects with institutions intact. The flexibility of the Constitution proved a godsend, and many of the robber baron "public be damned" abuses so prevalent in the Gilded Age would eventually be corrected by new Federal regulatory acts tacked on to the ever-lengthening tail of the Constitution. Also, tycoons like John D. Rockefeller, Sr.—while undoubtedly ruthless—provided the energy and drive that made America a great industrial power, increasing the production of petroleum, steel, coal and other products to unheard-of heights. American will and ingenuity were perfecting the telephone, the electric light, and the use of complex machinery to speed up production and solve a huge variety of problems. It was an age that scorned such ideas as "It can't be done!"

Symbolic of the dynamic spirit of the time was the growing network of railroads that spread across the country, cutting through mountains, crossing rivers and deserts, uniting cities and towns. The labor gangs that built the railroads provided one of America's favorite folk heroes, the great Negro steel-driver, John Henry. Traditionally, he is supposed to have died, hammer in hand, after winning a steel-driving race with a mechanical steam drill at the Big Bend Tunnel in West Virginia, in 1870. Whether or not it is partially based on fact, John Henry's story has come to symbolize the classic struggle between the man who earns his living with his hands and the machine that threatens to steal his job away.

JOHN HENRY

Anonymous

John Henry was a lil baby,
Sittin' on his mama's knee,
Said: "De Big Bend Tunnel on de C. & O.
    road
Gonna cause de death of me,
Lawd, lawd, gonna cause de death of me."

Cap'n says to John Henry,
"Gonna bring me a steam drill 'round,
Gonna take dat steam drill out on de job,
Gonna whop dat steel on down,
Lawd, Lawd, gonna whop dat steel on
    down."

John Henry tol' his cap'n,
Lightnin' was in his eye:
"Cap'n, bet yo' las' red cent on me,

Fo' I'll beat it to de bottom or I'll die,
Lawd, Lawd, I'll beat it to de bottom or
    I'll die."

Sun shine hot an' burnin',
Wer'n't no breeze a-tall,
Sweat ran down like water down a hill,
Dat day John Henry let his hammer fall,
Lawd, Lawd, dat day John Henry let his
    hammer fall.

John Henry went to de tunnel,
An' dey put him in de lead to drive,
De rock so tall an' John Henry so small,
Dat he lay down his hammer an' he cried,
Lawd, Lawd, dat he lay down his hammer
    an' he cried.

John Henry started on de right hand,
De steam drill started on de lef'—
"Before I'd let dis steam drill beat me down,
I'd hammer my fool self to death,
Lawd, Lawd, I'd hammer my fool self to
    death."

White man tol' John Henry,
"Driver, cuss yo' soul,
You might beat dis steam an' drill of mine,
When de rocks in dis mountain turn to gol',
Lawd, Lawd, when de rocks in dis mountain
    turn to gol'."

John Henry said to his shaker,
"Shaker, why don' you sing?
I'm throwin' twelve poun's from my hips on
    down,
Jes' listen to de col' steel ring,
Lawd, Lawd, jes' listen to de col' steel ring."

Oh, de captain said to John Henry,
"I b'lieve this mountain's sinkin' in."
John Henry said to his captain, oh my!
"Ain' nothin' but my hammer suckin' win',
Lawd, Lawd, ain' nothin' but my hammer
    suckin' win'."

John Henry tol' his shaker,
"Shaker, you better pray,
For, if I miss dis six-foot steel,
Tomorrow'll be yo' buryin' day,
Lawd, Lawd, tomorrow'll be yo' burying
    day."

John Henry tol' his captain,
"Look yonder what I see—
Yo' drill's done broke an' yo' hole's done
    choke,
An' you cain' drive steel like me,
Lawd, Lawd, an' you cain' drive steel like
    me."

De man dat invented de steam drill,
Thought he was mighty fine.
John Henry drove his fifteen feet,
An' de steam drill only made nine,
Lawd, Lawd, an' de steam drill only made
    nine.

De hammer dat John Henry swung,
It weighed over nine pound;
He broke a rib in his lef'-han side,
An' his intrels fell on de groun',
Lawd, Lawd, an' his intrels fell on de groun'.

All de womens in de Wes',
When dey heared of John Henry's death,
Stood in de rain, flagged de eas'-boun' train,
Goin' where John Henry fell dead,
Lawd, Lawd, goin' where John Henry fell
    dead.

John Henry's lil mother,
She was all dressed in red,
She jumped in bed, covered up her head,
Said she didn' know her son was dead,
Lawd, Lawd, didn' know her son was dead.

Dey took John Henry to de graveyard,
An' dey buried him in de san',
An' every locomotive come roarin' by,
Says, "Dere lays a steel-drivin' man,
Lawd, Lawd, dere lays a steel-drivin' man."

195

One of the great engineering feats of American history was the building of the transcontinental railroad, uniting New York and California. Supported by government subsidy, the Union Pacific built westward from Iowa while the Central Pacific built eastward from California. The work took several years during the 1860s, and was carried out under conditions which included numerous raids on laboring gangs by plains Indians, who read their doom in the coming of the white man's iron horse. The two railroad lines approached each other in Utah, May, 1869, and friction promptly developed between the Chinese laborers on the Central Pacific and the Irish laborers on the Union Pacific. Grenville M. Dodge, chief engineer of the Union Pacific, has left us this description of how a meeting of the East and West was accomplished—in terms of both nationalities and railroad lines . . .

EAST MEETS WEST ON THE TRANSCONTINENTAL RAILROAD

from "How We Built the Union Pacific"
by Grenville M. Dodge

The laborers upon the Central Pacific were Chinamen, while ours were Irishmen, and there was much ill feeling between them. Our Irishmen were in the habit of firing their blasts in the cuts without giving warning to the Chinamen on the Central Pacific working right above them. From this cause several Chinamen were severely hurt. Complaint was made to me by the Central Pacific people, and I endeavored to have the contractors bring all hostilities to a close; but

for some reason or other they failed to do so. One day the Chinamen, appreciating the situation, put in what is called a "grave" on their work and, when the Irishmen right under them were all at work, let go their blast and buried several of our men. This brought about a truce at once. From that time the Irish laborers showed due respect for the Chinamen, and there was no further trouble.

When the two roads approached in May, 1869, we agreed to connect at the summit of Promontory Point; and the day was fixed so that trains could reach us from New York and California. We laid the rails to the junction point a day or two before the final closing. . . . The two trains pulled up facing each other, each crowded with workmen who sought advantageous positions to witness the ceremonies and literally covered the cars. The officers and invited guests formed on each side of the track, leaving it open to the south. The telegraph lines had been brought to that point, so that in the final spiking, as each blow was struck the telegraph recorded it at each connected office from the Atlantic to the Pacific. Prayer was offered; a number of spikes were driven in the two adjoining rails, each one of the prominent persons present taking a hand, but very few hitting the spikes, to the great amusement of the crowd. When the last spike was placed, light taps were given upon it by several officials, and it was finally driven home by the chief engineer of the Union Pacific Railway. The engineers ran up their locomotives until they touched, the engineer upon each engine breaking a bottle of champagne upon the other one, and thus the two roads were wedded into one great trunk line from the Atlantic to the Pacific. Spikes of silver and gold were brought specially for the occasion and later were manufactured into miniature spikes as mementoes of the occasion. It was a bright but cold day. After a few speeches we all took refuge in the Central Pacific cars, where wine flowed freely and many speeches were made.

With the nation joined together by railroad ties, the siren call of the train whistle began to replace that of the river steamboat as the summons to high adventure, escape, new horizons . . .

TRAVEL

by Edna St. Vincent Millay

The railroad track is miles away,
    And the day is loud with voices speaking;
Yet there isn't a train goes by all day
    But I hear its whistle shrieking.

All night there isn't a train goes by,
    Though the night is still for sleep and
        dreaming,
But I see its cinders red on the sky,
    And hear its engine steaming.

My heart is warm with the friends I make,
    And better friends I'll not be knowing;
Yet there isn't a train I wouldn't take,
    No matter where it's going.

The railroad enormously speeded up settlement of the West. Railroad companies wanted towns, farms, and businesses to spring up in the wilderness so that they could increase their freight as well as their passenger traffic. They used every kind of promotional device to entice emigrants to buy tickets to "God's country"—and the people responded in the thousands. Travel by train across the plains in those days had few of the comforts that we associate with the streamlined, air-conditioned Pullman coaches of today. Famed English author Robert Louis Stevenson made the trip in 1879, and here are a few of his comments.

ROUGHING IT ON THE RAILROAD

from "Across the Plains"
by Robert Louis Stevenson

It was about two in the afternoon of Friday that I found myself in front of the Emigrant House [Council Bluffs, Iowa], with more than a hundred others, to be sorted and boxed for the journey. A white-haired official with a stick under one arm and a list in the other hand stood apart in front of us and called name after name in the tone of a command. At each name you would see a family gather up its brats and bundles and run for the hindmost of the three cars that stood awaiting us, and I soon concluded that this was to be set apart for the women and children. The second or central car, it turned out, was devoted to men traveling alone, and the third to Chinese. The official was easily moved to anger at the least delay, but the emigrants were both quick at answering their names and speedy in getting themselves and their effects on board.

The families once housed, we men carried the second car without ceremony by simultaneous assault. I suppose the reader has some notion of an American railroad car, that long, narrow wooden box like a flat-roofed Noah's ark, with a stove and a convenience, one at either end, a passage down the middle, and transverse benches upon either hand. Those destined for emigrants on the Union Pacific are only remarkable for their extreme plainness, nothing but wood entering in any part into their constitution, and for the usual inefficacy of the lamps, which often went out and shed but a dying glimmer even while they burned. The benches are too short for anything but a young child. Where there is scarce elbow-room for two to sit, there will not be space enough for one to lie. Hence the company, or rather, as it appears from certain bills about the transfer station, the company's servants, have conceived a plan for the better accommodation of travelers. They prevail on every two to chum together. To each of the chums they sell a board and three square cushions stuffed with straw and covered with thin cotton. The benches can be made to face each other in pairs, for the backs are reversible. On the approach of night the boards are laid from bench to bench, making a couch wide enough for two and long enough for a man of the middle height; and the chums lie down side by side upon the cushions with the head to the conductor's van and the feet to the engine. . . .

And when I think how the railroad has been pushed through this unwatered wilderness and haunt of savage tribes and now will bear an emigrant for some twelve pounds from the Atlantic to the Golden Gates; how at each stage of the construction roaring, impromptu cities, full of gold and lust and death, sprang up and then died away again, and are now but wayside stations in the desert; how in these uncouth places pigtailed Chinese pirates worked side by side with border ruffians and broken men from Europe, talking together in a mixed dialect, mostly oaths, gambling, drinking, quarreling, and murdering like wolves; how the plumed hereditary lord of all America heard, in this last fastness, the scream of the "bad medicine wagon" charioting his foes; and then when I go on to remember that all this epical turmoil was conducted by gentlemen in frock coats and with a view to nothing more extraordinary than a fortune and a subsequent visit to Paris, it seems to me, I own, as if this railway were the one typical achievement of the age in which we live, as if it brought together into one plot all the ends of the world and all the degrees of social rank, and offered to some great writer the busiest, the most extended, and the most varied subject for an enduring literary work. If it be romance, if it be contrast, if it be heroism that we require, what was Troy town to this?

The first white men to arrive on the plains found them teeming with vast herds of buffalo—bison, really—and other wild animals, all roaming free . . .

OH, GIVE ME A HOME WHERE THE BUFFALO ROAM

Anonymous

Oh, give me a home where the buffalo roam,
Where the deer and the antelope play,
Where seldom is heard a discouraging word,
And the skies are not cloudy all day.

Chorus:
Home, home on the range,
Where the deer and the antelope play,
Where seldom is heard a discouraging word,
And the skies are not cloudy all day.

How often at night when the heavens are
  bright
With the light of the glittering stars,
Have I stood there amazed and ask'd as I
  gazed,
If their glory exceeds that of ours.

Chorus:
Home, home on the range,
Where the deer and the antelope play,
Where seldom is heard a discouraging word,
And the skies are not cloudy all day.

The coming of the railroad, bearing ever-increasing streams of settlers, changed all this. The great herds of buffalo were practically exterminated by white hunters in the '70s and '80s. The Indians, who had depended on them for subsistence, were gradually subdued and penned up on reservations (but not before numerous last-ditch uprisings, which included the Sioux massacre of Custer and his men at Little Big Horn in 1876). As the buffalo disappeared, herds of branded beef cattle took over the open range. The railroad made cattle ranching enormously profitable, since now beef could be shipped quickly and in great numbers to the stock markets in the East. Cattlemen let their steers grow fat on the plains grass, then rounded them up for the "long drive" to one of the cow-towns on the Kansas or Union Pacific railroads, where they would be loaded into cattle cars and shipped to

market. The cowboys who were chosen to ride night-herd would sing softly to the cattle to keep them from getting nervous and stampeding. Here's one of the most famous of the old cowboy songs. (The "dogies" referred to are yearling calves, which tend to lag behind the herd.)

WHOOPEE TI YI YO, GIT ALONG, LITTLE DOGIES

Anonymous

As I was a-walking one morning for pleas-
  ure,
I spied a cow-puncher all riding alone;
His hat was throw'd back and his spurs was
  a-jinglin',
As he approach'd me a-singin' this song:

Whoopee ti yi yo, git along, little dogies,
It's your misfortune and none of my own.
Whoopee ti yi yo, git along, little dogies,
For you know Wyoming will be your new
  home.

Early in the spring we round up the dogies,
Mark and brand and bob off their tails;
Round up our horses, load up the chuck-
  wagon,
Then throw the dogies upon the trail.

It's whooping and yelling and driving the
  dogies;
Oh, how I wish you would go on;
It's whooping and punching and go on, little
  dogies,
For you know Wyoming will be your new
  home.

Some boys goes up the trail for pleasure,
But that's where you get it most awfully
    wrong;
For you haven't any idea the trouble they
    give us
While we go driving them all along.

When the night comes on and we hold them
    on the bedground,
These little dogies that roll on so slow;
Roll up the herd and cut out the strays,
And roll the little dogies that never rolled
    before.

Your mother she was raised way down in
    Texas,
Where jimson weed and sand-burrs grow;
Now we'll fill you up on prickly pear and
    cholla
Till you are ready for the trail to Idaho.

Oh, you'll be soup for Uncle Sam's Injuns;
"It's beef, heap beef," I hear them cry.
Git along, git along, git along, little dogies;
You're going to be beef steers by and by.

As the backwoods hunter-trapper faded
out of the picture, the cowboy took over as
American boyhood's (and, to be honest,
manhood's) favorite hero. The lean, soft-
spoken, hard-drinking, straight-shooting, tall-
in-the-saddle figure of the cowboy in his ten-
gallon hat has become America's favorite
symbol of both manly virility and escape
from the hemming-in complexities of modern industrial civilization. His horse and cattle have thundered across the pages of countless pulp novels . . . On the silver screen, the
face beneath the ten-gallon hat has changed
from Tom Mix to Gary Cooper, Gene Autry,

Roy Rogers, John Wayne—and now, a whole new crop of television cowboys is talking small and acting big on the network range. (Actually, most movie and television cowboys wouldn't be worth their keep to a rancher, since they seem to spend most of their time getting involved in shooting matches and solving other people's problems.) The legendary hero of real cowboys —Pecos Bill—was a rip-snorting, ring-tailed roarer in spurs.

THE SAGA OF PECOS BILL

by Edward O'Reilly

According to the most veracious historians, Bill was born about the same time Sam Houston discovered Texas. His mother was a sturdy pioneer woman who once killed forty-five Indians with a broom-handle, and weaned him on moonshine liquor when he was three days old. He cut his teeth on a bowie-knife, and his earliest playfellows were the bears and catamounts of east Texas.

When Bill was about a year old, another family moved into the country and located about fifty miles down the river. His father decided the place was gettin' too crowded, and packed his family in a wagon and headed west.

One day after they crossed the Pecos River, Bill fell out of the wagon. As there were sixteen or seventeen other children in the family, his parents didn't miss him for four or five weeks, and then it was too late to try to find him.

That's how Bill came to grow up with the coyotes along the Pecos. He soon learned the coyote language, and used to hunt with them and sit on the hills and howl at night. Being so young when he got lost, he always thought he was a coyote. That's where he learned to kill deer by runnin' them to death.

One day when he was about ten years old a cow-boy came along just when Bill had matched a fight with two grizzly bears. Bill hugged the bears to death, tore off a hind leg, and was just settin' down to breakfast when this cow-boy loped up and asked him what he meant by runnin' around naked that way among the varmints.

"Why, because I am a varmint," Bill told him. "I'm a coyote."

The cow-boy argued with him that he was a human, but Bill wouldn't believe him.

"Ain't I got fleas?" he insisted. "And don't I howl a-round all night, like a respectable coyote should do?"

"That don't prove nothin'," the cow-boy answered. "All Texans have fleas, and most of them howl. Did you ever see a coyote that didn't have a tail? Well, you ain't got no tail; so that proves you ain't a varmint."

Bill looked, and, sure enough, he didn't have a tail.

"You sure got me out on a limb," says Bill. "I never noticed that before. It shows what higher education will do for a man. I believe you're right. Lead me to them humans, and I'll throw in with them."

Bill went to town with his cow-hand, and in due time he got to enjoyin' all the pleasant vices of mankind, and decided that he certainly was a human. He got to runnin' with the wild bunch, and sunk lower and lower, until finally he became a cow-boy. . . .

He saddled up his horse and hit for the

West. One day he met an old trapper and told him what he was lookin' for.

"I want the hardest cow outfit in the world," he says. "Not one of these ordinary cow-stealin', Mexican-shootin' bunches of amateurs, but a real hard herd of hand-picked hellions that make murder a fine art and take some proper pride in their slaughter."

"Stranger, you're headed in the right direction," answers the trapper. "Keep right on down this draw for a couple of hundred miles, and you'll find that very outfit. They're so hard they can kick fire out of a flint rock with their bare toes."

Bill single-footed down that draw for about a hundred miles that afternoon; then he met with an accident. His horse stubbed his toe on a mountain and broke his leg, leavin' Bill afoot.

He slung his saddle over his shoulder and set off hikin' down that draw, cussin' and a-swearin'. Profanity was a gift with Bill.

All at once a big ten-foot rattlesnake quiled up in his path, set his tail to singin', and allowed he'd like to match a fight. Bill laid down his saddle, and just to be fair about it, he gave the snake the first three bites. Then he waded into that reptile and everlastingly frailed the pizen out of him.

By and by that old rattler yelled for mercy, and admitted that when it came to fightin', Bill started where he let off. So Bill picked up his saddle and started on, carryin' the snake in his hand and spinnin' it in short loops at the Gila monsters.

About fifty miles further on, a big old mountain-lion jumped off a cliff and lit all spraddled out on Bill's neck. This was no ordinary lion. It weighed more than three steers and a yearlin', and was the very same lion the State of Nuevo León was named after down in old Mexico.

Kind of chucklin' to himself, Bill laid down his saddle and his snake and went into action. In a minute the fur was flyin' down the cañon until it darkened the sun. The way Bill knocked the animosity out of that lion was a shame. In about three minutes that lion hollered:

"I'll give up, Bill. Can't you take a joke?"

Bill let him up, and then he cinched the saddle on him and went down that cañon whoopin' and yellin', ridin' that lion a hundred feet at a jump, and quirtin' him down the flank with the rattlesnake.

It wasn't long before he saw a chuck-wagon with a bunch of cow-boys squattin' around it. He rode up to that wagon, splittin' the air with his war-whoops, with that old lion a-screechin', and that snake singin' his rattles.

When he came to the fire he grabbed the old cougar by the ear, jerked him back on his haunches, stepped off him, hung his snake around his neck, and looked the outfit over. Them cow-boys sat there sayin' less than nothin'.

Bill was hungry, and seein' a boilerful of beans cookin' on the fire, he scooped up a few handfuls and swallowed them, washin' them down with a few gallons of boilin' coffee out of the pot. Wipin' his mouth on a handful of prickly-pear cactus, Bill turned to the cow-boys and asked:

"Who the hell is boss around here?"

A big fellow about eight feet tall, with seven pistols and nine bowie-knives in his belt, rose up and, takin' off his hat, said:

"Stranger, I was; but you be." . . .

There is a great difference of opinion as to the manner of Bill's demise. Many claim that it was his drinkin' habits that killed him. You see, Bill got so that liquor didn't have any kick for him, and he fell into the habit of drinkin' strychnine and other forms of wolf pizen.

Even the wolf bait lost its effect, and he got to puttin' fish-hooks and barbed wire in his toddy. It was the barbed wire that finally killed him. It rusted his interior and gave him indigestion. He wasted away to a mere skeleton, weighin' not more than two tons; then up and died, and went to his infernal reward.

Many of the border bards who knew Pecos Bill at his best have a different account of his death.

They say that he met a man from Boston one day, wearing a mail-order cow-boy outfit, and askin' fool questions about the West; and poor old Bill laid down and laughed himself to death.

Gradually, as more and more emigrants poured into Western territories, the open range was fenced in, most of the good land was taken up by farms, ranches and town lots, and towns themselves began to fill up. People who had made the long trek to "God's country" began to find themselves faced with unemployment or reduced to scrabbling for a living on land nobody else wanted. Many of them ended up trickling back East. The nature of the country was changing, the wide-open geographical frontier coming to an end. As the land filled up, the figure who had dominated so much of American history —the "Westering" pioneer with his long rifle, his axe, and his exuberant cry of

"Room, boys, room!"—began to fade away . . .

THE BALLAD OF WILLIAM SYCAMORE

by Stephen Vincent Benét

My father, he was a mountaineer,
His fist was a knotty hammer;
He was quick on his feet as a running deer,
And he spoke with a Yankee stammer.

My mother, she was merry and brave,
And so she came to her labor,
With a tall green fir for her doctor grave
And a stream for her comforting neighbor.

And some are wrapped in the linen fine,
And some like a godling's scion;
But I was cradled on twigs of pine
In the skin of a mountain lion.

And some remember a white, starched lap
And a ewer with silver handles;
But I remember a coonskin cap
And the smell of bayberry candles.

The cabin logs, with the bark still rough,
And my mother who laughed at trifles,
And the tall, lank visitors, brown as snuff,
With their long, straight squirrel rifles.

I can hear them dance, like a foggy song,
Through the deepest one of my slumbers,
The fiddle squeaking the boots along
And my father calling the numbers.

The quick feet shaking the puncheon floor,
And the fiddle squealing and squealing,
Till the dried herbs rattled above the door
And the dust went up to the ceiling.

203

There are children lucky from dawn to dusk,
But never a child so lucky!
For I cut my teeth on "Money Musk"
In the Bloody Ground of Kentucky!

When I grew tall as the Indian corn,
My father had little to lend me,
But he gave me his great, old powder horn
And his woodsman's skill to befriend me.

With a leather shirt to cover my back,
And a redskin nose to unravel
Each forest sign, I carried my pack
As far as a scout could travel.

Till I lost my boyhood and found my wife,
A girl like a Salem clipper!
A woman straight as a hunting knife
With eyes as bright as the Dipper!

We cleared our camp where the buffalo feed,
Unheard-of streams were our flagons;
And I sowed my sons like the apple seed
On the trail of the Western wagons.

They were right, tight boys, never sulky or
    slow,
A fruitful, goodly muster.
The eldest died at the Alamo.
The youngest fell with Custer.

The letter that told it burned my hand.
Yet we smiled and said "So be it!"
But I could not live when they fenced the
    land,
For it broke my heart to see it.

I saddled a red, unbroken colt
And rode him into the day there;
And he threw me down like a thunderbolt
And rolled on me as I lay there.

The hunter's whistle hummed in my ear
As the city men tried to move me,
And I died in my boots like a pioneer
With the whole wide sky above me.

Now I lie in the heart of the fat, black soil,
Like the seed of a prairie thistle;
It has washed my bones with honey and oil
And picked them clean as a whistle.

And my youth returns, like the rains of
    Spring,
And my sons, like the wild geese flying;
And I lie and hear the meadowlark sing
And I have much content in my dying.

Go play with the towns you have built of
    blocks,
The towns where you would have bound me!
I sleep in my earth like a tired fox,
And my buffalo have found me.

The balance of American society began to shift from the rural to the urban. Industrial towns were springing up, great cities like New York were booming . . .

MANNAHATTA

by Walt Whitman

I was asking for something specific and per-
    fect for my city,
Whereupon lo! upsprang the aboriginal
    name.

Now I see what there is in a name, a word,
    liquid, sane, unruly, musical, self-suf-
    ficient,
I see that the word of my city is that word
    from of old,
Because I see that word nested in nests of
    water-bays, superb,

Rich, hemm'd thick all around with sailships and steamships, an island sixteen miles long, solid-founded.

Numberless crowded streets, high growth of iron, slender, strong, light, splendidly uprising toward clear skies,

Tides swift and ample, well-loved by me, toward sundown,

The flowing sea-currents, the little islands, larger adjoining islands, the heights, the villas,

The countless masts, the white shore-steamers, the lighters, the ferry-boats, the black sea-steamers well-model'd,

The down-town streets, the jobbers' houses of business, the houses of business of the ship-merchants and money-brokers, the river-streets,

Immigrants arriving, fifteen or twenty thousand in a week . . .

Immigration—not emigration—was the symbol of the '80s and '90s. The Western land frontier might be closing up, but America was still the magic land of opportunity to the steerage passengers in rough caps and shawls who lined the decks of incoming ships, waiting eagerly for their first glimpse of the Statue of Liberty. The great statue—a gift from France in the '80s—still lifts its torch of freedom high above New York harbor. It bears this poem.

THE NEW COLOSSUS

by Emma Lazarus

Not like the brazen giant of Greek fame,
With conquering limbs astride from land to
    land;
Here at our sea-washed, sunset gates shall
    stand
A mighty woman with a torch, whose flame
Is the imprisoned lightning, and her name
Mother of Exiles. From her beacon-hand
Glows world-wide welcome; her mild eyes
    command
The air-bridged harbor that twin cities frame.
"Keep, ancient lands, your storied pomp!"
    cries she
With silent lips. "Give me your tired, your
    poor,
Your huddled masses yearning to breathe
    free,
The wretched refuse of your teeming shore.
Send these, the homeless, tempest-tost to me,
I lift my lamp beside the golden door!"

Immigrants streamed ashore, expecting to find the streets of American cities paved with gold. Instead, they often found discrimination, exploitation by sweatshop proprietors and slum landlords who charged high rates for miserable living quarters in tenements. But there were still precious advantages over the Old Country. In America they had freedom of speech and movement, a voice in the making of their government, the opportunity to rise as high as their own talents and initiative could take them. The great social reformer, Jacob Riis, in the following selection, condemns the conditions under which first-generation immigrants had to live—and, at the same time, praises their pioneer-style determination not only to survive but to *thrive*.

TENEMENT DWELLERS IN 1890

from "How the Other Half Lives" by Jacob Riis

New York's wage earners have no other place to live, more is the pity. They are truly poor for having no better homes; waxing poorer in purse as the exorbitant rents to which they are tied, as ever was serf to soil, keep rising. The wonder is that they are not all corrupted, and speedily, by their surroundings. If on the contrary there be a steady working *up,* if not *out* of the slough, the fact is a powerful argument for the optimist's belief that the world is after all growing better not worse, and would go far toward disarming apprehension were it not for the steadier growth of the sediment of the slums and its constant menace. Such an impulse toward better things there certainly is. The German ragpicker of thirty years ago, quite as low in the scale as his Italian successor, is the thrifty tradesman or prosperous farmer of today.

The Italian scavenger of our time is fast graduating into exclusive control of the corner fruit stands, while his black-eyed boy monopolizes the bootblacking industry in which a few years ago he was an intruder. The Irish hod carrier in the second generation has become a bricklayer, if not the alderman of his ward, while the Chinese coolie is in almost exclusive possession of the laundry business. The reason is obvious. The poorest immigrant comes here with the purpose and ambition to better himself and, given half a chance, might be reasonably expected to make the most of it. To the false plea that he prefers the squalid homes in which his kind are housed there could be no better answer. The truth is his half chance has too long been wanting, and for the bad result he has been unjustly blamed.

When things seemed too tough, newcomers could remind themselves of the example set by such as the Scottish-American steel magnate Andrew Carnegie. Hadn't he started out as an overworked, underpaid immigrant lad? Here is his own recollection of his first job in America.

ANDREW CARNEGIE MAKES $1.20 A WEEK

from "The Gospel of Wealth" by Andrew Carnegie

On arriving in Allegheny City (there were four of us: Father, Mother, my younger brother and myself), my father entered a cotton factory. I soon followed and served as a "bobbin boy," and this is how I began my preparation for subsequent apprenticeship as a businessman. I received one dollar and twenty cents a week and was then just about twelve years old.

I cannot tell you how proud I was when I received my first week's own earnings. One dollar and twenty cents made by myself and given to me because I had been some use in the world! No longer entirely dependent upon my parents, but at last admitted to the family partnership as a contributing member and able to help them! I think this makes a man out of a boy sooner than almost anything else, and a real man, too, if there be any germ of true manhood in him. It is everything to feel that you are useful. . . .

For a lad of twelve to rise and breakfast every morning, except the blessed Sunday morning, and go into the streets and find his way to the factory and begin to work while it was still dark outside, and not be released until after darkness came again in the evening, forty minutes' interval only being allowed at noon, was a terrible task.

But I was young and had my dreams, and something within always told me that this would not, could not, should not last—I should some day get into a better position.

Carnegie—and many immigrants who followed him—worked themselves up to positions of wealth and prestige. Immigrants who didn't make it in their own generation might scrimp and save so that their children could go to college, enter professions. Wasn't a great American President "born without a chance," of poor parents, in a humble cabin? Above all, in America, there was always hope of tomorrow . . .

HOPE IS THE THING WITH FEATHERS

by Emily Dickinson

Hope is the thing with feathers
That perches in the soul,
And sings the tune without the words,
And never stops at all.

And sweetest in the gale is heard;
And sore must be the storm
That could abash the little bird
That kept so many warm.

I've heard it in the chillest land,
And on the strangest sea;
Yet, never, in extremity,
It asked a crumb of me.

Each new immigrant group added its own unique flavor and contribution to the vast American melting pot. Among the first to come were the Irish, many of them among the early pioneers. During the 1840s, '50s, and '60s, the combination of potato famine in Ireland and railroad building—with its demand for labor in the States—greatly increased Irish immigration.

During the '80s and '90s, there were many new waves of immigration from other parts of Europe—Italians, Poles, Jews, Lithuanians, Scandinavians and others. Those who had come a generation earlier tended to feel superior to "Johnny-come-latelies"—in the same way that seniors traditionally look down their noses at freshmen. How an Italian immigrant handled this sort of prejudice is humorously shown in our next poem.

TWO 'MERICANA MEN

by Thomas Augustine Daly

Beeg Irish cop dat walks hees beat
    By dees peanutta stan',
First two, t'ree week w'en we are meet
    Eees call me "Dagoman."
An' w'en he see how mad I gat,
    Wheech eesa pleass heem, too,
Wan day he say: "W'at's matter dat,
    Ain't 'Dago' name for you?
Dat's 'Mericana name, you know,
    For man from Eetaly;

Eet ees no harm for call you so,
    Den why be mad weeth me?"

First time he talka deesa way
    I am too mad for speak,
But nexta time I justa say:
    "All righta, Meester Meeck!"
O! my, I nevva hear bayfore
    Sooch langwadge like he say;
An' he don't look at me no more
    For mebee two, t'ree day.
But pretta soon agen I see
    Dees beeg poleecaman
Dat com' an' growl an' say to me:
    "Hallo, Eyetalian!
Now, mebee so you gon' deny
    Dat dat's a name for you."
I smila back, an' mak' reply:
    "No, Irish, dat'sa true."
"Ha! Joe," he cry, "you theenk dat we
    Should call you 'Merican?"
"Dat's gooda 'nough," I say, "for me,
    Eef dat's w'at you are, Dan."

So now all times we speaka so
    Like gooda 'Merican:
He say to me, "Good morna, Joe,"
    I say, "Good morna, Dan."

Outstanding Americans have been produced by every race, color and creed. Bernard Baruch, Fiorello Laguardia, Jacob Riis, Ralph Bunche—the list stretches on and on. Late nineteenth and early twentieth century boys who dreamed of becoming great men devoured Horatio Alger success stories and took full advantage of America's free public schools. As well as absorbing the usual courses of study, they paid serious attention

208

to elocution lessons—for it was common knowledge that, since the days of Patrick Henry, great Americans were forever making speeches. One elocution manual provided the following speech exercise. It is certainly among the champion tongue twisters of all time.

THEOPHILUS THISTLE

from "Brook's Manual of Elocution and Reading"

Theophilus Thistle, the successful thistle-sifter, in sifting a sieve full of unsifted thistles, thrust three thousand thistles through the thick of his thumb. Now, if Theophilus Thistle, the successful thistle-sifter, in sifting a sieve full of unsifted thistles, thrust three thousand thistles through the thick of his thumb, see that *thou,* in sifting a sieve full of unsifted thistles, thrust not three thousand thistles through the thick of *thy* thumb. Success to the successful thistle-sifter.

As a reward for mastering that tongue-twisting gem, a young boy with a very tired tongue might be taken by his proud parents to the circus. His first visit to the big top might cause a youngster to transfer his allegiance from Buffalo Bill or Jesse James to the hero of the following ballad.

THE MAN ON THE FLYING TRAPEZE

Anonymous

Oh, the girl that I loved she was handsome,
I tried all I knew her to please.
But I couldn't please her a quarter as well
As the man on the flying trapeze.

Chorus:

Oh, he flies through the air with the greatest
    of ease,
This daring young man on the flying trapeze.
His figure is handsome, all girls he can please
And my love he purloined her away.

Last night as usual I went to her home.
There sat her old father and mother alone.
I asked for my love and they soon made it
    known
That she-e had flown away.

She packed up her box and eloped in the
    night,
To go-o with him at his ease.
He lowered her down from a four-story
    flight,
By means of his flying trapeze.

He took her to town and he dressed her in
    tights,
That he-e might live at his ease.
He ordered her up to the tent's awful height,
To appear on the flying trapeze.

Now she flies through the air with the great-
    est of ease,
This daring young girl on the flying trapeze.
Her figure is handsome, all men she can
    please,
And my love is purloined away.

Once I was happy, but now I'm forlorn,
Like an old coat that is tattered and torn,
Left to this wide world to fret and to mourn,
Betrayed by a maid in her teens.

During the "Gay Nineties," Americans loved to waltz and shed tears in equal doses. Strong men wept at such magnificently mournful songs ground out by Tin Pan Alley as *A Bird in a Gilded Cage* or *After the Ball Is Over*. People who felt they were going to drown in a sea of sentimentality could always take refuge in such outrageous parodies as the following:

AFTER THE BALL IS OVER

(Parody version)

Anonymous

After the ball is over,
Mary takes out her glass eye,
Puts her false teeth in cold water,
Corks up her bottle of dye;
Throws her cork leg in the corner,
Hangs up her wig on the wall,
Then what is left goes to slumber,
AF-TER THE BALL.

Actually, this listing of vital statistics would have brought a furious blush to the cheeks of a respectable lady—for the Gay Nineties period was also the tail end of the Victorian Age. Even the legs of couches were still referred to as "limbs," and often covered modestly with little pantalettes. Father was the undisputed master of the middle-class Victorian household, presiding royally over a large family in a cluttered, gingerbready house, sallying forth each weekday morning to that financial battlefield which seems to bear the same name in practically every age: *downtown*. A well-loved tyrant, Father was not without his little human frailties, as demonstrated by our next poem.

WHEN FATHER CARVES THE DUCK

by E. V. Wright

We all look on with anxious eyes
    When father carves the duck,
And mother almost always sighs
    When father carves the duck;
Then all of us prepare to rise,
And hold our bibs before our eyes,
And be prepared for some surprise,
    When father carves the duck.

He braces up and grabs a fork
    Whene'er he carves a duck,
And won't allow a soul to talk
    Until he's carved the duck.
The fork is jabbed into the sides,
Across the breast the knife he slides,
While every careful person hides
    From flying chips of duck.

The platter's always sure to slip
    When father carves a duck,
And how it makes the dishes skip!
    Potatoes fly amuck!
The squash and cabbage leap in space,
We get some gravy in our face,
And father mutters Hindoo grace
    Whene'er he carves a duck.

We then have learned to walk around
    The dining-room and pluck
From off the window-sills and walls
    Our share of father's duck.
While father growls and blows and jaws

And swears the knife was full of flaws,
And mother laughs at him because
   He couldn't carve a duck.

When the mangled bird—well-cushioned with stuffing—was finally distributed in various stomachs, the whole family might take to their bicycles to work off the calories. During the '90s, all America went bike crazy. Everybody pedalled—Father, Mother, Sister, Brother—and as they wheeled through Central Park or some little country lane, they pushed their pedals to the rhythm and refrain of an ever-popular song.

A BICYCLE BUILT FOR TWO

by Harry Dacre

Daisy, Daisy, give me your answer do!
I'm half crazy, all for the love of you!
It won't be a stylish marriage,
I can't afford a carriage,

But you'll look sweet
On the seat
Of a bicycle built for two!

What happened to the lusty, brawling, wide-open-spaces-loving ring-tailed roarers? The Western frontiers were closing in, and developing law and order were making things tough for the apprentice badman. However, there was still an exciting, precarious existence to be had working in the booming oil fields or in the roaring lumber camps of the Pacific Northwest and Great Lakes regions. As the mythical Pecos Bill captured the spirit of the devil-may-care, broncobusting cowboy, Paul Bunyan would become the folk hero of the giant, hardy lumberjack.

The growth of lumbering meant the destruction of larger and larger areas of forest land by competing timber barons. A strong feeling began to grow about the necessity for protecting America's natural resources. This was the beginning of the Conservation-

ist movement. Its basic forest-prevention idea was to save young trees and plant new trees for old ones destroyed, but few Conservationists would fail to feel sentimental about our next poem, written way back in 1830.

WOODMAN, SPARE THAT TREE

by George P. Morris

Woodman, spare that tree!
Touch not a single bough!
In youth it sheltered me,
And I'll protect it now.
'Twas my forefather's hand
That placed it near his cot;
There, woodman, let it stand
Thy ax shall harm it not!

That old familiar tree,
Whose glory and renown
Are spread o'er land and sea,
And wouldst thou hew it down?
Woodman, forbear thy stroke!
Cut not its earth-bound ties!
Oh! spare that aged oak,
Now towering to the skies.

When but an idle boy
I sought its grateful shade;
In all their gushing joy
Here too my sisters played.
My mother kissed me here
My father pressed my hand—
Forgive this foolish tear,
But let that old oak stand!

My heart-strings round thee cling,
Close as thy bark, old friend!
Here shall the wild-bird sing,
And still thy branches bend.
Old tree, the storm still brave!
And, woodman, leave the spot!
While I've a hand to save,
Thy ax shall harm it not.

Fighting for the rights of trees was all very well, but there were other areas of American life—involving the impoverished existences of human beings—that were sadly in need of reform. While big business was booming, the lot of the industrial worker and small farmer was growing increasingly grim. The farmer suffered from overproduction of farm goods and money deflation, which drove his profits down, while his debts mounted higher and higher as a result of the exorbitant prices he had to pay for farm equipment and for freight in sending his goods to market. Meanwhile, the industrial worker suffered from long hours, short pay, and depressing living and working conditions.

The next important American frontier was destined to be the frontier of social justice. In the 1890s, Edwin Markham registered a powerful protest against the exploitation of labor in the following poem.

THE MAN WITH THE HOE

by Edwin Markham

Bowed by the weight of centuries he leans
Upon his hoe and gazes on the ground,
The emptiness of ages in his face,
And on his back the burden of the world.
Who made him dead to rapture and despair,
A thing that grieves not and that never
    hopes,
Stolid and stunned, a brother to the ox?
Who loosened and let down this brutal jaw?

Whose was the hand that slanted back this
brow?
Whose breath blew out the light within this
brain?

Is this the Thing the Lord God made and
gave
To have dominion over sea and land;
To trace the stars and search the heavens for
power;
To feel the passion of Eternity?
Is this the dream He dreamed who shaped
the suns
And marked their ways upon the ancient
deep?
Down all the caverns of Hell to their last
gulf
There is no shape more terrible than this—
More tongued with censure of the world's
blind greed—
More filled with signs and portents for the
soul—
More packt with danger to the universe.

What gulfs between him and the seraphim!
Slave of the wheel of labor, what to him
Are Plato and the swing of Pleiades?
What the long reaches of the peaks of song,
The rift of dawn, the reddening of the rose?
Through this dread shape the suffering ages
look;
Time's tragedy is in that aching stoop;
Through this dread shape humanity be-
trayed,
Plundered, profaned, and disinherited,
Cries protest to the Judges of the World,
A protest that is also prophecy.

O masters, lords and rulers in all lands,
Is this the handiwork you give to God,

This monstrous thing distorted and soul-
quenched?
How will you ever straighten up this shape;
Touch it again with immortality;
Give back the upward looking and the light;
Rebuild in it the music and the dream;
Make right the immemorial infamies,
Perfidious wrongs, immedicable woes?
O masters, Lords and rulers in all lands,
How will the Future reckon with this man?
How answer his brute question in that hour
When whirlwinds of rebellion shake all
shores?
How will it be with kingdoms and with
kings—
With those who shaped him to the thing he
is—
When this dumb terror shall rise to judge
the world,
After the silence of the centuries?

One of the worst aspects of industrial life
was the employment of child labor. At the
turn of the century, there were still about
two million children under fifteen working
ten and twelve hours a day, many of them
under such dangerous conditions as the
following.

CHILDREN IN THE COAL BREAKERS

from "The Bitter Cry of the Children"
by John Spargo

Work in the coal breakers is exceedingly
hard and dangerous. Crouched over the
chutes, the boys sit hour after hour, picking
out the pieces of slate and other refuse from
the coal as it rushes past to the washers.
From the cramped position they have to assume, most of them become more or less de-

formed and bent-backed like old men. When a boy has been working for some time and begins to get round-shouldered, his fellows say that "he's got his boy to carry round wherever he goes." The coal is hard, and accidents to the hands, such as cut, broken, or crushed fingers, are common among the boys. Sometimes there is a worse accident; a terrified shriek is heard, and a boy is mangled and torn in the machinery or disappears in the chute to be picked out later, smothered and dead. Clouds of dust fill the breakers and are inhaled by the boys, laying the foundations for asthma and miners' consumption. I once stood in a breaker for half an hour and tried to do the work a twelve-year-old boy was doing day after day, for ten hours at a stretch, for sixty cents a day. The gloom of the breaker appalled me. Outside the sun shone brightly, the air was pellucid, and the birds sang in chorus with the trees and the rivers. Within the breaker there was blackness; clouds of deadly dust enfolded everything; the harsh, grinding roar of the machinery and the ceaseless rushing of coal through the chutes filled the ears. I tried to pick out the pieces of slate from the hurrying stream of coal, often missing them; my hands were bruised and cut in a few minutes; I was covered from head to foot with coal dust, and for many hours afterward I was expectorating some of the small particles of anthracite I had swallowed.

I could not do that work and live, but there were boys of ten and twelve years of age doing it for fifty and sixty cents a day. Some of them had never been inside of a school; few of them could read a child's primer.

What you have just read is a far cry from the generally enlightened child-labor laws and labor-management relations that we know today. These reforms would be won only after many decades of bitter struggle by such men as Samuel Gompers, founder of the American Federation of Labor, and John L. Lewis, former president of the United Mine Workers. In unions, alone, there was strength. The farmers—after the failure of their Grange organization and "free-silver" movement (championed by silver-tongued orator William Jennings Bryan)—slowly gained in political power in the Democratic party. However, their fight upward was also a long one, with hard times, droughts and depressions as well as successes ahead.

Meanwhile, starting in 1896, the country was once again diverted from its problems by the cry "There's gold in them hills!" This time gold-rushers had to bring their snowshoes along—for the great strike was in the frozen wastes of the Canadian Yukon and the Alaskan Klondike. However, some gold prospectors ended up falling under the spell of the strange Northern land . . .

THE SPELL OF THE YUKON

by Robert W. Service

I wanted the gold, and I sought it;
I scrabbled and mucked like a slave.
Was it famine or scurvy—I fought it;
   I hurled my youth into a grave.
I wanted the gold, and I got it—
   Came out with a fortune last fall—
Yet somehow life's not what I thought it,
   And somehow the gold isn't all.

No! There's the land. (Have you seen it?)
    It's the cussedest land that I know,
From the big, dizzy mountains that screen it
    To the deep, deathlike valleys below.
Some say God was tired when He made it;
    Some say it's a fine land to shun;
Maybe; but there's some as would trade it
    For no land on earth—and I'm one.

You come to get rich (damned good rea-
        son);
    You feel like an exile at first;
You hate it like hell for a season,
    And then you are worse than the worst.
It grips you like some kinds of sinning;
    It twists you from foe to a friend;
It seems it's been since the beginning;
    It seems it will be to the end.

I've stood in some mighty-mouthed hollow
    That's plumb-full of hush to the brim;
I've watched the big, husky sun wallow
    In crimson and gold, and grow dim,
Till the moon set the pearly peaks gleaming,
    And the stars tumbled out, neck and crop;
And I've thought that I surely was dreaming,
    With the peace o' the world piled on top.

The summer—no sweeter was ever;
    The sunshiny woods all athrill;
The grayling aleap in the river,
    The bighorn asleep on the hill.
The strong life that never knows harness;
    The wilds where the caribou call;
The freshness, the freedom, the farness—
    O God! how I'm stuck on it all.

The winter! the brightness that blinds you,
    The white land locked tight as a drum,

The cold fear that follows and finds you,
    The silence that bludgeons you dumb,
The snows that are older than history,
    The woods where the weird shadows
        slant;
The stillness, the moonlight, the mystery,
    I've bade 'em good-bye—but I can't.

There's a land where the mountains are
        nameless,
    And the rivers all run God knows where;
There are lives that are erring and aimless,
    And deaths that just hang by a hair;
There are hardships that nobody reckons;
    There are valleys unpeopled and still;
There's a land—oh, it beckons and beckons,
    And I want to go back—and I will.

While the gold rush was still on, America began to take a closer look at Cuba. This sugar-and-tobacco-rich island lying off our Atlantic coastline was in the midst of rebellion against harsh Spanish rule. American sympathies were deeply stirred in favor of the rebels. Weren't they fighting courageously against European oppression the way American patriots had done? Indignation was whipped up in the American masses by descriptions of Spanish atrocities published in the sensational "yellow" press. The following "purple" poem expresses the growing mood of the times.

CUBA LIBRE

by Joaquin Miller

Comes a cry from Cuban water—
    From the warm, dusk Antilles—
From the lost Atlanta's daughter,

215

Drowned in blood as drowned in seas;
Comes a cry of purpled anguish—
  See her struggles, hear her cries!
Shall she live, or shall she languish?
  Shall she sink, or shall she rise?

She shall rise, by all that's holy!
  She shall live and she shall last;
Rise as we, when crushed and lowly,
  From the blackness of the past.
Bid her strike! Lo, it is written,—
  Blood for blood and life for life.
Bid her smite, as she is smitten;
  Behold, our stars were born of strife!

Once we flashed her lights of freedom,
  Lights that dazzled her dark eyes
Till she could but yearning heed them,
  Reach her hands and try to rise.
Then they stabbed her, choked her, drowned
    her,
  Till we scarce could hear a note.
Ah! these rusting chains that bound her!
  Oh! these robbers at her throat!

And the kind who forged these fetters?
  Ask five hundred years for news.
Stake and thumbscrew for their betters?
  Inquisitions! Banished Jews!
Chains and slavery! What reminder
  Of one red man in that land?
Why, these very chains that bind her
  Bound Columbus, foot and hand!

She shall rise as rose Columbus,
  From his chains, from shame and wrong—
Rise as Morning, matchless, wondrous—
  Rise as some rich morning song—
Rise a ringing song and story,
  Valor, Love personified . . .

Stars and stripes, espouse her glory,
  Love and Liberty allied.

Other, more practical, emotions contributed to a desire to come to grips with the aging Spanish empire in the New World. This was an era of imperialism, in which European nations were "bearing the White Man's burden" with a good deal of profit in various underdeveloped areas of the world. The United States had purchased Alaska from Russia back in 1867, but now many Americans felt it was high time to do a little further expanding in good old "manifest destiny" style. At the time of the Spanish-American War, a Tennessee governor visualized Uncle Sam throwing out his chest in the following manner.

UNCLE SAM

from a Speech by Governor Robert L. Taylor

The most striking and picturesque in all history is the picture of a lean and sinewy old man, with long hair and chin whiskers, and wearing an old-fashioned plug hat. His pantaloons are in stripes of red and white, and his blue swallow-tailed coat is bespangled with stars. He is the personification of the United States, and we call him Uncle Sam.

He is the composite of the wildcat and the cooing dove, the lion and the lamb, and "summer evening's latest sigh that shuts the rose." He is the embodiment of all that is most terrible. The world stands appalled at his wonderful power and bows in admiration to his matchless magnanimity.

He is the tallest figure on this mundane sphere, and when he steps across the continent and sits down on Pike's Peak, and snorts in his handkerchief of red, white, and blue, the earth quakes and the monarchs tremble on their thrones. . . . He is boss of the Western Hemisphere, Sheriff of Cuba, Justice of the Peace of Porto Rico, and guardian *ad litem* of the Philippine Islands. He is as brave as Caesar and as meek as Moses.

He is as fierce as a tiger and as cool as a cucumber. He wears the tail feathers of the eagle of France in his hat and the scalp of Mexico in his belt. He laughs at the roar of the Russian bear and is always ready for a schooner of German beer.

All that is left of Spain is her "Honah," since her combat with Uncle Sam. No longer the lion of England roars at our door, but the twain now stand together for liberty and humanity.

The Spanish-American War was triggered in the spring of 1898 by the mysterious blowing up of the United States battleship *Maine* in Havana waters. Although proof was lacking, Spanish saboteurs were held responsible, the "yellow" press screamed for revenge, and Congress declared war. The war lasted exactly three months. It ended with America in possession of two new national heroes —Teddy Roosevelt of Rough Rider fame and Admiral Dewey—plus an assortment of islands in the Caribbean and Pacific. This sudden emergence as a world power presented problems. Was anticolonial America going to turn imperialistic herself? If the Philippines and Cuba were handed over to native patriots, would they be able to take charge of their own affairs? Or would ra-

pacious nations waiting on the sidelines move in as soon as America moved out? After a bit of hemming and hawing, President McKinley decided that the Philippines should be annexed for their own good. There was an immediate storm of anti-imperialist protest. One newspaper poet wrote:

O DEWEY AT MANILA

Anonymous

O Dewey at Manila
   That fateful first of May,
When you sank the Spanish squadron
   In almost bloodless fray,
And gave your name to deathless fame;
   O glorious Dewey, say,
Why didn't you weigh anchor
   And softly sail away?

Puerto Rico, Guam and, later, Hawaii were also annexed, and a protectorate established over Cuba, partial to American sugar interests. The Platt Amendment gave the United States the right to intervene in Cuban affairs. (It would be repealed in the 1930s.) The country split into "expansionist" and "anti-imperialist" factions. Those who endorsed the new acquisitions (the McKinley Republicans—he won a second term) saw Americans taking on the role of benevolent Big Brothers, guiding less-developed peoples toward civilization, self-government and prosperity. Others (the William Jennings Bryan Democrats—they also stood for free silver, and lost) saw it as a modern example of conquistadoring. "Grab the gold (in this case, sugar) and convert the heathen." These conflicting ideas are illustrated by the following verses, written around this time.

TAKE UP THE WHITE MAN'S BURDEN

(Kipling's version)

Take up the White Man's burden,
Send forth the best you breed . . .
To wait in heavy harness,
On fluttering folk and wild—
Your new-caught sullen peoples,
Half devil and half-child . . .

TAKE UP THE WHITE MAN'S BURDEN

(Cynic's version)

Take up the White Man's burden;
Send forth your sturdy sons,
And load them down with whiskey
And testaments and guns.
Throw in a few diseases
To spread in tropic climes,
For there the healthy [natives]
Are quite behind the times . . .

William Howard Taft, who was sent over as Governor-General of the Philippines, referred to Filipinos as "little brown brothers." American soldiers stationed there—who had to contend with mosquitoes, malaria and native hostility—felt somewhat differently.

I'M ONLY A COMMON SOLDIER-MAN

by Robert F. Morrison

I'm only a common soldier-man, in the
blasted Philippines;
They say I've got Brown Brothers here, but
I dunno what it means.
I like the word Fraternity, but still I draw
the line;
He *may* be a brother of William H. Taft, but
he ain't no friend of mine.

I never had a brother who would beg to get
a drink
To keep himself from dying when he hov-
ered on the brink;
And when my pal had give it him, and emptied out his sack,
Would take the opportunity to stick him in
the back . . .

You couldn't blame the Filipinos. They had fought long and courageously against Spanish domination, and now the Americans, whom they had welcomed as deliverers, seemed to be playing the same old game. Yet there was a vast difference. Americans weren't really cut out to be exploiters of other peoples. The weight of public opinion in the States made sure that American rule was both temporary and beneficial. Schools and hospitals were built, and the people were helped, as quickly as possible, toward self-government. In the future, the Philippines would become an independent republic. Hawaii was destined to become the fiftieth state, and Puerto Rico a territory slowly growing in prosperity, governed democratically by its own people as United States citizens . . .

While America was getting its feet wet in the Caribbean Sea and Pacific Ocean, things were humming on land back home, especially on the roads around Detroit. Horses were bolting at the sight of a wheezing, snorting, chugging, mechanical monstrosity, driven by a young inventor at reckless speeds up to twenty miles per hour. The young inventor was Henry Ford, and here is his own recollection of the first gasoline buggy in a city which would become the Mecca of the automobile industry.

HENRY FORD TRIES OUT HIS HORSELESS CARRIAGE

from "My Life and Work" by Henry Ford

My gasoline buggy was the first and for a long time the only automobile in Detroit. It was considered to be something of a nuisance, for it made a racket and it scared horses. Also it blocked traffic. For if I stopped my machine anywhere in town, a crowd was around it before I could start up again. If I left it alone even for a minute, some inquisitive person always tried to run it. Finally, I had to carry a chain and chain it to a lamp post whenever I left it anywhere. And then there was trouble with the police. I do not know quite why, for my impression is that there were no speed laws in those days. Anyway, I had to get a special permit from the mayor and thus for a time enjoyed the distinction of being the only licensed chauffeur in America. I ran that machine about one thousand miles through 1895 and 1896 and then sold it to Charles Ainsley of Detroit for two hundred dollars. That was my first sale. I had built the car not to sell but only to experiment with. I wanted to start another car.

As is well known, Henry Ford *did* start another car—and another, and another, and another ... America's horses were gradually put out to pasture as various automobile manufacturers got their assembly lines rolling. Instead of tightening harness straps, Father got accustomed to cranking up engines. And instead of *A Bicycle Built for Two*, American families—clad in dusters and goggles—began to sing the following song.

IN MY MERRY OLDSMOBILE

by Gus Edwards

Young Johnny Steele has an Oldsmobile,
He loves a dear little girl.
She is queen of his gas machine,
She has his heart in a whirl.
Now, when they go for a spin you know,
She tries to learn the auto, so
He lets her steer while he gets her ear,
And whispers soft and low:

Come away with me Lucille
In my merry Oldsmobile,
Down the road of life we'll fly
Automobubbling, you and I.
To the church we'll swiftly steal,
Then our wedding bells will peal,
You can go as far as you like with me,
In my merry Oldsmobile.

As the wheels of America began to roll faster and faster, not everybody shared the merry enthusiasm of Mr. Edwards. The following parody of "The Charge of the Light Brigade" appeared in the pages of the old *Life* magazine.

HALF A BLOCK, HALF A BLOCK, HALF A BLOCK ONWARD

Anonymous

Half a block, half a block,
  Half a block onward,
All in their motobiles
  Rode the Four Hundred.
"Forward!" the owners shout,
  "Racing-car!" "Runabout!"
Into Fifth Avenue
  Rode the Four Hundred.

"Forward!" the owners said.
  Was there a man dismayed?
No, though the chauffeurs knew
  Someone had blundered.
Theirs not to make reply,
  Theirs not to reason why,
Theirs but to kill or die.
  Into Fifth Avenue
Rode the Four Hundred.

While some hung back dismayed, the country as a whole rounded the turn of the century going full speed ahead. Forges, factories and assembly lines were booming. *The New York Times* editorialized on January 1st, 1900: "The year 1899 was a year of wonders . . . in business and production. . . ."

There were many shadows—labor unrest, various shades of discrimination, farm problems, growing slums, a cloudy international situation—but most Americans showed a supreme confidence in their ability to find the solution to any problem. Hadn't they licked a hostile wilderness? Hadn't they turned a bunch of weak, divided colonies into one of the strongest and most respected nations in the world? Hadn't they shown that democracy, with all its faults and excesses, was still the best system around for guaranteeing the widest variety of people a chance at life, liberty and the pursuit of happiness? Even the "nay-sayers" were infected by the over-all American spirit of vitality—they tended to shout angrily rather than grumble weakly, as in other more restricted lands.

Full of optimism, contentiousness, spit and vinegar, Uncle Sam stepped out onto the world stage, rolled up his sleeves, flexed his muscles, grinned, and strode briskly toward the century of new frontiers . . .

PART EIGHT

Century of New Frontiers

THE twentieth century was only a year old when the country was shocked by the assassination of President McKinley at the beginning of his second term. His Vice-President, Teddy Roosevelt, ascended to the Presidency and soon proved to be a far different sort than his earnest, plodding predecessor. Trust-buster, horseback rider, social reformer, wrestling enthusiast, insatiable reader and writer, international peace negotiator, "Big Stick" policy maker—Roosevelt shot off sparks wherever he went, and symbolized the dynamism of the age. It was a time of raw vitality, spilling over with power for both good and evil . . .

CHICAGO

by Carl Sandburg

Hog Butcher for the World,
Tool Maker, Stacker of Wheat,
Player with Railroads and the Nation's
    Freight Handler;
Stormy, husky, brawling,
City of the Big Shoulders:
They tell me you are wicked, and I believe
    them; for I have seen your painted
    women under the gas lamps luring the
    farm boys.
And they tell me you are crooked, and I an-
    swer: Yes, it is true I have seen the
    gunman kill and go free to kill again.

223

And they tell me you are brutal, and my reply is: On the faces of women and children I have seen the marks of wanton
hunger.

And having answered so, I turn once more
to those who sneer at this my city, and
I give them back the sneer and say to
them:

Come and show me another city with lifted
head singing so proud to be alive and
coarse and strong and cunning.

Flinging magnetic curses amid the toil of
piling job on job, here is a tall bold
slugger set vivid against the little soft
cities;

Fierce as a dog with tongue lapping for action, cunning as a savage pitted against
the wilderness,
    Bareheaded,
    Shoveling,
    Wrecking,
    Planning,
    Building, breaking, rebuilding,

Under the smoke, dust all over his mouth,
laughing with white teeth,

Under the terrible burden of destiny laughing as a young man laughs,

Laughing even as an ignorant fighter laughs
who has never lost a battle,

Bragging and laughing that under his wrist
is the pulse, and under his ribs the heart
of the people,
    Laughing!

Laughing the stormy, husky, brawling laughter of Youth; half-naked, sweating,
proud to be Hog Butcher, Tool Maker,
Stacker of Wheat, Player with Railroads, and Freight Handler to the
Nation.

When all this energy was linked to a sense
of fair play and public responsibility, good
resulted. But when greed and power un-
checked sat in the driver's seat, conditions
resulted like those revealed by Upton Sinclair in his novel *The Jungle*. His exposé of
the Chicago meat-packing industry, with its
brutal exploitation of labor and unsanitary
"corner-cutting" methods of operation, resulted in an investigation by Roosevelt and
the passing of the Pure-Food Legislation of
1906 . . . Roosevelt was optimistic about
putting a bridle on American energies, di-
verting them along constructive paths. There
were many, however, who shrank back from
the noisy, pushy, smoke-and-crowd-filled
cities. They yearned nostalgically for the past
—for the America of quiet, slow-paced rural
villages, white-steepled churches, and little
country stores where you could browse con-
tentedly without anybody telling you to hurry
up . . .

THE COUNTRY STORE

Anonymous

Far out beyond the city's lights, away from
din and roar,

The cricket chirps of summer nights beneath the country store;

The drygoods boxes ricked about afford a
welcome seat

For weary tillers of the ground, who here on
evenings meet.

A swinging sign of ancient make, and one
above the door,

Proclaim that William Henry Blake is owner
of the store;

Here everything from jam to tweed, from
    silks to ginghams bright,
Is spread before the folk who need from early
    morn till night.

Tea, sugar, coffee (browned or green), mo-
    lasses, grindstones, tar,
Suspenders, peanuts, navy beans, and home-
    made vinegar,
Fine combs, wash ringers, rakes, false hair.
    paints, rice, and looking glasses,
Side saddles, hominy, crockery ware, and
    seeds for garden grasses.

Lawn mowers, candies, books to read, corn
    planter, household goods,
Tobacco, salt, and clover seed, horsewhips
    and knitted hoods,
Canned goods, shoe blacking, lime and nails,
    straw hats and carpet slippers,
Prunes, buttons, codfish, bridal veils, cran-
    berries, clocks, and clippers.

Umbrellas, candles, scythes and hats, caps,
    boots and shoes and bacon,
Thread, nutmegs, pins and Rough on Rats,
    for cash or produce taken;
Birdseed, face powder, matches, files, ink,
    onions and many more,
Are found in heaps and stacks and piles
    within the country store.

While the character and values of rural
America would continue to contribute richly
to the American heritage, progress and invention were the dominating forces of the
age. However, there were still many doubters
who imposed limits on just how far American invention could go. For example, the
age-old dream man had of flying like a

bird . . . In 1903, after the failure of a gov-
ernment-sponsored experiment in flight, Simon Newcomb, a noted astronomer and
mathematician, had this to say:

FLYING IS FOR BIRDS ALONE

by Simon Newcomb

The example of the bird does not prove
that man can fly. . . . There are many problems which have fascinated mankind since
civilization began, which we have made little
or no advance in solving. . . . May not our
mechanicians . . . be ultimately forced to admit that aerial flight is one of that great class
of problems with which man can never cope,
and give up all attempts to grapple with it?

Just two months later (December 17,
1903), Wilbur and Orville Wright took off
at Kitty Hawk on their history-making flight.
Soon, the following song would be joining
A Bicycle Built for Two and *In My Merry
Oldsmobile* on the all-American hit parade.

COME, JOSEPHINE, IN MY FLYING MACHINE

by Alfred Bryan and Fred Fisher

Come, Josephine, in my flying machine,
Going up she goes, up she goes
Balance yourself like a bird on a beam
In the air she goes
There she goes
Up, up, a little bit higher
Oh! My! the moon is on fire . . .
Come, Josephine, in my flying machine,
Going up, all on, good-bye.

225

American inventiveness teamed up with American industrial know-how to send a host of new products rolling off the assembly lines.

Industry produced many self-made men who were able to give their children advantages that they themselves had lacked. "Advantages" meant, among other things, having their sons attend such a prestige college as Yale or Harvard. Yale students in the early 1900s—with typical undergraduate irreverence—showed their filial gratitude by singing this song.

WHAT'S THE MATTER WITH FATHER

Anonymous

What's the matter with father, he's all right,
What's the matter if father's hair is white?
I'm very strong for the other sex,
But Dad's the fellow who sends the checks,
What's the matter with father, he's all right!

Also part of the lighter scene were the various crazes that swept the country. In the 1840s it had been phrenology and dancing the polka. In 1902, it was the game of ping-pong. However, as always, there were dissenters. One wrote:

I KNOW I MUST BE WRONG

Anonymous

I know I must be wrong
But I cannot love ping-pong.

I cannot sing
In praise of ping;

I have no song
For pong.

The nation played its games, built its industries, and struggled with its various problems. Roosevelt, during his two terms, continued to fight for a whole host of reforms— control of monopolies, a "square deal" for the worker and little man, conservation and other causes. He knew that reform was necessary to save business from a violent popular revolt, and history has proved him right. He was criticized for interfering on the side of the Panamanians in their revolt against Columbia, but this ended up gaining America the Panama Canal (completed by American engineers in 1914). Roosevelt had the political power to pick his own successor, William Howard Taft, but he was disappointed by Taft's slow-moving conservatism, which resulted in a period of "dollar diplomacy." With typical maverick spirit,

Roosevelt formed his own progressive "Bull Moose" party to support him in the election of 1912. This split the Republicans (the regulars were rerunning Taft), and made nobody but the Democrats happy. The Democratic candidate, Woodrow Wilson, was elected. He continued along the reforming path of Roosevelt, supporting such measures as an eight-hour labor law, new antitrust and farm loan acts. And then in 1914 came the threat of the First World War.

America had been acting pretty much as an international peacemaker, but German militarists—like those of a later era—were more interested in conquest than peace. The Kaiser's generals swept into Belgium and France. The Kaiser's submarines ruthlessly attacked civilian vessels, resulting in the loss of many American lives. America didn't want to go to war, but it became increasingly obvious that, in the modern age, isolationism wouldn't work. If the war lords were permitted to ravage Europe today, tomorrow they might be able to turn their full attention to the Western Hemisphere. A sense that the fates of all opposed to tyranny were bound up together caused Vachel Lindsay to invoke the spirit of Abraham Lincoln in the following poem, written in 1914.

ABRAHAM LINCOLN WALKS AT MIDNIGHT

by Vachel Lindsay

It is portentous, and a thing of state
    That here at midnight, in our little town
A mourning figure walks, and will not rest
    Near the old court-house pacing up and
        down.

Or by his homestead, or the shadowed yards
    He lingers where his children used to play,
Or through the market, on the well-worn
    stones
    He stalks until the dawn-stars burn away.

A bronzed, lank man! His suit of ancient
    black,
    A famous high-top-hat and plain worn
    shawl
Make him the quaint great figure that men
    love,
    The prairie-lawyer, master of us all.

He cannot sleep upon his hillside now.
    He is among us, as in times before!
And we who toss and lie awake for long
    Breathe deep, and start, to see him pass
    the door.

His head is bowed. He thinks on men and
    kings.
    Yea, when the sick world cries, how can
    he sleep?
Too many peasants fight, they know not why,
    Too many homesteads in black terror
    weep.

The sins of all the war-lords burn his heart.
    He sees the dreadnaughts scouring every
    main.
He carries on his shawl-wrapt shoulders now
    The bitterness, the folly and the pain.

He cannot rest until a spirit-dawn
    Shall come;—the shining hope of Europe
    free;
    The league of sober folk, the Workers'
    Earth

Bring long peace to Cornland, Alp and
    Sea.

It breaks his heart that kings must murder
    still,
    That all his hours of travail here for men
Seem yet in vain. And who will bring white
    peace
    That he may sleep upon his hill again?

Wilson tried to keep America at peace, and was re-elected on that basis in 1916. But then the Germans, after promising to stop indiscriminate torpedoing of civilian vessels, suddenly went back on their promise early in 1917, and sent five American merchant ships to the bottom. Wilson knew the time had come. He went before Congress on April 2, 1917, and called for war in a speech that reaffirmed American ideals—one of the great speeches in American history. It included the following statements.

WILSON CALLS FOR WAR, TO MAKE THE WORLD "SAFE FOR DEMOCRACY"

from Woodrow Wilson's Address to Congress
April 2, 1917

With a profound sense of the solemn and even tragical character of the step I am taking and of the grave responsibilities which it involves, but in unhesitating obedience to what I deem my constitutional duty, I advise that the Congress declare the recent course of the imperial German government to be in fact nothing less than war against the government and people of the United States, that it formally accept the status of belligerent which has thus been thrust upon it, and that it take immediate steps not only to put the country in a more thorough state of defense but also to exert all its power and employ all its resources to bring the government of the German Empire to terms and end the war. . . .

We are now about to accept gauge of battle with this natural foe to liberty and shall, if necessary, spend the whole force of the nation to check and nullify its pretensions and its power. We are glad, now that we see the facts with no veil of false pretense about them, to fight thus for the ultimate peace of the world and for the liberation of its peoples, the German people included: for the rights of nations great and small and the privilege of men everywhere to choose their way of life and of obedience. The world must be made safe for democracy. Its peace must be planted upon the tested foundations of political liberty. We have no selfish ends to serve. We desire no conquest, no dominion. We seek no indemnities for ourselves, no material compensation for the sacrifices we shall freely make. We are but one of the champions of the rights of mankind. We shall be satisfied when those rights have been made as secure as the faith and the freedom of nations can make them. . . .

It is a distressing and oppressive duty, gentlemen of the Congress, which I have performed in thus addressing you. There are, it may be, many months of fiery trial and sacrifice ahead of us. It is a fearful thing to lead this great peaceful people into war, into the most terrible and disastrous of all wars, civilization itself seeming to be in the balance. But the right is more precious than peace, and we shall fight for the things which we have always carried nearest our hearts—for democracy, for the right of those who submit to authority to have a voice in their own governments, for the rights and liberties of small nations, for a universal dominion of right by such a concert of free peoples as shall bring peace and safety to all nations and make the world itself at last free. To such a task we can dedicate our lives and our fortunes, everything that we are and everything that we have, with the pride of those who know that the day has come when America is privileged to spend her blood and her might for the principles that gave her birth and happiness and the peace which she has treasured. God helping her, she can do no other.

Once war was declared, young men rallied to the Colors, and marched to training camps singing *Over There!* Two million men were shipped overseas to fight in France. They indulged in time-honored complaints about their sergeants, food and K.P. duty. They sang "Oh, how I hate to get up in the morning . . ." and made up uncomplimentary verses about the "big brass."

THE OFFICERS GET ALL THE STEAK

Anonymous

The officers get all the steak
And all we get is the bellyache.
The general got the *croix-de-guerre,*
And the son of a gun was never there.

However, once the fighting started, American soldiers proved they could more than hold their own against the Prussian-trained troops of the Kaiser. In 1918, General Pershing's army unleashed a powerful offensive in the Argonne, helping to break the German lines. There were 1,200,000 American troops who took part in this action. They demonstrated a hard-bitten courage and devotion to duty which caused many of them to fall in action, to rest forever beneath the soil of France.

BUTTONS

by Carl Sandburg

I have been watching the war map slammed
    up for advertising in front of the news-
    paper office.
Buttons—red and yellow buttons—blue and
    black buttons—are shoved back and
    forth across the map.
A laughing young man, sunny with freckles,
Climbs a ladder, yells a joke to somebody in
    the crowd,
And then fixes a yellow button one inch west
And follows the yellow button with a black
    button one inch west.

(Ten thousand men and boys twist on their
    bodies in a red soak along a river edge,
Gasping of wounds, calling for water, some
    rattling death in their throats.)
Who would guess what it cost to move two
    buttons one inch on the war map here
    in front of the newspaper office where
    the freckle-faced young man is laughing
    to us?

A young American soldier-poet, who served with the Foreign Legion during the war, pledged his life to the cause of freedom in the following poem. He was later killed in battle.

I HAVE A RENDEZVOUS WITH DEATH

by Alan Seeger

I have a rendezvous with Death
At some disputed barricade,
When Spring comes back with rustling shade
And apple-blossoms fill the air—
I have a rendezvous with Death
When Spring brings back blue days and fair.

It may be he shall take my hand
And lead me into his dark land
And close my eyes and quench my breath—
It may be I shall pass him still.
I have a rendezvous with Death
On some scarred slope of battered hill,
When Spring comes round again this year
And the first meadow-flowers appear.

God knows 'twere better to be deep
Pillowed in silk and scented down,
Where love throbs out in blissful sleep,
Pulse nigh to pulse, and breath to breath,
Where hushed awakenings are dear . . .
But I've a rendezvous with Death
At midnight in some flaming town,
When Spring trips north again this year,
And I to my pledged word am true,
I shall not fail that rendezvous.

This was the first war in which air power played a part. Admittedly, it was a comparatively minor part, and the airplanes involved have been described as chicken crates held together with baling wire, but that speaks all the more for the daring of pilots who engaged in many a thrilling machine-gun duel with enemy "aces" in the wild blue yonder . . .

THE DYING AIRMAN

Anonymous

A handsome young airman lay dying,
And as on the aerodrome he lay,
To the mechanics who round him came sighing,
These last dying words he did say:

"Take the cylinders out of my kidneys,
The connecting-rod out of my brain,
Take the cam-shaft from out of my backbone,
And assemble the engine again."

In 1918, Wilson issued his Fourteen Points program. It called for an honorable peace settlement with the people of Germany, plus such international reforms as removing the economic barriers between countries, recognizing the right of European peoples to live under governments of their own choice, setting up a "general association of nations." It was a grand new concept of international relations that captured the imagination of the world. The government of the Kaiser, whose armies were being pushed back steadily toward the borders of Germany, sent peace feelers to Wilson, but he would only deal with a new government representing not militarists but *people*. Public pressure in Germany forced the Kaiser to abdicate, flee to Holland, and start his new wood-chopping career. The war ended on November 11, 1918.

GRASS

by Carl Sandburg

Pile the bodies high at Austerlitz and Waterloo.
Shovel them under and let me work—
　　I am the grass; I cover all.

And pile them high at Gettysburg
And pile them high at Ypres and Verdun.
Shovel them under and let me work.
Two years, ten years, and passengers ask the conductor:
　　What place is this?
　　Where are we now?

I am the grass.
Let me work.

Wilson's plan for an "association of nations" became the League of Nations—ironically, without American participation. This broke Wilson's heart. He appealed to the public to elect a liberal Congress, and in a wave of isolationism, they promptly elected conservative majorities in both houses. The Senate rejected American involvement in the League, as a mood of isolationism—brought about by weariness with both war and the tangled affairs of Europe—swept the country. It was an unfortunate decision: Had America been behind the League when Hitler and his fellow gangsters started their aggressions, the Second World War might never have occurred.

But war was the last thing America felt like dwelling on, as the Twenties got under way. Wilson was replaced by easy-going Warren Harding and then Calvin Coolidge, and the country got back to "normalcy" and to "business as usual." There were a few changes however. Women finally got their right to vote written into the Constitution, in spite of the sentiments expressed by such masculine die-hards as the author of the following parody. (The song being parodied is *Gee, But There's Class to a Girl Like You*.)

GEE, BUT THERE'S CLASS TO A MAN LIKE THAT

by Charles A. Jones

My friend, he wed a suffragette,
He calls her dovey, dear and pet;
He cooks the meals and the table sets,
And rocks the cradle too.
She wears his hat, also his vest,
She smokes the brand he likes the best,
To get the housework through,
That her club she may go to,
To spin a yarn or two.

Gee, but there's class to a man like that.
Honest, isn't he great?
Now I'll bet my old straw hat
He goes to bed at eight.
Give him a chance and he will soon wear
Corsets and frocks, a comb and a rat;
He will look sweet with long, wavy hair.
Gee there's class to a man like that.

In spite of the fear lurking beneath the scorn of those lyrics, most American women had no desire either to smoke cigars or to wear the pants in the family. They were simply tired of being treated as second-class citizens in a country they had helped to build. Their contributions in many fields— social reform, literature, education and the like—had enriched American society beyond measure. American wives and mothers had managed to keep their homes together and send strong, healthy children out into the world, in spite of Indian attacks, epidemics, wars and depressions. Many of them just seemed to toughen with age, turning into peppery "no nonsense!" grandmothers, setting an example of sparkling-eyed, nimble-fingered vitality for the younger generation. Who would begrudge giving the vote to such as Edgar Lee Master's *Lucinda Matlock?*

LUCINDA MATLOCK

from "Spoon River Anthology"
by Edgar Lee Masters

I went to the dances at Chandlerville,
And played snap-out at Winchester.
One time we changed partners,
Driving home in the moonlight of middle June,
And then I found Davis.
We were married and lived together for seventy years,
Enjoying, working, raising the twelve children,
Eight of whom we lost
Ere I had reached the age of sixty.
I spun, I wove, I kept the house, I nursed the sick,
I made the garden, and for holiday
Rambled over the fields where sang the larks,
And by Spoon River gathering many a shell,
And many a flower and medicinal weed—
Shouting to the wooded hills, singing to the green valleys.
At ninety-six I had lived enough, that is all,
And passed to a sweet repose.
What is this I hear of sorrow and weariness,
Anger, discontent, and drooping hopes?

232

Degenerate sons and daughters,
Life is too strong for you—
It takes life to love Life.

The "flappers" and "sheiks" of the Roaring Twenties loved life, all right, but in a rootless, frenzied sort of way that had little to do with the pioneer spirit. Release from the tensions of war, plus the feeling that all that loss of life had accomplished very little, created a mood of general disillusionment. A "lost generation" of young people was made even more cynical by such evidence of widespread corruption in high places as the Teapot Dome scandals, when the Secretary of the Interior was convicted of accepting a bribe from an oil tycoon. Idealism didn't seem to have much future, but there was plenty of easy money to be made playing the stock market. Stay young, live high today, let tomorrow take care of itself—that was the popular philosophy of the era. As morals dropped, skirts rose, and Prohibition made liquor forbidden fruit—which, of course, made it twice as desirable. "Lips that touch liquor shall never touch mine" was paraphrased as follows.

LIPS THAT TOUCH LIQUOR

by J. Gillespie

Lips that touch liquor
Shall always touch mine.
Blood should run red
With the ruby of wine.
Those who cloak virtue
In teetotal toil—
Have no blood in their veins:
It's cod liver oil!

Actually, Flaming Youth was more likely to guzzle "bathtub" gin or whiskey than sip wine. Prohibition was a godsend to the criminal elements. They manufactured various kinds of alcoholic poison for which they charged outrageous prices to their customers in home or speakeasy. But the customers didn't really care, money flowed as easily as liquor, as stocks continued to climb . . . When flappers weren't kicking up their heels in the Charleston or emptying flasks while snuggling close to their raccoon-coated boy friends at college football games, they "ooh'ed" and "ah'ed" at the exploits of Rudolph Valentino, Douglas Fairbanks and others on the silver screen. Movie stars built enormous palaces in Hollywood, and many of them lived even more colorful lives off screen than on. One of the most colorful characters of all was the great comedian W. C. Fields. He had many ups and downs during a career which extended before, during and after the Twenties, but he always demonstrated a knack for both indulging in and spoofing the grand gesture, so dear to Hollywood hearts. The following anecdote describes Fields' triumphant return to Hollywood after one of his "down" periods.

W. C. FIELDS MAKES A GRAND RE-ENTRY INTO HOLLYWOOD

from "W. C. Fields" by R. L. Taylor

After a trip filled with pleasant dalliance, Fields entered Hollywood in the shiniest possible condition . . . According to subsequent accounts, he pulled up in front of the most gorgeous hotel he could find, climbed down, tossed his keys to a uniformed lackey, whom he scrutinized carefully, in order to remember his face, and descended upon the lobby somewhat in the manner of Caesar returning from Carthage. He made "quite a procession," as he described it afterward. Several bellhops struggled along behind with his luggage, all of it picturesque, including one valise which seemed to be leaking, and others plastered with promotional labels on the order of "W. C. Fields, Greatest Juggler on Earth." He was wearing his cutaway and morning trousers, into which he had slipped in the lavatory of the filling station, and he was carrying a gold-headed cane. His step was jaunty; as he trod the flowered carpet he lifted a frayed and dented silk hat to various startled persons in the lobby, one of whom, an elderly lady in a wheel chair, sniffed suspiciously and broke into a rolling sprint for the side exit.

At the desk Fields rapped with his cane and asked for the bridal suite. The manager, recoiling slightly, causing Fields to start and clutch his hat, informed him that the bridal suite was usually reserved for gentlemen with brides.

"I'll pick one up in town," the comedian told him.

The "ritzy" big-city hotel — with its doormen uniformed like gold-epauletted admirals, its thick-carpeted lobby blossoming forth with potted palms, its eddying streams of cigar-chomping, stock-market-quoting financiers accompanied by long-legged, short-skirted "mamas," sprinkled with the occasional turban of an Indian prince—symbolized the transient and tinsel-wrapped nature

of the Roaring Twenties. However, an even greater symbol was that thirsty man's best friend—the bootlegger. The curious morality of the age was characterized by the general public's attitude toward Prohibition, summed up in the following speech by "the man who knew Coolidge."

NOT THAT I NEVER TAKE A DRINK

from "The Man Who Knew Coolidge"
by Sinclair Lewis

Not that I never take a drink. What I say about Prohibition is: Once a law has been passed by the duly elected and qualified representatives of the people of these United States, in fact once it's on the statute books, it's *there,* and it's there to be enforced. There hadn't ought to be any blind pigs or illegal stills. But the same time, that don't mean you got to be a fanatic.

If a fellow feels like making some good home-brewed beer or wine, or if you go to a fellow's house and he brings out some hootch or gin that *you* don't know where he got it and it isn't any of your business, or if you have a business acquaintance coming to your house and you figure he won't loosen up and talk turkey without a little spot and you know a good dependable bootlegger that you can *depend* on, well then, that's a different matter, and there ain't any reason on God's green earth that *I* can see why you shouldn't take advantage of it, always providing you aren't setting somebody a bad example or making it look like you sympathized with law-breaking.

No, sir!

Naturally, this attitude was encouraged by such leading executives of the illicit liquor trade as Al Capone. The last thing *he* wanted was repeal of Prohibition. All through the Twenties, rival crime syndicates entered into congenial competition with each other, complete with Tommy guns, for control of various lucrative rackets. Other murky forces were at work beneath the gaudy surface of the era. Pressure from labor groups forced the passage of laws restricting immigration. Intolerance against minorities, radicals and aliens increased, spurred by the fear that international communism would attempt to take over this country as it had taken over Russia. Two Italian radicals—Sacco and Vanzetti—were convicted of a payroll robbery and murder, even though the evidence was inconclusive. It was felt by many that Vanzetti especially had been convicted out of prejudice rather than fact, and the conduct of the case stirred world-wide indignation. Before being sentenced to death, he made the following extemporaneous speech to the judge.

VANZETTI ADDRESSES THE JUDGE WHO IS ABOUT TO SENTENCE HIM TO DEATH

by Bartolomeo Vanzetti

This is what I say: I would not wish to a dog or to a snake, to the most low or misfortunate creature of the earth—I would not wish to any of them what I have had to suffer for things that I am not guilty of. But my conviction is that I have suffered for things that I am guilty of. I am suffering because I am a radical and indeed I am a radical; I have suffered because I was an Italian, and indeed I am an Italian; I have suffered more for my family and for my beloved than for myself; but I am so convinced to be right that if you could execute me two times, and if I could be reborn two other times, I would live again to do what I have done already.

I have finished. Thank you.

Many Americans, while disagreeing with Vanzetti's radical political philosophy, had to admire the dignity and integrity with which he met his fate. Both men were electrocuted in 1927 . . .

The year 1927 was a year of human drama. Young Charles Lindbergh achieved a historic "first" and became a national hero as a result of his solo flight across the Atlantic. Babe Ruth cracked sixty homers and achieved baseball immortality. Americans went sports crazy. They cheered the exploits of Jack Dempsey in the ring, Bobby Jones on the golf course, Bill Tilden on the tennis court; but baseball was the national sport, and "The Babe" the all-time champ. However, he does have one rival in the hearts of Americans: a certain fictional bush leaguer named Casey . . .

CASEY AT THE BAT

by Ernest Lawrence Thayer

It looked extremely rocky for the Mudville
    nine that day;
The score stood two to four, with but one
    inning left to play.
So, when Cooney died at second, and Burrows did the same,
A pallor wreathed the features of the patrons of the game.

235

A straggling few got up to go, leaving there
the rest,
With that hope which springs eternal within
the human breast.
For they thought: "If only Casey could get
a whack at that,"
They'd put even money now, with Casey at
the bat.

But Flynn preceded Casey, and likewise so
did Blake,
And the former was a pudd'n, and the latter
was a fake.
So on that stricken multitude a deathlike
silence sat;
For there seemed but little chance of Casey's
getting to the bat.

But Flynn let drive a single, to the wonder-
ment of all.
And the much-despised Blakey "tore the
cover off the ball."
And when the dust had lifted, and they saw
what had occurred,
There was Blakey safe at second, and Flynn
a-huggin' third.

Then from the gladdened multitude went up
a joyous yell—
It rumbled in the mountaintops, it rattled in
the dell;
It struck upon the hillside and rebounded on
the flat;
For Casey, mighty Casey, was advancing to
the bat.

There was ease in Casey's manner as he
stepped into his place,
There was pride in Casey's bearing and a
smile on Casey's face;
And when responding to the cheers he lightly
doffed his hat,
No stranger in the crowd could doubt 'twas
Casey at the bat.

Ten thousand eyes were on him as he rubbed
his hands with dirt,
Five thousand tongues applauded when he
wiped them on his shirt;
Then when the writhing pitcher ground the
ball into his hip,
Defiance glanced in Casey's eye, a sneer
curled Casey's lip.

And now the leather-covered sphere came
hurtling through the air,
And Casey stood a-watching it in haughty
grandeur there.

Close by the sturdy batsman the ball unheeded sped;
"That ain't my style," said Casey. "Strike one," the umpire said.

From the benches, black with people, there went up a muffled roar,
Like the beating of the storm waves on the stern and distant shore.
"Kill him! kill the umpire!" shouted someone on the stand;
And it's likely they'd have killed him had not Casey raised his hand.

With a smile of Christian charity great Casey's visage shone;
He stilled the rising tumult, he made the game go on;
He signaled to the pitcher, and once more the spheroid flew;
But Casey still ignored it, and the umpire said, "Strike two."

"Fraud!" cried the maddened thousands, and the echo answered "Fraud!"
But one scornful look from Casey and the audience was awed;
They saw his face grow stern and cold, they saw his muscles strain,
And they knew that Casey wouldn't let the ball go by again.

The sneer is gone from Casey's lips, his teeth are clenched in hate,
He pounds with cruel vengeance his bat upon the plate;
And now the pitcher holds the ball, and now he lets it go,
And now the air is shattered by the force of Casey's blow.

Oh, somewhere in this favored land the sun is shining bright,
The band is playing somewhere, and somewhere hearts are light;
And somewhere men are laughing, and somewhere children shout,
But there is no joy in Mudville—Mighty Casey has struck out.

We're sure that Casey redeemed himself another day. However, the Roaring Twenties itself was destined to strike out—disastrously. Wild speculation and buying "on margin" caused the stock market to climb to dizzy, unsteady heights. The few voices of warning were ignored—"Don't be a gloomy grouch. Everybody's making money, aren't they? Come on, join the fun!" Americans would have done well to have read and reread the following poem . . .

CASSANDRA

by Edwin Arlington Robinson

I heard one who said: "Verily,
    What word have I for children here?
Your Dollar is your only Word,
    The wrath of it your only fear.

"You build it altars tall enough
    To make you see, but you are blind;
You cannot leave it long enough
    To look before you or behind.

"When Reason beckons you to pause,
    You laugh and say that you know best;
But what it is you know, you keep
    As dark as ingots in a chest.

"You laugh and answer, 'We are young;
    O leave us now, and let us grow.'—

Not asking how much more of this
   Will Time endure or Fate bestow.

"Because a few complacent years
   Have made your peril of your pride,
Think you that you are to go on
   Forever pampered and untried?

"What lost eclipse of history,
   What bivouac of the marching stars,
Has given the sign for you to see
   Millenniums and last great wars?

"What unrecorded overthrow
   Of all the world has ever known,
Or ever been, has made itself
   So plain to you, and you alone?

"Your Dollar, Dove and Eagle make
   A Trinity that even you
Rate higher than you rate yourselves;
   It pays, it flatters, and it's new.

"And though your very flesh and blood
   Be what your Eagle eats and drinks,
You'll praise him for the best of birds,
   Not knowing what the Eagle thinks.

"The power is yours, but not the sight;
   You see not upon what you tread;
You have the ages for your guide,
   But not the wisdom to be led.

"Think you to tread forever down
   The merciless old verities?
And are you never to have eyes
   To see the world for what it is?

"Are you to pay for what you have
   With all you are?"—No other word

We caught, but with a laughing crowd
   Moved on. None heeded, and few heard.

People heard all right when the stock market exploded and collapsed like an overblown, rose-tinted soap bubble late in October, 1929. Thousands of businesses and bank accounts were wiped out overnight. The Golden Age of the Twenties traded in its white tie and tails for the tattered cloak of the Great Depression. As bankrupt businesses closed down their factories and offices, hordes of the gray-faced unemployed became common sights, selling apples on city street corners, wandering listlessly through the countryside, looking for food, work, anything. Newly elected President Hoover, who had served the country brilliantly in the past, fought to lift the gloom with various relief measures and the promise that "prosperity is just around the corner." But worsening conditions gave the slogan a hollow ring, and people abandoned it in favor of singing "Brother, can you spare a dime?" or "Hallelujah, I'm a bum . . ."

HALLELUJAH, BUM AGAIN

Anonymous

When springtime does come,
Oh, won't we have fun!
We'll all throw up our jobs
And we'll go on the bum.

Chorus:
Hallelujah, I'm a bum,
Hallelujah, bum again,
Hallelujah, give us a handout
To revive us again.

Oh, springtime has come,
And I'm just out of jail,
Ain't got no money,
It all went for bail.

I went up to a house
And I knocked on the door.
A lady came out, says,
"You been here before!"

I went up to a house,
Asked for some bread;
A lady came out, says,
"The baker is dead."

I went up to a house,
Asked for a pair of pants;
A lady came out, says,
"I don't clothe no tramps!"

I went into a saloon,
And I bummed him for a drink;
He give me a glass
And he showed me the sink.

Oh, I love my boss,
And my boss loves me;
That is the reason
I'm so hun-ga-ree!

"Why don't you go to work
Like all the other men do?"
"How the hell we going to work
When there ain't no work to do?"

In 1932, the public—which was ready to try anything—decided to see if a change of party would improve the situation, and elected Democratic Franklin D. Roosevelt to the Presidency. F.D.R. swept into office with the same brand of dynamic energy and boundless optimism that had characterized his fifth cousin, Teddy Roosevelt. Having fought his way back from infantile paralysis, he had little patience with defeatism. "The only thing we have to fear is fear itself," he said in his Inaugural Address, and proceeded to conduct Congress—with a long cigarette holder instead of a baton—like an orchestra, pushing through sweeping measures of reform and aid that came to be labeled the New Deal.

Although he endorsed relief measures for those who needed them, Roosevelt believed in the strength of the American people as a whole. They might fall down, but they always got up again.

CABOOSE THOUGHTS

by Carl Sandburg

It's going to come out all right—do you
 know?
The sun, the birds, the grass—they know.
They get along—and we'll get along.

Some days will be rainy and you will sit
 waiting
And the letter you wait for won't come,
And I will sit watching the sky tear off grey
 and grey
And the letter I wait for won't come.

There will be ac-ci-dents.
I know ac-ci-dents are coming.
Smash-ups, signals wrong, washouts, trestles
 rotten,
Red and yellow ac-ci-dents.

But somehow and somewhere the end of the
    run
The train gets put together again
And the caboose and the green tail lights
Fade down the right of way like a new white
    hope.

I never heard a mocking bird in Kentucky
Spilling its heart in the morning.

I never saw the snow on Chimborazo.
It's a high white Mexican hat, I hear.

I never had supper with Abe Lincoln.
Nor a dish of soup with Jim Hill.

But I've been around.
I know some of the boys here who can go a
    little.
I know girls good for a burst of speed any
    time.

I heard Williams and Walker
Before Walker died in the bughouse.

I knew a mandolin player
Working in a barber shop in an Indiana
    town,
And he thought he had a million dollars.

I knew a hotel girl in Des Moines.
She had eyes; I saw her and said to myself
The sun rises and the sun sets in her eyes.
I was her steady and her heart went pit-a-pat.
We took away the money for a prize waltz
    at a brotherhood dance.
She had eyes; she was safe as the bridge over
    the Mississippi at Burlington; I married
    her.

Last summer we took the cushions going
    west.
Pike's Peak is a big old stone, believe me.
It's fastened down; something you can count
    on.

It's going to come out all right—do you
    know?
The sun, the birds, the grass—they know.
They get along—and we'll get along.

All through the Thirties, the country struggled upward from the slough of the Depression. There were setbacks, droughts, hardships of various kinds; but when times were
at their toughest, parents could always raise
their spirits by watching their children at
play. Even a Depression couldn't stop
American children from climbing trees,
breaking windows with baseballs, trampling
dirt all over the living-room rug, and making
a good deal of healthy noise. On a visit to a
crowded city street during the Thirties, you
might hear a chorus of pint-sized versifiers
chanting the following immortal lines.

CHILDREN'S SIDEWALK RHYMES OF NEW YORK

*from "Songs of Innocence"**
by Dorothy Mills and Morris Bishop

Roses are red,
Violets are blue,
I like pecans,
Nuts to you.

Roses are red,
Violets are blue,

*Copyright © 1937 *The New Yorker Magazine, Inc.*

240

Elephants are fat
And so are you.

Roses are red,
Violets are blue,
If I had your mug,
I'd join the zoo.

Roses are red,
Violets are blue,
Everybody stinks
And so do you.

Roses are red,
Violets are blue,
I use Lifebuoy.
Why don't you?

Looie, pooie,
You're full of hooey.

It was during the Thirties that a major change in children's fashions occurred. Knickers, the sturdy, knee-length pants worn by boys before graduating into the dignity of long trousers, gradually faded from the scene ...

ON THE PASSING OF KNICKERS

by John Tobias

When I was swinging a seventh-grade satchel,
Crammed with geography, comic books,
And assorted etceteras—
I ballooned with pride in my corduroy knickers.

They were my midway mark of caste
Between the short and the long of life.

Babe Ruth wore 'em, golf champs wore 'em—
So did I. Or rather: they wore me;
For when I put them on, I was possessed by a need
To collect cockleburrs, grass stains,
But mostly to run. God, how I could run in my knickers!

I have traded my satchel for an attaché case,
And knickers are passé.
I am air-borne now, at hundreds of miles per.
But sometimes, as I strap into my cushioned seat,
Waiting to take off,
I think—
God! How I could run ...

As the country approached the Forties, the economy began to pick up again. One obvious—sometimes too-obvious—symbol of this was the vast increase in the giant advertising signs that lined America's highways, cajoling the Sunday driver to stop depriving his family of a wide variety of new products.

SONG OF THE OPEN ROAD

by Ogden Nash

I think that I shall never see
A billboard lovely as a tree.
Indeed, unless the billboards fall,
I'll never see a tree at all.

While America was struggling up out of the Depression, Hitler, Mussolini, and the Japanese war lords began their careers of aggression. Country after country fell, and American public opinion was split between those who felt that neutrality was becoming increasingly impossible and the isolationists who insisted, "It can't happen here—let's mind our own business, and everything will be all right . . ." The controversy still raged in 1940, when the following poem was written.

NIGHTMARE AT NOON

by Stephen Vincent Benét

There are no trenches dug in the park, not yet.
There are no soldiers falling out of the sky.
It's a fine, clear day, in the park. It is bright and hot.
The trees are in full, green, summer-heavy leaf.
An airplane drones overhead but no one's afraid.
There's no reason to be afraid, in a fine, big city
That was not built for a war. There is time and time.

There was time in Norway and time, and the thing fell.
When they woke, they saw the planes with the black crosses.
When they woke, they heard the guns rolling in the street.
They could not believe, at first. It was hard to believe.
They had been friendly and thriving and inventive.
They had had good arts, decent living, peace for years.
Those were not enough, it seems.
There were people there who wrote books and painted pictures,

Worked, came home tired, liked to be let alone.
They made fun of the strut and the stamp and the strained salute,
They made fun of the would-be Caesars who howl and foam.
That was not enough, it seems. It was not enough.
When they woke, they saw the planes with the black crosses.

There is grass in the park. There are children on the long meadow
Watched by some hot, peaceful nuns. Where the ducks are fed
There are black children and white and the anxious teachers
Who keep counting them like chickens. It's quite a job
To take so many school-kids out to the park,
But when they've eaten their picnic, they'll go home.
(And they could have better homes, in a rich city.)
But they won't be sent to Kansas or Michigan
At twenty-four hours' notice,
Dazed, bewildered, clutching their broken toys,
Hundreds on hundreds filling the blacked-out trains.
Just to keep them safe, just so they may live not die.
Just so there's one chance that they may not die but live.
That does not enter our thoughts. There is plenty of time.

In Holland, one hears, some children were less lucky.
It was hard to send them anywhere in Holland.

242

It is a small country, you see. The thing happened quickly.

The bombs from the sky are quite indifferent to children.

The machine-gunners do not distinguish. In Rotterdam

One quarter of the city was blown to bits.

That included, naturally, ordinary buildings

With the usual furnishings, such as cats and children.

It was an old, peaceful city, Rotterdam,

Clean, tidy, full of flowers.

But that was not enough, it seems.

It was not enough to keep all the children safe.

It was ended in a week, and the freedom ended.

There is no air-raid siren yet, in the park.

All the glass still stands, in the windows around the park.

The man on the bench is reading a Yiddish paper.

He will not be shot because of that, oddly enough.

He will not even be beaten or imprisoned.

Not yet, not yet.

You can be a Finn or a Dane and an American.

You can be German or French and an American,

Jew, Bohunk, Nigger, Mick—all the dirty names

We call each other—and yet American.

We've stuck to that quite a while.

Go into Joe's Diner and try to tell the truckers

You belong to a Master Race and you'll get a laugh.

What's that, brother? Double-talk?

I'm a stranger here myself but it's a free country.

It's a free country . . .

Oh yes, I know the faults and the other side,

The lyncher's rope, the bought justice, the wasted land,

The scale on the leaf, the borers in the corn,

The finks with their clubs, the grey sky of relief,

All the long shame of our hearts and the long disunion.

I am merely remarking—as a country, we try.

As a country, I think we try.

They tried in Spain but the tanks and the planes won out.

They fought very well and long.

They fought to be free but it seems that was not enough.

They did not have the equipment. So they lost.

They tried in Finland. The resistance was shrewd,

Skilful, intelligent, waged by a free folk.

They tried in Greece, and they threw them back for a while

By the soul and spirit and passion of common men.

Call the roll of fourteen nations. Call the roll

Of the blacked-out lands, the lands that used to be free.

But do not call it loud. There is plenty of time.

There is plenty of time, while the bombs on London fall

And turn the world to wind and water and fire.

There is time to sleep while the fire-bombs
    fall on London.
They are stubborn people in London.

We are slow to wake, good-natured as a
    country.
(It is our fault and our virtue.) We like to
    raise
A man to the highest power and then throw
    bricks at him.
We don't like war and we like to speak our
    minds.
We're used to speaking our minds.
                    There are certain words,
Our own and others', we're used to—words
    we've used,
Heard, had to recite, forgotten,
Rubbed shiny in the pocket, left home for
    keepsakes,
Inherited, stuck away in the back-drawer,
In the locked trunk, at the back of the quiet
    mind.
Liberty, equality, fraternity.
To none will we sell, refuse or deny, right or
    justice.
We hold these truths to be self-evident.

I am merely saying—what if these words
    pass?
What if they pass and are gone and are no
    more,
Eviscerated, blotted out of the world?
We're used to them, so used that we half-
    forget,
The way you forget the looks of your own
    house
And yet you can walk around it, in the
    darkness.
You can't put a price on sunlight or the air,
You can't put a price on these, so they must

be easy.
They were bought with belief and passion, at
    great cost.
They were bought with the bitter and anony-
    mous blood
Of farmers, teachers, shoemakers and fools
Who broke the old rule and the pride of
    kings.
And some never saw the end and many were
    weary,
Some doubtful, many confused.
They were bought by the ragged boys at
    Valmy mill,
The yokels at Lexington with the long light
    guns
And the dry, New England faces,
The iron barons, writing a charter out
For their own iron advantage, not the people,
And yet the people got it into their hands
And marked it with their own sweat.
It took long to buy these words.
It took a long time to buy them and much
    pain.

Thenceforward and forever free.
Thenceforward and forever free.
No man may be bound or fined or slain till
    he has been judged by his peers.
To form a more perfect Union.

The others have their words too, and strong
    words,
Strong as the tanks, explosive as the bombs.

The State is all, worship the State!
The Leader is all, worship the Leader!
Strength is all, worship strength!
Worship, bow down or die!

I shall go back through the park to my safe
    house,

This is not London or Paris.
This is the high, bright city, the lucky place,
The place that always had time.
The boys in their shirtsleeves here, the big,
     flowering girls,
The bicycle-riders, the kids with the model
     planes,
The lovers who lie on the grass, uncaring of
     eyes,
As if they lay on an island out of time,
The tough kids, squirting the water at the
     fountain,
Whistled at by the cop.
The dopes who write "Jimmy's a dope" on
     the tunnel walls.
These are all quite safe and nothing will
     happen to them.
Nothing will happen, of course.
Go tell Frank the Yanks aren't coming, in
     Union Square.
Go tell the new brokers' story about the
     President.
Whatever it is. That's going to help a lot.
There's time to drink your highball—plenty
     of time.
Go tell fire it only burns in another country,
Go tell the bombers this is the wrong address,
The hurricane to pass on the other side.
Go tell the earthquake it must not shake the
     ground.

The bell has rung in the night and the air
     quakes with it.

I shall not sleep tonight when I hear the
     plane.

On December 7, 1941, the Japanese attacked Pearl Harbor, and the United States found itself in World War II. Once again, young men gave up homes and jobs to re-port at training camps that sprang up all over the nation. Instead of *Over There,* they sang *This Is the Army, Mr. Jones,* and kissed their wives and sweethearts good-bye to the tune of *Don't Sit under the Apple Tree with Anyone Else but Me* . . . In camp, they submitted to the fastest—and shortest— haircut most of them had ever had, and began to learn the fine art of complaining about food and sergeants in equal doses. They also learned how to kill efficiently. They didn't want to. They hadn't asked to. But they would do what was necessary to bring peace home to their families. After training, they filed aboard troop trains for the first leg of a journey that might end up in a jungle on Okinawa . . . a desert in North Africa . . . a beachhead in Italy or France . . .

TROOP TRAIN

by Karl Shapiro

It stops the town we come through. Workers
     raise
Their oily arms in good salute and grin.
Kids scream as at a circus. Business men
Glance hopefully and go their measured way.
And women standing at their dumbstruck
     door
More slowly wave and seem to warn us back,
As if a tear blinding the course of war
Might once dissolve our iron in their sweet
     wish.

Fruit of the world, O clustered on ourselves
We hang as from a cornucopia
In total friendliness, with faces bunched
To spray the streets with catcalls and with
     leers.
A bottle smashes on the moving ties
And eyes fixed on a lady smiling pink

Stretch like a rubber-band and snap and
    sting
The mouth that wants the drink-of-water
    kiss.

And on through crummy continents and
    days,
Deliberate, grimy, slightly drunk we crawl,
The good-bad boys of circumstance and
    chance,
Whose bucket-helmets bang the empty wall
Where twist the murdered bodies of our
    packs
Next to the guns that only seem themselves.
And distance like a strap adjusted shrinks,
Tightens across the shoulder and holds firm.

Here is a deck of cards; out of this hand
Dealer, deal me my luck, a pair of bulls,
The right draw to a flush, the one-eyed jack.

Diamonds and hearts are red but spades are
    black,
And spades are spades and clubs are clovers
    —black.
But deal me winners, souvenirs of peace.
This stands to reason and arithmetic,
Luck also travels and not all come back.

Trains lead to ships and ships to death or
    trains,
And trains to death or trucks, and trucks to
    death,
Or trucks lead to the march, the march to
    death,
Or that survival which is all our hope;
And death leads back to trucks and trains
    and ships.
But life leads to the march, O flag! at last
The place of life found after trains and death
—Nightfall of nations brilliant after war.

The broad outlines of the war are still sharp in memory: the terribly costly invasion of island after island in the Pacific . . . the final defeat of Rommel in the North African campaign . . . the landing in Normandy and the battle across France and into Germany . . .

Hitler's dream of glory ended in 1945 with suicide in a bunker, while Allied tanks rumbled through the streets of Berlin overhead. The Japanese had been driven back practically to the shores of their homeland, but they still had powerful armies, and it was estimated that a million American soldiers would die in an invasion of Japan. President Truman called upon the Japanese to surrender. They refused. To save a huge loss of American lives, he ordered the newly developed atomic bomb dropped on Hiroshima. It exploded over the city on August 6, 1945, almost wiped it out, and killed more than seventy thousand people . . .

The terrifying launching of the age of the atom brought the war to a swift end. When a second bomb was dropped on Nagasaki, Japan surrendered.

There was much controversy over the use of the bomb, with its gigantic slaughter of innocent civilians. Those who defended its use cited the millions of helpless civilians slaughtered by the Axis powers since they began their unjustified bombings and invasions of peaceful countries. Using Mr. Truman's argument, they pointed out that many more people, including Japanese, would have been killed by withholding the bomb than were killed by dropping it and forcing a quick surrender. America hadn't asked for the war. The explosion of the atomic bomb was the end of a chain of destructive events triggered by Mussolini's bombing of defenseless Ethiopia . . . Hitler's murder of countless "non-Aryans" . . . the Japanese war lords' rape of China and treacherous attack on Pearl Harbor . . .

American joy at peace was tempered with the sobering knowledge that twice within thirty years aggressors had been permitted to turn the civilized world into a slaughterhouse. After 1918, America had isolated itself, turned its back on global problems, until it was almost too late. It must not happen again. Those who died in two wars that the world might be made "safe for democracy" must be remembered . . .

THE YOUNG DEAD SOLDIERS
(For Lieutenant Richard Myers)

by Archibald MacLeish

The young dead soldiers do not speak.
Nevertheless, they are heard in the still
    houses: who has not heard them?
They have a silence that speaks for them at
night and when the clock counts.
They say: We were young. We have died.
    Remember us.
They say: We have done what we could but
    until it is finished it is not done.
They say: We have given our lives but until
    it is finished no one can know what our
    lives gave.
They say: Our deaths are not ours; they are
    yours; they will mean what you make
    them.
They say: Whether our lives and our deaths
    were for peace and a new hope or for
    nothing we cannot say; it is you who
    must say this.

They say: We leave you our deaths. Give
    them their meaning.
We were young, they say. We have died.
    Remember us.

This time, America remembered. It
helped establish the United Nations and par-
ticipated fully, accepting its responsibilities
as a world leader. Under the Marshall Plan
and other measures, America helped the war-
ravaged nations and peoples of Europe to
pull themselves up again. It was a time of
change, of building and rebuilding—and
what was America basically, if not a nation
of dedicated, enthusiastic builders?

PRAYERS OF STEEL

by Carl Sandburg

Lay me on an anvil, O God.
Beat me and hammer me into a crowbar.
Let me pry loose old walls.
Let me lift and loosen old foundations.
Lay me on an anvil, O God.
Beat me and hammer me into a steel spike.
Drive me into the girders that hold a sky-
    scraper together.
Take red-hot rivets and fasten me into the
    central girders.
Let me be the great nail holding a sky-
    scraper through the blue nights into
    white stars.

There was need in the years ahead for
every bit of energy and determination that
America could bring to bear. An icy wind
blowing from the Communist East soon
turned peace into the Cold War. Through
the Berlin Airlift and its actions in Korea

and elsewhere, the United States demonstrated its will to resist aggression. The
country made mistakes in the "battle for
men's minds"—sometimes expediency placed
it in the embarrassing position of supporting
governments opposed to reform in their own
countries. But America made no claims to
perfection; it had a hard, complicated fight
on its hands, and it knew that the mainte-
nance of a strong, free, democratic America,
with all its faults, was still the best hope the
world had. The Communists erected an
"iron curtain" around the countries they
ruled, as a protective measure. But the
American ideal taught that an open society
is a healthy society. Fences were all right
for holding in livestock, but walls between
peoples were made to be torn down.

MENDING WALL

by Robert Frost

Something there is that doesn't love a wall,
That sends the frozen-ground-swell under it,
And spills the upper boulders in the sun;
And makes gaps even two can pass abreast.
The work of hunters is another thing:
I have come after him and made repair
Where they have left not one stone on a
    stone,
But they would have the rabbit out of hiding,
To please the yelping dogs. The gaps I
    mean,
No one has seen them made or heard them
    made,
But at spring mending-time we find them
    there.
I let my neighbor know beyond the hill;
And on a day we meet to walk the line

To each the boulders that have fallen to
each.
And some are loaves and some so nearly balls
We have to use a spell to make them
balance:
"Stay where you are until our backs are
turned!"
We wear our fingers rough with handling
them.
Oh, just another kind of out-door game,
One on a side. It comes to little more:
There where it is we do not need the wall:
He is all pine and I am apple orchard.
My apple trees will never get across
And eat the cones under his pines, I tell him.
He only says, "Good fences make good
neighbors."
Spring is the mischief in me, and I wonder
If I could put a notion in his head:
"*Why* do they make good neighbors? Isn't it
Where there are cows? But here there are no
cows.
Before I built a wall I'd ask to know
What I was walling in or walling out,
And to whom I was like to give offense.
Something there is that doesn't love a wall,
That wants it down." I could say "Elves" to
him,
But it's not elves exactly, and I'd rather
He said it for himself. I see him there
Bringing a stone grasped firmly by the top
In each hand, like an old-stone savage
armed.
He moves in darkness as it seems to me,
Not of woods only and the shade of trees.
He will not go behind his father's saying,
And he likes having thought of it so well
He says again, "Good fences make good
neighbors."

The ideal of an open society is freedom to
sample, express, accept, reject ideas . . . freedom to choose directions of growth. The
Communist system orders its people to serve
The Party. American society *offers* its people the chance to serve the party of their
choice, to serve themselves—or to serve and
love one another . . .

POEM IN PROSE

by Archibald MacLeish

This poem is for my wife.
I have made it plainly and honestly:
The mark is on it
Like the burl on the knife.

I have not made it for praise.
She has no more need for praise
Than summer has
Or the bright days.

In all that becomes a woman
Her words and her ways are beautiful:
Love's lovely duty,
The well-swept room.

Wherever she is there is sun
And time and a sweet air:
Peace is there,
Work done.

There are always curtains and flowers
And candles and baked bread
And a cloth spread
And a clean house.

Her voice when she sings is a voice
At dawn by a freshening sea
Where the wave leaps in the
Wind and rejoices.

Wherever she is it is now.
It is here where the apples are:
Here in the stars,
In the quick hour.

The greatest and richest good,
My own life to live in,
This she has given me—

If giver could.

Communism teaches its children that the primary wonder of life rests in such things as a successful Five Year Plan or sputnik. In America, wise parents strive to teach their children that the primary wonder of life rests in such things as creation, renewal, the coming of spring . . .

IN JUST-SPRING

by E. E. Cummings

in Just-
spring   when the world is mud-
luscious the little
lame balloonman

whistles   far   and wee

and eddieandbill come
running from marbles and
piracies and it's
spring

when the world is puddle-wonderful

the queer
old balloonman whistles
far   and   wee
and bettyandisbel come dancing

from hop-scotch and jump-rope and

it's
spring
and
        the

              goat-footed

balloonMan   whistles
far
and
wee

There were, as always, shadows as well as lights. The "payola" scandal, the hysteria of McCarthyism, the exploitation of migrant workers, chronic unemployment in depressed areas—these were among the problems of American society which, as long as they remained unresolved, would continue to make the reality fall short of the American dream, while providing heavy ammunition for Communist propaganda.

McCarthyism finally shrilled itself out, but one of the outstanding problems that remained involved discrimination against American Negroes and other minority groups that had contributed richly to the building of the nation.

In 1954, the Supreme Court, as the result of a case brought before it by the legal arm of the N.A.A.C.P., declared school segregation unconstitutional. In 1957, nine qualified Negro children applied for admission to Central High School in Little Rock, Arkansas. A federal judge ordered that they be admitted. Governor Faubus called out the Arkansas National Guard, not to protect the children's right to enter, but to keep them *out* on the pretext of avoiding violence. At this sign of encouragement from Faubus, the white-supremacist lunatic fringe formed a mob at the school. Mrs. Daisy Bates, head of the Arkansas N.A.A.C.P., warned the children not to walk to school alone. Fifteen-year-old Elizabeth Sheckford failed to receive that warning. She started off for her first day in high school. Here is the account of what Elizabeth experienced.

A GIRL WALKS TO SCHOOL IN LITTLE ROCK

from "The Daisy Bates Story" by Mrs. Daisy Bates

The day before we were to go in, we met Superintendent Blossom at the school board office. He told us what the mob might say and do, but he never said we wouldn't have any protection. He told our parents not to come because he wouldn't be able to protect us if they did.

That night I was so excited I couldn't sleep, and next morning I was about the first one up. I pressed the black and white dress I had made for the first day of school, and while I was doing this, my little brother turned on TV. They started telling about a large crowd gathered at the school. The commentator said he wondered if we were going to show up that day. Mother called from the kitchen, where she was fixing breakfast, "Turn that TV off!" She was so worried I wanted to comfort her, so I said, "Mother, don't worry."

Dad was walking back and forth from room to room with a sad expression. He was chewing on his pipe and had a cigar in his hand, too, and he didn't light either one. It would have been funny, only he was so nervous.

Before I left home Mother called us into the living room, saying we should have a word of prayer, and then I caught the bus and got off a block from school. I saw a large crowd of people before I reached the guards. When I walked toward them, the crowd got very quiet. Superintendent Blossom had told us to enter by the front door. I looked at all the people and thought—maybe I will be safer if I walk down the block to the front entrance behind the guards. At the corner of Fourteenth and Park, I tried to pass the guards so as to enter the grounds. One of the guards pointed across the street. So I pointed in the same direction and asked if he meant for me to cross the street and walk down. He nodded "yes." I walked across the street and the crowd moved away from me.

For a moment all I could hear was the shuffling of their feet. Then someone shouted, "Here she comes; get ready." I moved away from the crowd on the sidewalk and into the street, so that I could cross back over to the protection of the guards if they came at me.

They moved in closer as they followed me, calling me names. I still wasn't afraid, just very nervous, and my knees were shaking so much I wondered if I could make it to the entrance at the center of the two blocks. That was the longest block I ever walked in my whole life.

But I still wasn't too scared because I thought the guards would protect me.

When I got right in front of the school, I went up to a guard again. But this one just looked straight ahead and did not move to let me pass. I didn't know what to do. Then I looked down and saw that the path to the front entrance was a little farther on, so I walked until I was right in front of the path to the front door.

I stood looking at the school—it looked so big. Just then, the guards let some white students go through.

The crowd was quiet. I guess they were waiting to see what was going to happen. When my knees were steady enough, I walked up to the guard who had let the white students in. He did not move. When I tried to squeeze past him, he raised his bayonet, and the other guards closed in and raised their bayonets.

They glared at me with a mean look, and I was very frightened and didn't know what to do. I turned around and the crowd came at me.

They moved closer and closer, shouting "Lynch her!"

I tried to see a friendly face, someone to help, somewhere. I looked into the face of an old woman; it seemed a kind face, but when I looked at her again, she spat on me.

They came closer, shouting, "No nigger is going to get in our school. Get out of here! Get!"

I turned back to the guards, but their faces told me I wouldn't get help from them. Then I looked down the block and saw a bench at the bus stop. I thought, if I can only get there I will be safe. I don't know why the bench seemed to be a safe place to me, but I started walking toward it. I closed my mind to what they were shouting and kept saying to myself, if I can only make it to the bench I will be safe.

When I finally got to the bench, I don't think I could have gone another step. I sat down and the mob crowded up shouting. Someone hollered, "Drag her over to this tree. Let's take care of the nigger." Just then a white man put his arm around me and patted my shoulder. He raised my chin and said, "Don't let them see you cry."

The bus came and a white lady got off and saw me. She came through the mob and helped me on the bus. She asked me my name and tried to talk to me, but I don't think I answered. I can't remember much about the bus ride, but the next thing I remember I was standing in front of the School for the Blind where Mother works.

I thought, maybe she isn't here. She has to be here! I ran upstairs, and I think some teachers tried to talk to me, but I kept running until I reached Mother's classroom.

Mother was standing at the window with her head bowed, but she must have sensed I was there because she turned around. She looked as if she had been crying, and I wanted to tell her I was all right, but I couldn't talk. She put her arm around me and I cried.

Many Americans are becoming increasingly aware that prejudice and discrimination not only cause pain and injustice—they help to divide and weaken the country. Gradually, progress is being made. As prejudice becomes "tolerance," America is a little less weak. When tolerance is turned into the warm handclasp of American brotherhood, then the shining future envisioned by Walt Whitman becomes possible.

I HEAR AMERICA SINGING

by Walt Whitman

I hear America singing, the varied carols I
hear,

Those of mechanics, each one singing his as
it should be blithe and strong,

The carpenter singing his as he measures his
plank or beam,

The mason singing his as he makes ready
for work, or leaves off work,

The boatman singing what belongs to him
in his boat, the deckhand singing on the
steamboat deck,

The shoemaker singing as he sits on his
bench, the hatter singing as he stands,

The wood-cutter's song, the plowboy's on
his way in the morning, or at noon in-
termission or at sundown,

The delicious singing of the mother, or of
the young wife at work, or of the girl
sewing or washing,

Each singing what belongs to him or her and
to none else,

The day what belongs to the day—at night
the party of young fellows, robust,
friendly,

Singing with open mouths their strong melodious songs.

What's there to sing about in an age
fraught with such towering anxieties? Every
age has had its "towering anxieties"—
whether from fear of the Black Plague or the
Hydrogen Bomb. Every age has also had its
affirmation of life, humanity, beauty . . .

BARTER

by Sara Teasdale

Life has loveliness to sell—
   All beautiful and splendid things,
Blue waves whitened on a cliff,
   Climbing fire that sways and sings,
And children's faces looking up
Holding wonder like a cup.

Life has loveliness to sell—
   Music like a curve of gold,
Scent of pine trees in the rain,
   Eyes that love you, arms that hold,
And for your spirit's still delight,
Holy thoughts that star the night.

Spend all you have for loveliness,
   Buy it and never count the cost,
For one white singing hour of peace
   Count many a year of strife well lost,
And for a breath of ecstasy
Give all you have been or could be.

"Count many a year of strife well lost . . ." The early settler fought the wilderness, buried his dead, cleared his land. When he had a brief moment's rest, he pulled a knife out of his pocket and whittled a toy for his child's birthday . . .

Today, America faces a new frontier. In his speech accepting the Democratic nomination in 1960, future President John F. Kennedy said:

THE NEW FRONTIER

by John F. Kennedy

But I tell you the New Frontier is here, whether we seek it or not. Beyond that frontier are uncharted areas of science and space, unsolved problems of peace and war, unconquered pockets of ignorance and prejudice, unanswered questions of poverty and surplus. . . .

Can a nation organized and governed such as ours endure? That is the real question. Have we the nerve and the will? Can we carry through in an age where we will witness not only new breakthroughs in weapons of destruction—but also a race for mastery of the sky and the rain, the ocean and the tides, the far side of space and the inside of men's minds?

Are we up to the task? Are we equal to the challenge? . . .

All mankind waits upon our decision.

Are we up to the challenge? Listen—and you will hear a Pilgrim's axe biting through a stubborn tree as he grunts and sings *"Pump*kins at morning, and *pump*kins at noon, if it *was* not for pumpkins we *should* be undone . . ."

You will hear an officer (holding up a pamphlet in front of some shivering troops at a Godforsaken place called Valley Forge) reading, "These are the times that try men's souls . . ."

You will hear the creak of hundreds of wooden axles and the uneasy stirring of oxen and the sudden thrilling cry, "Wagons roll!"

And if you listen especially hard, you will hear the high, nasal voice of a tall, gaunt man as he says:

". . . that this nation, under God, shall have a new birth of freedom; and that government of the people, by the people, and for the people, shall not perish from the earth."

As long as Americans can still respond to this heritage, the story of America will have no end.

Index

Let the word go forth from this time and place, to friend and foe alike, that the torch has been passed to a new generation of Americans—born in this century, tempered by war, disciplined by a cold and bitter peace, proud of our ancient heritage, and unwilling to witness or permit the slow undoing of those human rights to which the nation has always been committed, and to which we are committed today. . . .

Together let us explore the stars, conquer the deserts, eradicate disease, tap the ocean depths and encourage the arts and commerce. . . . Let both sides join in the next task: Creating not a new balance of power, but a new world of law, where the strong are just and the weak secure and the peace preserved forever.

All this will not be finished in the first one hundred days. Nor will it be finished in the first one thousand days, nor in the life of this Administration, nor even perhaps in our lifetime on this planet. But let us begin.

President John F. Kennedy
from the Inaugural Address